DISPUTED EARTH

Military geology may be defined simply enough as the application of geology to the art of war.

C.E. Erdmann, 1943[1]

DISPUTED EARTH

Geology and Trench Warfare on the Western Front 1914-1918

Peter Doyle

UNIFORM

This edition first published by Uniform
an imprint of Unicorn Publishing Group

Unicorn Publishing Group
101 Wardour Street
London W1F 0UG

www.unicornpublishing.org

A catalogue record for this book is available from the British Library

ISBN 978-1-910500-87-3

Printed and bound in Spain

Cover design Uniform Press
Typeset by Vivian@Bookscribe

The military history of any country is largely determined by its Topography, that is, by the nature of its soil: where run its ranges of hills: how high, steep or barren these may be: the situation of its better lands, with their chief towns: the position, depth and rapidity of its rivers, etc., etc. The importance of such features lies in this: that such features aided or impeded the march of armies.

H. Belloc, 1914[2]

The consideration of the manner of occurrence, behaviour, and adaptability of earth materials is essential to the effective and intelligent conduct of military operations. Earth materials are dealt with in the tunnels and mines under 'No Man's Land' and in the trenches, gun pits, and dug-outs along the front. The nature of the materials that make up the surface of the ground determines the form and size of shell craters and in a measure the effect of shell fire. Earth materials form the foundations of heavy artillery… They are in many places the source of water supply.

H.E. Gregory, 1918 [3]

CONTENTS

NOTE ON GEOLOGICAL TERMINOLOGY

Geological terms are explained in text where they first appear. Older stratal terms are used in preference to newer ones, established by the modern geological surveys of France and Belgium; this is to avoid confusion with historical literature; equivalence to the new units is given where they are first mentioned, however. Geology is governed by a geological time scale which has two components, *relative* time, marked by named time periods, and *absolute* time, given in millions of years before present. The relative intervals, Mesozoic, Cretaceous, Ypresian, and so on, are agreed upon by international convention, and allow rocks to be assigned to them using tools like the recognisable fossils that belong to them. Absolute time estimates will vary, as these are dependent upon the accuracy of the method. A Geological Time Scale relevant to the interval covered is supplied, to assist the reader.

NOTE ON FLEMISH PLACE NAMES

During the war, most place names in Belgium were in French, used widely by the Allies on their maps. Today, where those places are in Flemish speaking Flanders (Vlaanderen), the Flemish equivalent is used – with Ypres being Ieper, Passchendaele becoming Passendale, and so on. However, given that the French spellings were used during the Great War, these have been retained in this book to avoid complication.

Opposite: **Geological Time scale**.
Only those intervals of relevance here are included.
(Note: geological time is given in millions of years before present, Ma)

Era	Period	Epoch	Age	Time (Ma)
Cenozoic	Quaternary	Holocene		0.0117
		Pleistocene		2.58
	Neogene	Pliocene		5.333
		Miocene		23.03
	Palaeogene	Oligocene		33.09
		Eocene	Priabonian	37.8
			Bartonian	41.02
			Lutetian	47.80
			Ypresian	56.00
		Paleocene	Thanetian	59.20
			Selandian	61.60
			Danian	66.00
Mesozoic	Cretaceous	Upper	Maastrictian	72.01
			Campanian	83.60
			Santonian	86.30
			Coniacian	89.80
			Turonian	93.90
			Cenomanian	100.50
		Lower		145.00
	Jurassic			201.30
	Triassic			251.902
Palaeozoic	Permian			298.90
	Carboniferous	Pennsylvanian		323.20
		Mississippian		358.90
	Devonian			419.20
	Silurian			443.80
	Ordovician			485.40
	Cambrian			541.00
Proterozoic				2500
Archaean				4000
Hadaean				~4600

Echoes of the past: excavated trenches in the chalk soils of the Champagne region of France. Soldiers' instincts were to draw them close to the earth. (P. Doyle)

1 THE GREAT WAR

Belgium
Mud: and a thin rain coming down to make more mud.
Mud: with scraps of iron lying in it and the straggling fragment of a nation,
lolling, hanging about in the mud on the edge of disaster.[4]

The Great War. One of the bloodiest wars in history, and one that has become irrevocably linked with trench warfare, a species of war that favours the defender over the attacker. And in this war of position the science of geology played its part, right from the point where the first soldiers broke the surface of the earth with their spades in 1914. In so doing they made an intimate connection with the *ground*, the earth, the soil, in a bid to escape the rapid artillery fire and the hail of machine gun bullets. It was at this point that a link with the earth's embrace was forged strongly – an instinctive urge to return to the protective succour of the land – that would not be easily broken.

Digging in; use of the pick (*Manual of Field Works*, 1921)

The idea of digging trenches was sound, of course, and it was not just to satisfy the soldiers' desire to 'go to ground' under fire. Trenches would stop invading armies in their tracks, and create a barrier against further progress. It would not only protect the infantry from the attentions of the artillery, it would also create a linear fortress that was ultimately so difficult to destroy. Yet with all the advantages of digging trenches, all too often it was a matter of circumstance – rather than planning – that led to their construction. This was to be expected, as the British manual *Military Engineering (Part 1) Field Defences* noted in 1908:

> No precise rules can be laid down as to the manner in which a defensive position is to be occupied or intrenched[5], as so much depends on the character of operations, the physical features of the ground, and the composition of the troops engaged. The only reliable guides are a thorough knowledge of the effects of fire, and a practiced eye for ground.[6]

Such 'practiced eyes' demanded experience, and in 1914 this experience had yet to be earned. The opening of the war saw the invasion of the German armies through Flanders, in an open attack that swept across the fields in a manner that had much in common with the battles of Napoleonic times. But by 1918, in these same fields, there had evolved a war that was, as historian John Horne has noted, the 'polar opposite of the war that had been imagined'.[7] A new term emerged, 'the front', which embodied the stalemate conditions of a new type of warfare, of mutual siege, where matters of 'microgeography' assumed great importance. Here the 'practised eye for ground' would attempt to pick out the most suitable conditions for the lines of trenches that snaked across Europe – though opportunities to choose the ground where trenches could be dug, and where barriers could be created were not always available. (All too often the defender had limited time to choose ground, and the attacker less inclined to yield ground won.) By 1918 the war of position assumed immense importance and levels of great sophistication.

It was on the Western Front that this new warfare was prosecuted, as in the east, the vast geography and challenging conditions dictated more variable outcomes. And the war was not confined to these fronts alone; it spread worldwide, with perhaps lesser-known land campaigns in Alpine Europe, the Balkans, the Middle East, Asia and Africa (not to mention the extension of those land engagements to a naval war that raged from the South Atlantic to the North Sea). Though siege conditions would also appear on some of these fronts, they were variable and spasmodic in form, defined by tactical issues and geographic constraints, all of which would test their commanders.

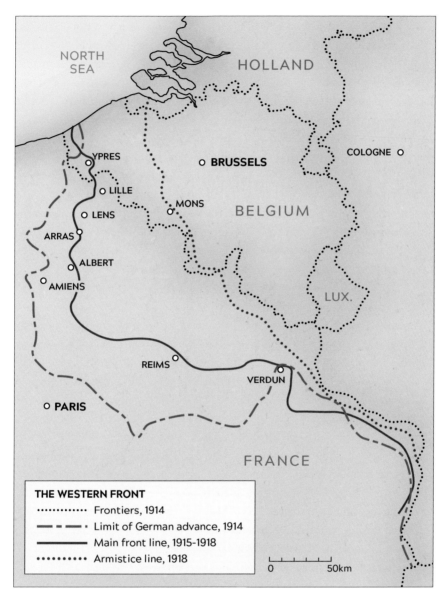

The Western Front, 1914–1918: showing the line of maximum penetration, the line of siege (the main front line), and the Armistice line.

Throughout history, the most effective military commanders have been those who have understood topography and the nature of terrain, with records at least back to 512 BC recorded in the Chinese text attributed to Sun Tzu, in the *Art of War*.[8] Of its 13 chapters, some seven of them refer explicitly to the use of terrain in battle and manoeuvre, the need to understand terrain types, and of the pitfalls and advantages of defensive positions: 'How to make the best of both strong and weak – that is a question involving the proper use of ground.' This doctrine would still apply centuries later. Tellingly, the first English translation of this classic of military literature appeared in 1910; the Great War that followed its publication provided ample opportunities to test Sun Tzu's assertions.

The 'nature of ground' has so often controlled the outcome of battle and the planning of campaigns, that it is taken for granted that 'a reading' of the terrain is fundamental to the outcome of battle.[9] Yet the details of the impact of ground, of the many nuances of nature, are not always fully appreciated. As C.E. Erdmann put it, on the eve of the Allied invasion of Europe in 1944, 'The mutual relationship between geology and terrain, or, as the soldier sees it, the landscape, is axiomatic. There is an equally close connection between land warfare and terrain. Without some good earth the terrain factor would not exist.'[10] The definition of 'good ground' or 'good earth' is all too often overlooked or dismissed by some historians, simply forming a backdrop to battle that, in some circumstances, have been seen primarily as a product of fate. Instead there deserves to be specialist considerations of the effect of terrain on the outcome of battle, even *post facto*, to understand that it is so. As an example, in a now classic case-history of military geology studies, the Battle of Gettysburg (1863), the pivotal engagement of the American Civil War, has been scrutinised in some detail.

Since at least the early 1960s geologists have attempted to examine the role of geology in the battle, to deconstruct its main events from a military perspective, and to examine the way in which geology contributed to them, particularly in providing the essential framework – the stage – on which it was fought. The first major study to examine Gettysburg from this perspective was Andrew Brown of the Pennsylvania State Geological Survey.[11] Publishing an article in the early 1960s, Brown examined the campaign that led to the battle, the movement of the Union Armies from the south, and the progression of the Confederates along the Great Valley from Virginia into Pennsylvania – part of General Robert E. Lee's plan to invade the north, putting pressure on the Union in its own territory. Subsequent studies have explored the detail of the battle more fully, with terrain – geology in its roundest sense – rightly held up by all concerned as a major influence in the outcome of battle.[12] The Round Tops, the Seminary and Cemetery ridges, the Devil's Den – all famous features of the battlefield topography – are surface expressions of the outcrop of harder rocks (a crystalline rock known as 'diabase') which had been forced into softer sandstones and shales. The battle hinged on geology, the Union forces holding the so-called 'topographic fishhook'; a curving

Battle of Gettysburg, July1st–3rd, 1863. The outcome of the pivotal battle of the American Civil War was largely determined by geology; view of the 'Devil's Den' from Little Round Top. (P. Doyle)

Confederate sharpshooter in the Devil's Den; the use of geological features by soldiers is a common feature of most battlefields. (Library of Congress)

ridge formed by distinctive rocks that the Confederacy assaulted in vain over the three days of the battle. Brown's work led the way in demonstrating that such forensic dissection of battlegrounds could be applied to other campaigns.

In the Great War, the most obvious aspects of the impact of terrain were not only to figure on the Western Front, but in all other theatres too. Perhaps the first analysis of the impact of terrain in the war overall was that of D.W Johnson, Professor of Physiography [physical geography] at Colombia University in New York. Writing in 1917, at the point of America's involvement, Johnson commented on the war that was then raging on many fronts. 'If the surface features of Europe control in important measure the issues of the various campaigns, contributing to success in one field and imposing failure in another, then obviously a knowledge of the topographic elements peculiar to each front is essential to an intelligent understanding of the war…'[13] Johnson followed this up with a more detailed examination in his book *Battlefields of the World War*, published in 1921.

Johnson's studies were focused primarily on the European fronts, drawing out the details of their physiography and commenting upon how they were influenced by it. He considered the geology of Europe and the landforms that resulted from it; he examined the distribution of lowlands and uplands, the nature of the soil, the influence of watercourses. He considered barriers to manoeuvre and obstacles to fortification. His conclusions were that even in the 'modern warfare' of the Great War, terrain was master, for 'despite the enormous improvement in the artillery and other arms of the service, it is still the infantry which must drive back the enemy and conquer the ground on which he stands, and that whatever affects the movement of infantry remains a vital element in the fighting.'[14]

Notably, Johnson did not consider those theatres in which the fighting had ended before his work had commenced in 1917. One such battlefront was the ill-fated Gallipoli Campaign of 1915; yet a study of the campaign is especially rewarding in this respect, especially when examining the features he identified as worthwhile on other fronts. At Gallipoli, such features are the effects of the coastal geography on the failure of the Allies to push inland, the difficulty of the terrain once bridgeheads had been established, and the total inadequacy of the landscape to provide sufficient water for men or animals.[15] Examination of all these aspects would take another volume, as would indeed the study of many of the other theatres that Johnson did consider, such as the Alpine warfare of the Italo–Austro-Hungarian Front, the supply, terrain and medical problems of the Salonika Front, and the desert warfare in Mesopotamia and Palestine. Echoing Johnson's studies, and drawing upon some of the detailed examinations of the battlefield of Gettysburg, this book examines what was seen arguably as the principal front of the Great War, then as

The 'badland' topography of the Anzac Sector of the Gallipoli Battlefield; the nature of the topography made it difficult to capture, and its arid nature meant it provided little sustenance to the men entrenched here in 1915. (P. Doyle)

now, and indeed that sector where it was felt the war could be ended: northern France and Flanders.

It was in this part of northern Europe that the war started, a function of the Schlieffen Plan of 1904. The intention was to despatch recent enemy France – losers in the Franco-Prussian War of 1870–71 – before an attack could be mounted against Russia, with its countless millions, and its vast territories. The plan predicted that in a future war there would be an early exit for France (and its allies) as the armies of von Moltke pivoted their 'swinging door', forcing everything ahead of them en route to the French capital. The idea, of course, was to prevent the horror of a conflict fought simultaneously on two fronts, with Germany caught in a vice-like grip between its enemies, the plan predicated on geographical principles.

The plan was enacted in the wake of the Kaiser's backing of Austria-Hungary, in its bid to subjugate Serbia following the assassination of the Archduke Franz Ferdinand in late June, 1914. With Russia bound to follow, supporting the smaller Slavic nation, it followed that France would become embroiled, and the Schlieffen Plan brought into play. Germany declared war on France on 3 August 1914, and

Still from the 1933 film *La Bataille de la Marne*: German officers discuss the failure of the Schlieffen Plan.

started the door swinging. Yet that door would inevitably move slower through 'friction', a concept first introduced by the military theorist Carl von Clausewitz, 'Everything is very simple in war, but the simplest thing is difficult. These difficulties accumulate and produce a friction, which no man can imagine exactly who has not seen war.'[16] Friction is made up of those simple aspects of a campaign that cannot be planned for, but which will inevitably slow down any advance. Not surprisingly, geographical and geological factors feature significantly in this, and helped slow the German advance.

The Schlieffen Plan also ensured that Britain would be part of the story – as with the German troops streaming across neutral Belgium's borders, then it followed that the British could not simply stand aside and allow this to happen. Not only had Britain guaranteed Belgium's sovereignty in the Treaty of London in 1839, but with the *Entente Cordiale* of 1904 had also agreed to take France's interests into account. And in the light of the pre-war naval arms race played out between Britain and Imperial Germany (with the Kaiser vying to equal or outdo the power of the Royal Navy) the prospect of hostile Germans occupying the Channel ports, just miles away from the English coast, was not to be relished – or accepted.

On that point, in an address to London's Royal Geographical Society in January 1915, the military and political geographer Vaughan Cornish set out why occupation of the Channel Ports would be unacceptable to the British.

> The conception of there being lands on the Continent of Europe which are part of a British military area may be illustrated by reference to the Monroe Doctrine of the United States. The foreign policy of that power is based upon the declaration that the acquisition of territory on the American continents will be regarded as a *casus belli*…The importance of the Low Countries, with the harbours of the Rhine and the Scheldt, is as great for us now as it was in the days of Marlborough and Wellington; but the French departments of Nord and Pas de Calais have an increased importance to us owing to the development of marine mines and submarine craft…A German occupation of the opposite shore of the Straits of Dover would entail imminent danger of invasion.[17]

It was clear, then, that conditions for an Allied response to the Schlieffen Plan were in place, and the British Expeditionary Force (BEF) arrived in France in early August. The BEF was soon embroiled a battle of movement, retreating in the face of German pressure alongside their French allies, stopping where they could to delay the onslaught. Yet the weight of the German invasion that commenced on 4 August 1914 was such that the French and British troops fell back, retreating to take up a position along the line of the River Marne before Paris. In the battle that ensued from 6–12 September 1914, the German advance was stopped in its tracks. The Schlieffen Plan's 'swinging door' had met the doorjamb of the Marne, just in front of Paris. From this point on, and until the end of 1914, the battles that would become known as the 'Race for the Sea' would witness the two sides trying to turn the flank of the other in the traditional 'cockpit of Europe' – Flanders – the flat manoeuvring ground of European armies for centuries.

This distinctive region of northern Europe had seen warfare since the Middle Ages. Low-lying, as a region Flanders stretches from the chalk uplands of Artois and Picardy in northern France to the coastal strip of sand dunes between Dunkirk and Ostend. Squeezed between the rugged Ardennes mountains and the North Sea, it is not surprising that Flanders has throughout history been the main route for countless invading and retreating armies intent on east-west movement, and vice versa. Later in his 1915 lecture to the Royal Geographical Society, Dr Cornish reflected on this point, centring on its importance to Britain:

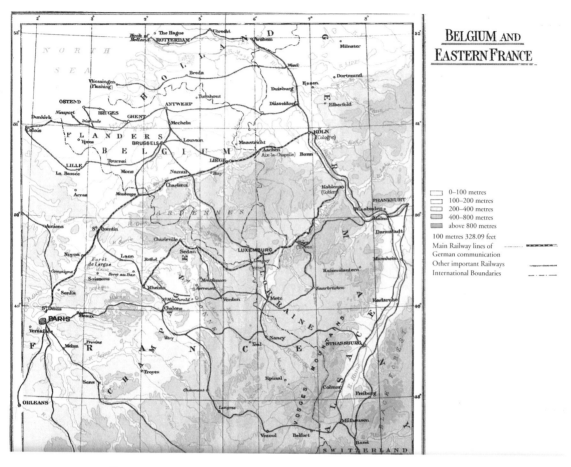

0–100 metres
100–200 metres
200–400 metres
400–800 metres
above 800 metres
100 metres 328.09 feet
Main Railway lines of
German communication
Other important Railways
International Boundaries

Contemporary topographic map of Northern France and Belgium; this shows the flat plain of
Flanders, the uplands of the Ardennes (and the Vosges mountains to the south), and the position
of Paris at the centre of a bowl; it also demonstrates the main east-west rail routes across Europe.

Belgium between the line of the Lys and the lower Scheldt on the one hand
and the line of the Sambre on the other is a strip of country not too broad
to be correctly described as a 'defile' [a pass between mountains] between
Germany and France, a character which…is moreover enforced by the
locality of such battles as Ramillies, Ligny, Mons, Waterloo, Oudenarde and
Fontenoy. The fact that the country stands in a somewhat similar relation
between Metropolitan England and the Cologne district of Germany was
not obvious to the general reader…[18]

Replete with rapid communication lines, and squeezed between natural barriers,

The Champagne region of France; the region lies in front of Paris and the plateau of the Marne. (P. Doyle)

it is no surprise that Flanders would once again be the target of intense military activity. The reasons were plain to the military geographer Douglas W. Johnson:

> In 1914, the Flanders Plain offered the German General Staff something more than the smoothest pathway between mountains and sea along which to launch its enveloping movement designed to crush the French armies in the space of a few weeks. The plan was provided with that abundant network of roads, railways and canals which is the natural product of a dense population inhabiting a region of very little relief.[19]

If Flanders was to be the through route to Paris, then it was the line of the River Marne that would be the roadblock. Here, in September 1914, French commander Joseph Joffre held the Germans, as they attempted to move from the chalky lowlands of the Champagne region to the heavily dissected plateau of the Marne, beyond the river. The Champagne is a rich, verdant and open landscape, perfect for rapid manoeuvre with just a few hills to disturb its flat chalk lands. But the Marne – that plateau that commences with slopes that had nurtured countless generations

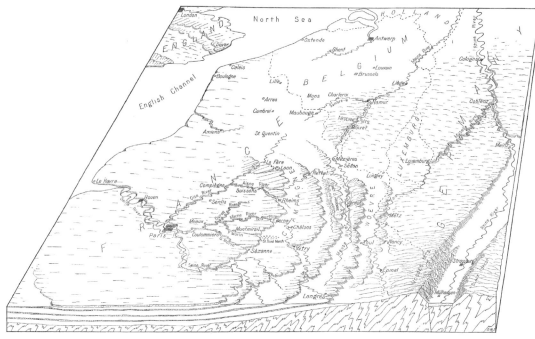

Block diagram showing the topography of the Western Front, showing the Flanders Plain between the Ardennes mountains and the North Sea, and the location of Paris in a basin, with successive strata dipping down beneath it. Scarp slopes are presented to any invader from the east. (D.W. Johnson, 1917).

of grapes for the most special of all wines – was a different proposition altogether. This plateau of the Marne is capped with hard limestone, and softer marls (a type of lime-rich clay), creating positions that are easy to defend, a last bastion before the French capital.[20] Planning an assault on Paris, the German intentions were compromised by the fact that the city sits squarely within a bowl; a bowl formed of successive strata that dip into the ground to the west. While these layers descend below the capital, they present a series of scarps in their wake, cliffs and steep slopes that are easy to defend, and difficult to attack. It was a challenging prospect for any enemy of France, as Douglas Johnson recognised:

> Every enemy movement would be open to observation from the crest of the scarp, and could be broken up by fire from artillery concealed in ravines back from the plateau face. Assaults on intrenched positions on the slopes and crest of the scarp would be made with every advantage on the side of the defending troops. The level plain below offers little opportunity for

Ypres was a focus of endeavour for the British; here the Medieval Cloth Hall is under bombardment in 1914. The Salient that surrounded the city on three sides gave superb vantage to the Germans.

the offensive to secure concealed artillery positions from which to make preparation for the uphill infantry charges.[21]

With the topography of the Marne plateau acting to multiply the difficulties for the attacking forces, the Germans were held. A counterattack followed on another river line, the Aisne, and out-flanking positional warfare developed as both sides attempted to trap their enemies, and to 'turn their flanks' – literally to surround them and force them to retreat or surrender. From 17 September to 19 October 1914 the Allied and German armies attempted to outflank each other in what has become known as the 'Race to the Sea'. With the armies locked into a fierce struggle to find open flanks, the battles moved inexorably closer to the Belgian Coast, and the line became a static one. By November 1914, both armies in the west had ground to a halt in parallel lines that stretched from the North Sea to the Swiss Frontier.

For the British Expeditionary Force, sandwiched between what remained of the Belgian armies (reinforced by the French) at the coast, and the French armies in Artois, Flanders would become the place of battle for another four years of a hard war. Ypres became a centre of British endeavour, with battles there

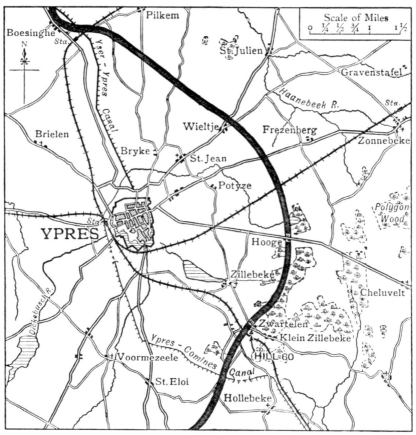

The Ypres Salient, after the Second Battle of Ypres, in 1915. The German line followed the trace of the high ground to the east of the city.

from late 1914 right the way through to the end of the war in 1918. The First Battle of Ypres, in November–December 1914 was an outcome of the 'Race to the Sea', with British troops holding on grimly in the face of a determined German army. Here there would be waterlogged ground, hasty scrapes in the earth, and the birth of the legend of the old BEF and its fire rate of fifteen-rounds-a-minute from Lee Enfield rifles. With the German line held by the close of the year, the early part of 1915 saw the development of the tradition of trench warfare that has come to represent the Great War to so many people. Grimly holding on, the British toiled in and around the clay plain of Ypres, while the Germans set about holding the high ground that faced the town on three sides, in what became known as the Ypres Salient.

A 'salient' is a bulge in the front line, usually jutting forward into enemy held territory. Such bulges are dangerous as, over extended, they are easier to attack and observe, and at certain points they even allow the enemy to fire into the rear of the line. The Ypres Salient was particularly dangerous, formed in the early days of the German drive towards the coast. The Salient had been born in November 1914, when the German attacks from Armentières to Nieuport ran out of steam. 'The Germans had driven in wedges towards Ypres until our lines had fallen back closer to the city, and the ground was a bastion thrust out dangerously in a wide arc, like an English bow full-drawn, and encompassed by the enemy whose skill and strength had seized the high ground everywhere'.[22]

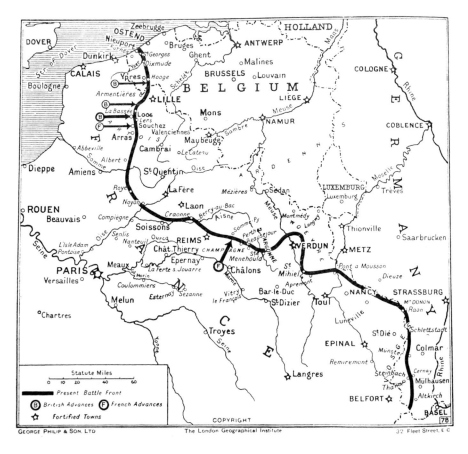

The Noyon Salient. Joffre's plans for 1914–15 were to drive in the line to the north (in Artois), and east (on the Champagne) of Noyon. The line is anchored at the Fortress of Verdun, and the city of Ypres.

Following the low rising hills to the east of the town, the Salient defined an arc of trenches with a long axis running approximately north–south, facing east–west. Running around the hills, the German line, and British line following it, passed southwards over its saddle back, and down to the damp valley of the Lys and on to Armentières. Farther south, the line passed through French Flanders to the canal of La Bassée, in that flat tract of land between the Lys and the Scarpe rivers. South from this the line was in French hands and ran towards Noyon, before tracking westwards to Verdun and the St Mihiel Salient, from there arcing around to the Swiss Frontier. Stabilised in late 1914, this line would form the linear fortress of the Western Front, scene of the titanic battles of 1916–18, and successive attempts to break the line and sweep to victory.

For the French, the occupation of home soil by the Germans was a national disgrace. General Joffre, Commander in Chief of the French armies, and hero of the Marne, was a strong character. Joffre enacted plans in late 1914 and 1915 that would throw the might of the French Tenth Army at the Germans in Artois, close to the city of Arras, and particularly the natural stronghold of Vimy Ridge; while committing the French Fourth and Second armies in the Champagne. In attacks that commenced in the winter of 1914–15 Joffre hoped that the right-angled dogleg of the German front around the town of Noyon would be driven in, thereby allowing for mobile warfare to be resumed. This plan would form the basis of French planning throughout 1915, and would figure again as the centre of General Nivelle's ill-fated plans for a rapid knock-out blow in 1917. All would contribute to a vast toll of French casualties that mounted up in these war-blighted areas. Artois was challenged with its chalk uplands and ridges; while the Champagne, a vast area for manoeuvre, was one that was difficult to defend, or dominate.

In this way, and at other points in the line, the Great War in the west of 1914–1918 became largely static: a fortress war that bears comparison with the siege warfare prevalent centuries before. Trench warfare in the west began when the race for the sea came to its abrupt conclusion. Despite all the protestations from the military manuals that trench warfare was just a passing phase, a temporary halt in the proceedings of open battle, it had become the norm.[23] It would last until the breakthrough battles of 1918, when first the Germans and then the Allies found a way to punch through the defensive lines.

The form of the Western Front was decided, as a static line with little change of 'turning a flank', when the sluice gates of the canal system in the low ground near the Flanders town of Nieuport were opened in 1914. Stopping the advancing Germans by flooding, for almost four years the armies of the Western Front to the south of the polders endured a troglodyte existence as artillerymen vied with engineers to weaken the line and provide opportunities for advance. 'Understanding the ground' was an important task in the development of this underground war, and a sophisticated science of ground engineering was deployed in its development.

For the British and the Germans facing them, the impact of geology was particularly significant along the line of the largely static front, from the coastal town of Nieuport Bains along the line of the Yser River to Dixmude, crossing the Flanders plain to Boesinghe on the outskirts of Ypres, then following the Passchendaele and Wytschaete–Messines ridges, before dropping down onto the clay plain of the River Lys near Armentières in northern France. From here the line passed southwards through French Flanders (close to the cities of Armentières and Lens) and on to Arras and Albert in Artois-Picardy. All these places had differences in 'ground', differences that would be felt directly by the infantrymen who marched through its fields or dug trenches into its soil, and to all the Generals who stared at the maps and plans in front of them in those four years of war.

This book examines the role that geology and terrain had to play in the operations fought on the Western Front, and particularly in the area of Flanders, Artois and Picardy. Though many other fronts and sectors could have been considered, it is the section of the Western Front in France and Flanders that arguably saw the most important applications and implications of the science of geology in warfare. It examines geology's role in the creation of trench warfare and its many innovations for defence, and explores its impact on those new means of breaking the status quo that developed at the front, on artillery, mining, gas and tanks.

2 GEOLOGY, GEOLOGISTS AND WARFARE

The work of the geologists in the Great War was of a great many different kinds. There was, of course, the problem of water-supply, and there were the finding of rock materials for roads and concrete and the selection of sites for bridges and trenches, and, perhaps most important of all, for dug-outs and mine galleries.[24]

From the foregoing discussion it can be seen that geology has had a major role to play in most campaigns – though whether commanders were aware of this at the time is another matter. Certainly, the evaluation and use of terrain – the 'ground' – was the preoccupation of many great soldiers, with specific paths and gateways figuring often in the course of history, where 'certain characteristics of terrain have spelled the difference between success and defeat in particular battles or campaigns.'[25]

With such factors obviously significant, what are meant by the terms geology, ground, relief, terrain? Geology is the study of the Earth, its origin, structure, composition, history – and the nature of the processes that have shaped it. Geologists are those scientists who are committed to this study, as well as its application in human endeavour – including warfare. The term 'ground' is defined by the *Oxford English Dictionary* as 'the surface of the Earth or part of it'. This surface clearly creates an arena for human activity, once again, including warfare. Relief, used by some, is an expression of the variation in elevation shown by landforms and topographical features (with topography the detailed features of a region). Terrain is more complex. Once again the *OED* provides 'a tract of country considered with regard to its natural features, configuration, etc.; in military use… as affecting its tactical advantages, fitness for manoeuvring, etc'; when first used, it was in a military sense, in 1766. Terrain has also been described as 'the common denominator of land warfare and geology'.[26]

Though the use of the term 'terrain' in military matters has grown to dominate analysis of battlegrounds in the post Second World War era,[27] all of these terms have been used, interchangeably, through history, when military commanders have striven to grasp the significance of the surface over which they were fighting. As Erdmann put it in 1943, 'Military literature of all ages, from Sun Tzu (500 BC) to

Terrain 'as affecting its tactical advantages, fitness for manoeuvring…', at Pointe de Hoc, Normandy. In June 1944, on D-Day, this site had to be assaulted from sea, the Jurassic limestone cliffs scaled. Aerial and naval bombardment had left the terrain broken and cratered, easier to defend. (P. Doyle)

Foertsch (1940), is replete with references to terrain, or 'ground,' or 'country' (they all mean the same), and they convey such a definite picture to the soldier that he seldom bothers to define it.'[28]

With terrain the arena of battle, understanding how it came to be, its characteristics and features, and knowing how to use those effectively, provides the military commander greater opportunity to fight a war. It can be argued that geology had a major role in this way in campaigns as diverse as the Battle of Poitiers (1356), when Edward the Black Prince drew the heavily armoured French knights onto boggy ground; the Battle of the Plains of Abraham (1759), when General Wolfe outflanked the French in Quebec by an appreciation of the cliffs and ravine for his landings, or Napoleon's 'ignorance of the sunken road at Waterloo' (1815) that allowed Blücher to achieve surprise over his enemy.[29] The most astute commanders recognised that knowledge of ground, as complete as possible, was a desired result. Marshal Foch, advocate of the offensive, wrote in his *Principles of War*, first published in 1903:

Plains of Abraham, Quebec. General Wolfe outflanked his French opponent, Montcalm, in 1759, scaling the steep cliffs of the St Lawrence River to face the French general on the Plains, outside of the city. (P. Doyle)

Before coming to the combined use of troops of all arms, you have to know them, to be able to handle them. The same is true of the *ground*, a fourth arm at your disposal; it is necessary to master everything it contains in order to be able to find in it what you have made up your mind you must be looking for.[30]

The landscape of Waterloo; part of the plain of Flanders, the traditional fighting ground of Europe, and the scene of Napoleon's defeat in 1815. (P. Doyle)

While these and other achievements underline the role a successful commander has in the 'appreciation of ground', the first considered use of geological knowledge in warfare is tracked back to the late eighteenth or early nineteenth century.[31] Despite the fact that he was later defeated at Waterloo (1815), arguably for the want of geological knowledge, Napoleon reportedly took two geologists with him on his expedition to Egypt in 1798. But it was Professor K.A. von Raumer's analysis of terrain in Silesia that permitted the defeat of his forces at the Battle of Katzbach River (1813) that stands as the first actual *documented* use of geological information in war.[32] Nevertheless, it took some time for geology – a science that had grown in stature throughout the eighteenth century – to become fully accepted in military circles.

Geology became part of the syllabus of engineer or artillery officers in the mid to later part of the nineteenth century.[33] The famous British geologist and soldier, Major-General J.E. Portlock, RE, was one of the first to give serious consideration of the application of geology to warfare, though he may well have met with resistance, or at least ignorance in promoting his science in these early years.[34] Nevertheless, writing in 1868, as the science of geology gathered some acceptance, Portlock was alive to its military possibilities:

> Geology is now a true science, being founded on facts and reduced to the domination of definite laws, and in consequence has become a sure guide to the practical man... The soldier may also find in geology a most valuable guide in tracing his lines both of attack and defence.[35]

By the latter part of the century, geology was finding more favour in military circles. This was certainly the case for geologist O. Barré, commandant du genie, who lectured at *l'École d'application de l'artillerie et du genie* at Fontainebleau in the latter part of the century.[36] In Britain, Lt Col Charles Cooper King RE similarly gave lectures on military geology at the Camberley Staff College, another man credited as 'the first professional soldier to recognise the wide application of geology to military problems'.[36] His obituary noted that 'Col King drew a large class to geology, both in the lecture-room and the field; for, being a military expert himself, his explanations of the science in relation to military tactics and battle-fields were well appreciated.'[37]

Arguably, though, it was the development of the largely static conflict on the Western Front that was to see the first large-scale use of geology and geologists in war (though there were many examples in the trench-warfare battles of the American

Walter Kranz, the 'father' of modern military geology (Geologische Vereinigung, Universtätsbibliothek Freiburg/Breisgau)

Civil War of 1861–65 and the Russo-Japanese War of 1904-05).[39] Just prior to the war, in 1913, military fortification engineer Hauptmann Walter Kranz,[40] coined the phrase *Militärgeologie* – later, with the outbreak of war, transmuted to *Kriegsgeologie*.[41] Kranz' original idea – that geology would have a large role to play in warfare, and particularly in the type of fortress or static warfare that would be enacted just a year later – was taken seriously only when war broke out in Europe.[42]

It was natural that Kranz's approach should take root, however. After all, geology dealt with the nature of the land surface over which men, animals and machines travelled; it gave answers to the kind of obstacles that they may face; it controlled the way in which fortifications were built, above and below ground, and it provided answers for resourcing armies – particularly in the supply of that vital liquid, water.[43] A review of Kranz's work in 1915 laid down the basic principles of *Militärgeologie*.[44] Kranz also recognised the significance of expertise in wartime 'It is of utmost importance that all geologists under arms, and geological trained personnel or miners should be drawn in for these uses.'[45] These principles were built upon and expanded in a wartime lecture – *Kriegsgeologie* (1915) – by W. Salomon of Heidelberg University, once again recognising the most important activities for geologists:

> Geology is practical and necessary: to prove the stability of parapets and trenches and the stability of dug-outs; to identify the speed of digging excavations; to identify water supplies; to assist in rain water and waste water removal; to supply building materials; and to identify mineral raw materials.[46]

As the world would very soon experience, all of these factors would have a pivotal role in the successful prosecution of trench warfare.

From the foundations that Kranz built came the evolution of a subject that would help define the way that the second war that followed the first would be fought. Once again Kranz was at the forefront of this; his 1938 manual *Wehrgeologie* would be a standard text for the German army, and identified the fundamental principles of the subject. Many of the other nations would have to catch up with German expertise as the Second World War dawned, and it would not be until 1941–42 that British and US geologists got the chance to bring their knowledge to bear, working in the Western Desert, but also working towards the invasion of Europe and the opening of a 'second front' against Germany.[48] These experiences would influence the future generation of post-war military geologists, with new threats, but with the same challenges remaining.[49]

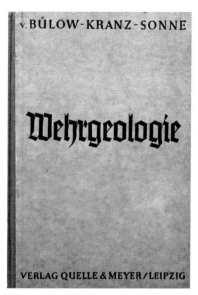

v. BÜLOW-KRANZ-SONNE

Wehrgeologie

VERLAG QUELLE & MEYER / LEIPZIG

Wehrgeologie: a 1938 text that would be carried by German military geologists in the Second World War.

What are these challenges? First identified by Kranz, they soon found application and use in world war, by both the practical experience of men in battle and the needs of the military to gain a tactical advantage over their enemy, and they remain pertinent today. Geologists under arms are engaged in a diversity of activities that would be familiar to the progenitors of *Kriegsgeologie,* namely:

1. Provision and interpretation of geological information in the planning and development of military operations (terrain intelligence and evaluation);
2. Consideration of observation, concealment and cover of military forces and personnel;
3. Trafficability, the capability of troops and materiel to move over terrain;
4. Military engineering geology, the influence of geology in the construction or excavation of military fortifications, fieldworks and infrastructure, in both offensive and defensive operations;
5. Water supply; and
6. The provision of construction materials and other resources.[50]

Terrain analysis, in particular, is a major role, with geologists being recognised as people who can 'analyse a terrain, appreciate its topography and understand its

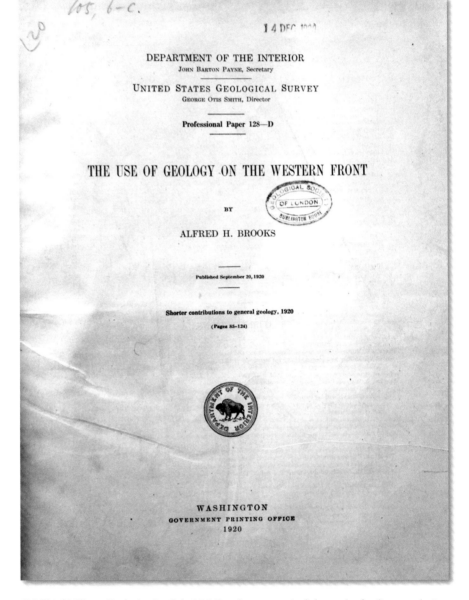

DEPARTMENT OF THE INTERIOR

John Barton Payne, Secretary

United States Geological Survey

George Otis Smith, Director

Professional Paper 128—D

THE USE OF GEOLOGY ON THE WESTERN FRONT

BY

ALFRED H. BROOKS

Published September 20, 1920

Shorter contributions to general geology, 1920

(Pages 85–124)

WASHINGTON
GOVERNMENT PRINTING OFFICE
1920

US Chief Military Geologist, Lt-Col. A.H. Brooks, summarised the work of military geologists in the Great War in this influential paper, published in 1920.

contours. This ability is a function of…particular training and with it a geologist is equipped to make complete and rapid analyses of the ground'.[51] Such activities would become an established part of military operations in the wake of the Second World War;[52] but this was long before they would dawn on the military of all nations in 1914. Though Walter Kranz had first advised that a geological service for the Imperial German Army be established in 1912 (prior to his ground-breaking article published in 1913), it took the outbreak of war for this to be considered in detail.[53] As noted by chief US military geologist Lt.-Col. Anthony Brooks in 1920:

> Kranz's recommendations published a year before the war, attracted little attention among geologists and apparently none at all among the military authorities. Therefore, when the war came German geologists were mobilised with their unit without regard to the possible value of their services in their own profession.[54]

This was certainly true. As late as April 1914 the Inspector General of the Imperial German Engineer Corps wrote to the Prussian minister of war:

> The Inspector General sees no need for the establishment of military geologist positions. In the field, events proceed so rapidly that even in trench warfare the employment of a geologist is out of the question. Moreover, his expertise would be worthless in most cases because it is tactical knowledge requirements that count…[55]

Fortunately, by 1915, many German press reports picked up on the point – that geologists really should be employed in the service of the army, and that officers should receive additional training as a matter of course (rather than as an optional component of their syllabus).[56]

A year later, the geological support provided to the German Army after its slow start grew to be impressively organised, and was embodied directly into the army structure by 1916.[57] Then, each of the twenty-eight field survey companies contained geological sections (*Geologen Stellen*), and requests for geological assistance would be made directly to them.[58] There would be some ~250 geologists employed in the German army by the end of the war (and a further 60 with the Austro-Hungarian army).[59] Though the actual number of geologists in German service during the Great War grew to be relatively large, their impact was reduced, as many served in lowly positions; they were expected simply to advise, but not supervise. But at least they were actively engaged on the ground.

A captured document for the German 5. Armee, serving opposite the French in Lorraine in late 1917, shows how far the Germans had got in applying the principles laid down by Kranz four years before. In it, geologists could be called upon 'at the first reconnaissance of the country before the lines are finally fixed..' to predict 'what difficulties are likely to occur arising out of the hardness of the strata, and their water-bearing qualities' and to advise on subways and galleries, providing information on 'which strata are the easiest to work' and whether there was a 'risk of landslide or inflow of water'. For water supply, geologists would be invaluable in 'ensuring water supply for the defensive battle' and for other supplies, they would be essential in assisting in the provision of 'gravel, sand, loam, building stone, material for cement and plaster, road metal, railway ballast and peat…'. It was a long list of duties and responsibilities.[60]

By way of contrast, at the outbreak of war in 1914 the British Army had no geological staff whatsoever, or even the will to provide one. Despite the commitment to geology given by the Royal Engineers in the mid to late part of the nineteenth century, the science had faded from view, no longer a significant component of the work of the Corps. It was the chronic need for water in both the Dardanelles and on the Western Front that led to the appointment of Britain's first practising geologist

French officers 'water divining' with a birch twig. Undue faith was placed in this practice; what was required was a full understanding of the geology of a region in order to locate groundwater supplies.

in uniform (many others would serve as infantry soldiers).[61] Lieutenant W.B.R. King, who had worked for the Geological Survey of Great Britain, was an infantry officer serving with the Royal Welsh Fusiliers. At the request of Major General W.A. Liddle, Director of Works at GHQ, and following a recommendation by his former employers, King became the first British geologist to receive a military

Lt (later Captain) W.B.R. King, the first British military (hydro)geologist of the Great War. (E.P.F Rose)

assignment in his own profession.[62] Seconded to Major-General G.H. Fowke, the Engineer-in-Chief of the British Expeditionary Force (BEF), he was put to work in Flanders and Artois exploring for water. In Flanders, King tackled the problem of polluted water supplies – surface waters contaminated by poison gases and the human detritus of war – and also determined a way of tapping the clean, water-filled, but extremely fine-grained sands that lay beneath the clay plain; on the Somme he examined the effect of fluctuating water levels in the porous, freely draining chalk rocks, and was able to predict how far the RE needed to sink boreholes to permanently tap the drinkable groundwaters at depth.[63] For a year King worked in isolation.

And then there was military mining. Such activity involves the excavation of tunnels, galleries and dug-outs – in fact in any subsurface excavation that can aid the army, whether in an offensive or defensive sense. The use of military mines is centuries-old.[64] Until the Great War the objectives of military miners had traditionally been large and clearly defined – forts and castles – with the besieger often better equipped and outnumbering the besieged. On the Western Front armies found themselves facing an enemy with roughly equal resources spread over a vast area, possessing not one but thousands of potential objectives, each of varying tactical value.

French miners at work in the Great War; a full appreciation of geology prevented many errors and problems.

The consideration of geology as a significant component of mine warfare was applied differently by the combatant nations. In fact, mining had been a component of military training schools in the United Kingdom during the nineteenth century, but had been dropped from the mainstream prior to the First World War.[65] This ambivalence was neatly encapsulated by the recollections of Brigadier-General R.N. Harvey, the British Inspector of Mines, in 1919:

> Although mining had been going on for nine months before I took over the appointment of Inspector of Mines, I did not realise that geology had anything to do with military mining. We were not mining very deeply in those days, and naturally if we came to a wet place, if the Germans were mining we continued, and if it was wet we pumped; but there was no geological science so far as that was concerned. It was when we came to deep mining that its importance was obvious.[66]

In fact, Harvey's wartime role was to bring order to the apparently endlessly expanding and complicated underground conflict; under him, the complete mining operation would be re-organised and coordinated, charges would no longer be blown without good reason, and no mining 'scheme' would be considered without consultation with other relevant and complimentary branches of the Army. He was eventually to administer his duties through three Assistant Inspectors, and locally through a Controller of Mines for each Army in the field. His initial disregard for – or ignorance of – geology was soon dissipated on the arrival on the scene of a distinguished Australian geologist.

In May 1916 the Australian Mining Corps detrained on the Western Front at Bailleul. With it came Major T.W. Edgeworth David FRS. Professor of Geology at Sydney University. David was an influential scientist who had helped raise and recruit the Australian Mining Corps. The Corps had originally been bound for Gallipoli, but before they could arrive, the Peninsula had been evacuated, the miners diverted to France.[67] Welsh-born, and at 58 already advanced in years, David was attached to Mines HQ and became the most senior British military geologist in the Great War, working directly to Harvey.[68]

Whilst with Harvey, David had a roving commission, and geology was soon taken seriously. His role was principally that of geological work in relation to mining and dug-outs, and providing practical advice and trouble-shooting where necessary for all the British armies in the field. In practice, although King was attached to the Engineer-in-Chief at GHQ, with a remit to concentrate upon water supply, both he and David were also to work closely together within all the

British sectors of the Western Front. A third geologist, another Australian, joined them in September 1916. Lieutenant C. Loftus Hills of the Australian Electrical and Mechanical, Mining and Boring Company (AEMMBC – or 'Alphabetical Company'), used test bores to ascertain water levels and strata,[69] carefully drawing up water-coloured logs of the sediments encountered that would provide the basis for a series of highly informative 'dug-out suitability' maps – specially created and annotated 1:10,000 sheets intended for the use of the British army in Flanders.[70]

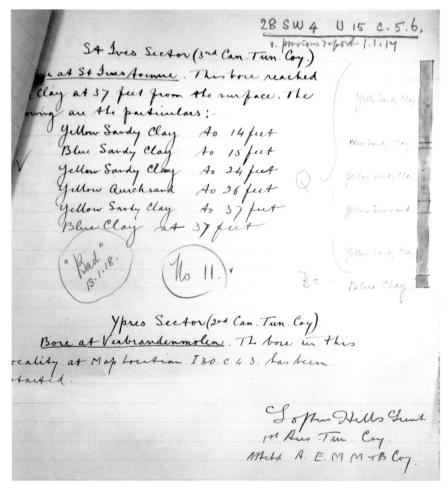

Borehole report from January 1917 by geologist Lt C. Loftus Hills of the Australian Electrical, Mechanical, Mining and Boring Company. The borehole, sunk in the Ypres Salient, identifies the ground here as 'bad' – unsuitable for deep dugouts.
(The National Archives)

By the end of the war, then, there would be three geologists employed full time in their professional capacity by the British army.[71] This was in stark contrast to the to the German's estimated 250 men on all fronts, in line with Kranz' original desire for the widespread use of military geologists. Two more geologists joined the British complement in the autumn of 1918 – Lieutenant G.A. Cook of the 2nd Australian Tunnelling Company (TC) and Lieutenant C.S. Homan of the 3rd Australian TC.[72] This establishment of five were to advise on geological conditions during the Allied advance in 1918.

The greatest success for the British tunnellers and their geological advisors was to come in June 1917, when the Messines–Wytschaete Ridge was captured in what could arguably be considered one of the most effective and successful battles of the Great War – meeting all objectives with limited casualties.[73] Not surprisingly, a deep understanding of geology had played a major role in prosecuting the coordinated mine offensive that launched the first attacks. Writing in 1935, Walter Kranz, the man who had done so much to precipitate geologists into their future role as military scientists, commented ruefully on the British dominance:

> If German geologists with military training had, immediately after the beginning of mining operations, at the latest in 1915, made a thorough survey of the whole Wytschaete salient, and if our miners from the beginning would have checked their advice tactically and technically, and if found correct would have followed this with all available means, the British would never have been so successful with their Wytschaete explosions – in spite of their excellent technical equipment and enormous willpower.[74]

3 GEOLOGY OF FLANDERS AND NORTHERN FRANCE

It was the geological features of western Europe which determined the general plan of campaign against Europe and the detailed movements of the invading armies. Geological history had favoured Belgium and northern France with valuable deposits of coal and iron…at the same time it had so fashioned the topography of these two areas as to insure the invasion of France through Belgium…[75]

Flanders and Artois-Picardy – that section of a long front that stretched 440 miles from the North Sea to the Swiss Frontier. It was a line that had run to a halt point after the failure of the Schlieffen plan, and was a line that was chosen, as far as military expertise could be brought to bear, to provide an advantage to the defender wherever possible. And as those defenders were the Germans – holding on to their occupied land as a buffer to their own territory, while the Russians were fought to a standstill in the East – it might have been thought that considerable geological or geographical expertise would be brought to bear. But it was not to be. It was left to their commanders to make their own choices (where they could): 'It would seem that the Germans may have prepared in some measure for trench warfare, if it should come, for they dug in with amazing rapidity after the First Battle of the Marne, on lines from which it took years to dislodge them. But they had planned a different kind of campaign…'[76]

One thing was clear, however, that the terrain of the line that became set in 1914 was least complex in the region of Flanders–Artois-Picardy, and here there was most to gain from a German advance, splitting the Allies, occupying the Channel Ports, and allowing rapid access to the capital of France, Paris.[77] With the notable exception of Verdun in 1916, the scene of the costly attempt of Falkenhayn to 'bleed the French army white', German attention was focussed in the northern sector of the front (as well as holding the French in the region of the Champagne).

The geology of Flanders-Picardy is not complex, but it was to have a major role in influencing the outcome of the war, both in its early days, and at its conclusion. For the British, the landscape of the region was familiar – at least those used to the chalk downs, or the clay plains of the South East of England. As noted in 1917 by Sir Aubrey Strahan, the Director of the Geological Survey of Great Britain, direct

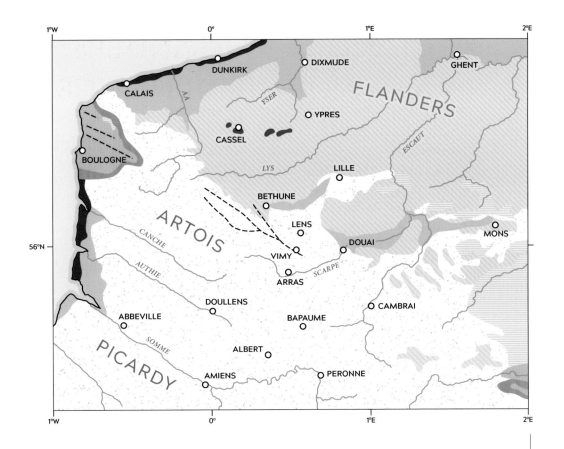

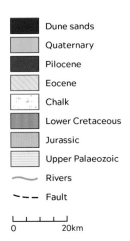

	Dune sands
	Quaternary
	Pilocene
	Eocene
	Chalk
	Lower Cretaceous
	Jurassic
	Upper Palaeozoic
	Rivers
	Fault

0   20km

Geological map of Flanders, Artois and Picardy, showing the distribution of the dune belt at the coast, the Polder Plain inland from this (Quaternary sediments), the Clay Plain (Eocene rocks), and the chalk of Artois and Picardy. At this scale, the Paniselian ridges are the same age as the Clay Plain (Eocene); higher hills are capped with younger (Pliocene) sediments. The Marqueffles Fault is the junction of Flanders and Artois. The coal bearing rocks of French Flanders are buried beneath younger rocks.

The rolling chalk downland of the Somme; a familiar topography for those from Kent and Sussex. (P. Doyle)

geological comparison could be made between the region of France and Flanders, and that of southern England.

> In connexion with the operations on the western Front a comparison of the geology with that of the South of England acquires a special interest. The severance of England from the Continent is, geologically speaking, a recent geographical incident. That the chalk escarpments of the North and South Downs are continued in the chalk escarpments which overlook Boulogne is obvious, and that the subdivisions of the Tertiary strata with which we are familiar in the London and Hampshire Basins are recognisable in the North of France and in Belgium is well known. Not only so, but the scenery characteristic of each formation is reproduced with fidelity.[78]

This comparison went beyond the geological. For the men of the British Expeditionary Force, most of whom would never have travelled to the continent before, the similarity of landscape of France and southern England must have been especially striking. It certainly impressed upon John Masefield, the future Poet Laureate, who examined the Somme battlefield in the aftermath of the battle in 1916.

> The whole field of the Somme is chalk hill and downland, like similar formations in England. It has about it, in every part of it, certain features well known to everyone who has ever lived or travelled in a chalk country.[79]

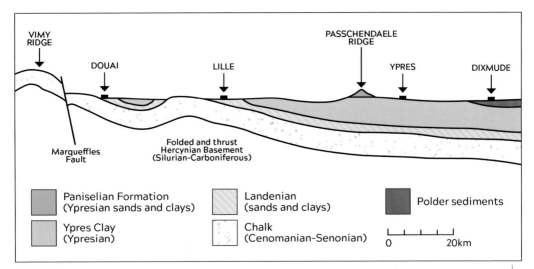

Geological cross section from Vimy Ridge to Dixmude, showing the relationship of the various layers. Beneath the chalk of French Flanders is an older 'basement' that has been folded and fractured during mountain building (the 'Hercynian' event that created the Ardennes).

In fact, a study of a topographic map of the 'war zone' in France and Belgium will reveal a pattern of distinct 'belts', zones of differing topography, controlled for the most part by the underlying geology and which were in turn to influence the outcome of the war – or at least the lives of the soldiers as they toiled across the battlefield, or struggled through the trenches.[80] It would even control the shape and form of shell and mine craters that marked out the war zone.[81] From the Belgian Coast to the Somme these fall into at least six zones or belts: the coastal dune belt; the Polder Plain; the clay plain; the sand ridges; the coal belt; and the chalk upland.

L. Dudley Stamp, geologist and former Royal Engineer Officer, made a special study of the geology of Belgium in the aftermath of war. Writing in professional geological journals in the early 1920s, he noted (with some personal experience) that Flanders was:

A low lying district, even marshy in places, consisting largely of Eocene Clay (*Argile des Flandres*) with a superficial covering of sand and 'limon' and on the west a fringe, termed the 'plaine maritime' of recent marine muds and sands. The plain is relieved by a few prominent hills [forming] a chain stretching from Cassel in France, through the hills north of Bailleul (Mont des Cats, Mont Noir, Rouge and Aigu) to Mont Kemmel and then to the central region.[82]

The clay rich soils of Flanders, here on the southern slopes of the Messines ridge at La Petit Douve Farm. (P. Doyle)

From a military viewpoint such features are critical, as each provides its own challenges – just as they did, and indeed still do, for the civil inhabitants. And there was nothing as distinct as the boundary between the chalk upland and the clay plain, the junction of Flanders and Artois-Picardy. The distinction was not lost on military geographer Douglas Johnson:

> Of the battlefields of the world war the rolling surface of the Somme region just to the south can be best compared with the Flanders plain. Yet how few the elements of correspondence, how many the points of contrast! Two different worlds seem to come together where the chalk of the Somme region meets the clay of Flanders. One is a rolling upland, the other a lowland. The even flowing, clear streams of the chalk country do not in the least suggest the unruly rivers whose turbid waters repeatedly flood the fields and homes of the Flemish peasant. Nothing could be further apart than the aridity of the chalk surface and the humidity of the water-soaked plain.[83]

These differences would regularly be remarked upon by all soldiers who served both in Flanders, and on the Somme. Just as the geology of the landscape of Flanders would become well known, inadvertently, to the soldiers who toiled there, it was also of significant interest to the military engineers of the day. Though the first military geologists only arrived on the scene in 1915, there was no mistaking the need of a greater understanding of the terrain than had been developed in the opening months of the war, when the expectation of a drawn-out positional warfare was small. In Belgium, it was the 1:40,000 scale maps produced by the country's Geological Survey in the late nineteenth century that served to provide the most detailed information available, and as the national survey and major universities were now in occupied territory, this would have to suffice. In fact, these maps remained widely used until the general geology of Flanders was revised according to modern geological practices in the mid 1990s.[84] (As such, the names given by geologists to some of the well-known geological layers changed). Learning how to read these maps was important. As with all such maps, they show the distribution of geological materials and their occurrence at the surface, and showed how they varied. Importantly, they marked the position of boreholes that revealed subsurface information, and gave other details, such as the thickness of soils and other materials likely to have an effect in the developing battlefield. All such data would be hungrily picked over by military engineers, future reference for the war ahead.

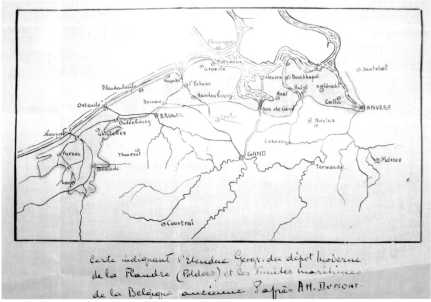

Manuscript sketch map of the dunes and Polder Plain prepared for the proposed Allied invasion of the Belgian coast in 1917. The dune belt is a narrow strip, while the Polders, the area that could be flooded at extremes of tide, extends inshore, particularly along the river valleys. (The National Archives)

The dune field looking back over the Polder Plain. (P. Doyle)

THE COASTAL DUNE BELT

The coastal dune belt comprises a 2-km-wide strip of coastal dunes that fringe the North Sea – a strip that is now a target for developers keen to exploit the real estate possibilities of the attractive Belgian coast. Each of the dunes is made up of loose sands, though stabilised by marram grass and other hardy vegetation that is typical of all the sand hills along the North Sea coast. Because of this, these dunes are static, unmoving, having been in place for some time. At their base they are just at sea level, and rising rapidly up from there, some them reach considerable heights. That they were also significant natural features during the Great War is shown by contemporary photographs, which show soldiers amongst their slopes. Douglas Johnson described the dunefield as it looked in 1917:

> Between the low maritime plain and the sea stretches the great barrier of sand, from one to several miles broad, capped by dunes that keep out the ocean waters. The dunes are from 30 to 100 feet high and, while sheltering more trees that the level plain, show large spaces of barren white or yellowish sand, conspicuous even at great distances.[85]

As noted by Johnson, the dunes, then and today, are irregular in form but are arranged in two bands parallel to the coast, just inland from the strandline of

Belgian soldiers dig hasty shelters in the dune field, 1914.

the beach, gently sloping into the sea with golden sands. The dune field was an effective barrier, not only to the storms of the North Sea coast, but also to any invader, albeit a temporary one.

The coastal dunes are largely dry. Despite this, and perhaps surprisingly, considering the proximity of sea water, in some areas fresh water lakes and 'lagoons' (known as 'pannes') may be found between individual dune clusters, indicating the fact that fully saturated ground is very close to the surface.[86] Historically, this has been an issue for warring nations intent on campaigning close to the coast.

> The sandy soil is much drier than that found on the plain; but the water lies close below the surface, as the Duke of York discovered when he found it impossible, during his siege of Dunkirk [in 1793], to protect his flanks by trenches because they encountered water at a depth of two feet.[87]

Nevertheless, trenches *were* dug there during the Great War, anchoring the end of the Western Front to the North Sea coast, and this made them an important feature for the armies that manned them. When the lines were set, the Western Front came to an abrupt end at the sea, the trench lines carving their way through lower dunes just to the east of the Allied-held town of Nieuport. Here the French, Belgian or British troops that held them watched anxiously for enemy activity, and

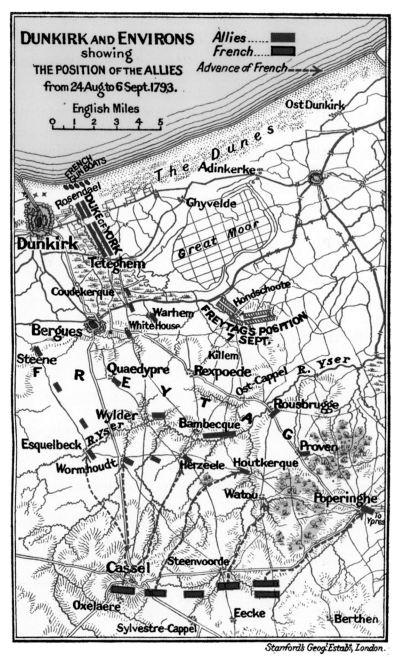

Map of the Battle of Hondshoote in 1793; in trying to besiege the City of Dunkirk, the Duke of York was beset with the difficulties of the wet Polder Plain and dune fields. Unable to deploy his cavalry, and under pressure, the Duke of York withdrew. (Bwcajp/CC–BY–SA–3.0)

worked tirelessly with the sands to ensure that fortifications improved as they did so.[88] Nevertheless, the dunes provided an incongruous backdrop to war, as noted by Lt. Charles Douie, who occupied this sector with his battalion in preparation for a possible amphibious attack in 1917:

> War seemed more than usually odd as one sat in some convenient fold of the dunes and watched the waves lapping the belts of wire on the sands where but a short while before men and women had kept holiday and children had built sandcastles. But the sand-dunes did not show the traces of shell fire in the same degree as the chalk country of the Somme. Shells exploding in the sand appeared to be choked in the loose texture and to have a limited effect.[89]

THE POLDER PLAIN

North of the Belgian city of Ypres, commencing for the most part at the village of Dixmude and passing north to Nieuport, is the coastal plain of Flanders, 'the Polders', a region sometimes known as 'Les Moëres' (the moors) or 'De Moeren'. It is a region that is under the control of fluctuations in sea level, sandwiched between the dune field and the clay plain of Flanders, where the land surface finally rises away from the influence of even the highest North Sea tides. This region was artificially drained in the seventeenth century by the celebrated Flemish engineer Wenceslas Cobergher, who strove to transform the wet and unhealthy marshland into the verdant farmland it is now. With the use of canals, locks and windmills to pump the water, Cobergher transformed the marshy Polders; but it was also left that the waters could be called upon to return if necessary.

The Polder plain is at best just five metres above sea level today, and its vulnerability to flooding remains, as it is lower that the highest sea levels that can be expected on this coast;[90] but farther south the rising clay provides a barrier to inundation by the sea. Across the coastal plain runs the Yser, joined and linked to the complex of artificial canals and drainage ditches between them. Not surprisingly, the many types of sedimentary layers that make up the wet plain are conspicuously water bearing.[91] Douglas Johnson described the predicament that originally faced the Flemish engineers, four centuries before the Great War.

> With the whole belt menaced by invasion from the sea on one side, by flooding from the rivers which flow into the lowland on the other side, by deluges of rain from a leaden sky above, and by eruption of brackish water from the earth beneath…only a severe and never-ending struggle can keep the land fit for human habitation.[92]

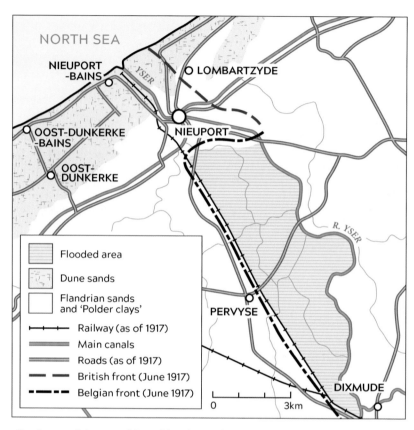

NORTH SEA

NIEUPORT-BAINS

OOST-DUNKERKE-BAINS

OOST-DUNKERKE

NIEUPORT

LOMBARTZYDE

YSER

PERVYSE

R. YSER

DIXMUDE

Flooded area

Dune sands

Flandrian sands and 'Polder clays'

Railway (as of 1917)

Main canals

Roads (as of 1917)

British front (June 1917)

Belgian front (June 1917)

0   3km

Sketch map of the area of the Polder Plain under inundation during the Great War.

Because of its history, the Polder plain is build from layers that include clays and sands that were formed by coastal processes, or fine sediments that settled out from estuaries.[93] This coastal plain represents the maximum flooding level in recent geological history, high and dry during the Ice Age, followed by a time of variability in sea levels with glacial melting. Here, the resulting sedimentary layers are up to at least 30 m thick, and are mixed below surface, often with a confusing interplay of peat beds, sands and thin clays, which together with buried valleys and other topographical features, mean it is difficult to predict just what is beneath your feet in this zone.[94] Moving across this zone was a concern for the armies of both world wars. A British report from 1917 recognised the constraints of the ground, with only infantry passing, and even then 'Manoeuvring with difficulty'.[95] This uncertainty was to exert its influence on the Second World War too. In 1940, the advancing German armies were equipped with military manuals and geological maps that

Belgian sentries on duty in the inundated zone; tracks, embankments and canal banks were fiercely defended.

advised: 'Predominant soil type: peat, groundwater near surface. Passability...: at all times passable with difficulty. Accessible to infantry in dry season.'[96] This, it is argued, could have been a material consideration in halting the tanks outside of the perimeter of Dunkirk, thereby allowing the British to escape in May–June 1940.[97]

Due to the availability of water, and of the complexity of the drainage system, it has been understood for centuries that the deliberate inundation of the Polder plain by flood waters has been an effective defensive tactic, and the high level of water saturation has meant that its suitability for trenches, tunnels and other defensive works has been limited.[98] From the fifteenth century the town of Nieuport, situated on the northern edge of the Polders, had been successfully defended by inundation during the various wars in the region five times between 1488 and 1677. In 1914, when Belgium was once again under attack from the invader, the lock gates controlling this system were opened and the land inundated to help impede the German advance. While to the south there were French and British soldiers, this particular part of the front was held through the war by Belgians. Stationed along the canalised River Yser, and the raised railway line which ran from Dixmude to Nieuport, the Belgians faced the grim inundated land surface to the east. In 1917, British subaltern Charles Douie examined the Polder defences for himself:

> The flooded country was traversed only by the high towpaths of the Yser Canal and by a number of causeways and duck-boarded tracks. The defences took the form of breastworks and strong points constructed of concrete or

fashioned out of the ruins of the farms. An active enemy could have made life intolerable in these marshes. The breastworks were inadequate and often unprotected from the rear. The causeways that led to them were few and wholly exposed.[99]

Not surprisingly, the inundations were a significant barrier to military operations, and dismal to lay eyes upon. Intelligence officer Maurice Baring observed the scene in January 1915:

> On the 2nd of January [1915] I went to Ypres, Furnes, Pervyse, and Dunkirk. Pervyse was on the edge of the inundated country, and we watched the wide grey floods from a rickety, shot-riddled little building. I never looked upon a more desolate scene. It was pouring with rain, and the world seemed to have been first destroyed and then flooded.[100]

THE CLAY PLAIN

From Ypres southwards, Flanders comprises an extensive, flat plain composed of thick deposits of clay, overlain by soils and other deposits. This plain has become the site of memory – the position of the Ypres Salient, held by the British for the four years of war. The topography of the clay plain is uncomplicated, its flatness relieved only by a series of low hills with elevations of no greater than 50 metres that partially embrace the city of Ypres. As author Leon Wolff would comment in his 1956 classic *In Flanders Fields*: 'The fields of Flanders are mostly flat, flatter than the plains of Kansas, flatter than the lowlands of Hungary. On such terrain a ten-foot rise is a military prize worth fighting for'.[101] Yet despite this flatness, there is still enough relief on the plain to define the route of the streams and rivers, draining downwards from the low hills and ridges to the clay plain and beyond.[102]

The plain itself is mostly made up of clays once called the 'Ypres Clay' – (indeed belonging to a geological time interval, the Ypresian, that was named after it) but which are now given a new, but perhaps less historically emotive, technical name – the Kortrijk Formation.[103] This thick blanket of clay underlying the city of Ypres and spreading its influence across the region consists of heavy clays of variable depth, reaching up to 130 m thick, but reducing to around 50 m in the west.[104] The clay would become both a blessing and a curse to the engineers who worked with it, and in it, during the course of the war.

As noted by many contemporary commentators – these clays are broadly equivalent to the London Clay common in southern England, formed in the same seas, under the same conditions. Both 'Ypres' and 'London' clays are blue-

Comparison of geological strata names used on geological maps of the Ypres (Ieper) region

1:40,000 (1900)		1:50,000 (1999)	British military (1918)
Quaternary		Quaternary	Alluvium
		Diest Formation	
		Maldegrem Formation	
		Lede Formation	
		Aalter Formation	
Paniselian	Pl*d* Fine Sands	Gent Formation	Wytschaete Sands
	Pl*c* Sandy Clay	Tielt Formation	Sandy Clays
	Pl*b* Sand & Clay		Kemmel Sands
	Pl*m* Clay	Kortrijk Formation	Paniselian Clay
Ypresian	Y*d* Fine sands		Ypres Sands
	Y*c* Clay		Ypres Clay

Sources: Rosenbaum & Rose (2011), Belgian Geological Survey maps (1900, 1999)

grey when freshly cut, oxidising a dull-brown, and both are a plastic material. In Flanders, the striking colour of freshly cut clay was a major issue for the British, particularly those engaged in deep mining. With the blue colour visible from the air, it would surely give away the fact that tunnels and mines were in the process of being dug, and even when put into sandbags to reinforce parapets, the blue colour would still shine through alarmingly. Fortunately, this blue colour did not last; it was the result of the presence of such minerals such as kaolinite, bentonite or glauconite, minerals that very quickly change in the presence of air, oxidising to a brownish colour. This colour would soon become the norm in the Ypres Salient, blending with the dun-coloured uniforms of the men who slogged through the fields, trenches and along the roads. Fortunately for those who had to live within this landscape, the process of oxidisation does not take long – but no doubt it was too long for the liking of the average soldier, under the threat of aerial observation, as every change and variance on the ground was seen as a potential threat – and shelled, when spotted.

There are other minerals too, tiny crystals that had a material effect on the lives of the infantry. Montmorillonite, also plentiful in the clay, has a microscopic platey structure that allows it to soak up considerable water, and therefore gives it a propensity to swell.[105] This moisture absorption aspect was a severe problem for military miners; with the clay swelling, so it followed that the tunnel walls would expand, exerting huge pressure on the timber supports. Nevertheless, the clay was an almost perfect material to work. As Aubrey Strahan noted '[the] Clay has its uses. Almost the whole of the system of tube-railways under London has been constructed in this watertight material'[106]: just as it was in London, so it would be in Ypres. But while mine galleries in clay could therefore be driven with relative ease – and silence – the amount of timber needed to keep them from being crushed was immense, and in some situations, steel supports were essential.[107]

Both clays, those of London and Ypres, are largely impervious to water, with very fine pore spaces meaning that ground water cannot easily travel through its clayey layers. Whereas water-bearing rock units are known as 'aquifers' – holding water – those layers that repel water like the clay of Ypres are known as 'aquicludes' – excluding water. In this way the 'Ypres Clay' layer acted as a barrier to downwards movement of water into the lower strata of Flanders, leading to a tendency for it to pool, and to create a number of semi-permanent lakes on the plain. It also meant

Blue clay exposed in beneath the duckboards in an archaeological excavation near Pilckem; disguising the colour from aerial reconnaissance was a challenge. (P. Doyle)

that this barrier had a major influence on the soils that sat above it.

The clay itself is of considerable thickness, and sits on water-bearing sands at depth, trapped beneath its thick blanket.[108] Again, the clay acts like a cap, keeping the water in the sands below under pressure. As more water is added to the pore spaces between the sand grains, so the pressure of water in those spaces builds in what is known as a 'confined aquifer'. This means that where the clay cap is breached, the water would be forced under this pressure to spurt upwards, acting as 'artesian water'. Aubrey Strahan of the Geological Survey made the direct comparison, in measured words, of the strata of Belgium with those of Britain in this respect. 'The [sand] beds pass below the [Ypresian] clay, and under suitable circumstances the water in them is held down under pressure by the impervious covering. In such cases, when a hole is bored through the clay, the water rises from the sand and overflows at the surface.'[109] That overflow could be dramatic.

Above the clay, there are soil layers – deposits of sands, gravels and other materials. These layers were added to the clay plain by rivers and streams, filling valleys and spreading over the plain itself, or were deposited during the Ice Age, when icy blasts of air moved fine particles blown from the land surface and deposited them elsewhere. Known as 'loess' around Europe, these deposits consist mostly of fine sands and silts that are capable of allowing water through before being stopped at the clay barrier below. These soils are variable in both thickness and extent,[110] but together act to gather water, creating what geologists call an 'unconfined aquifer' – layers that can soak up any amount of water, before being stopped on their

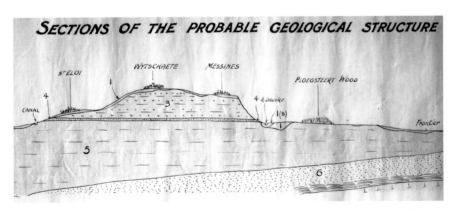

North-South geological section across the clay plain and sand ridges in the environs of Ypres, prepared for the Second Army School of Sanitation in December 1916. Numbered strata are: 1, surface loam and 1b, alluvium; 3, Paniselien clay and some sand; 4, Upper Ypresian fine sand; 5, Ypresian Clay; 6, Landenian sand and clayey sand (Louvil clay). Beneath this is the chalk. (Myers Coplans Archive)

On the Clay Plain, along the Menin Road, looking back to the City of Ypres. The clay soil is holding water after rain. (P. Doyle)

downwards journey by the clay beneath. As a consequence, the levels of water saturation (the 'water table') can be variable; the more water added, the higher the level of saturation. With increased rainfall, or with inadequate drainage, that level could be very high. This was of great concern to any soldier.

It is not surprising, then, that porous layers or soils that lie on top of the clay are very likely to be water logged, as the water has no way of escaping downwards. Water therefore sits naturally on the surface around Ypres, and soaks into the soils that cap the clay in normal times. Farmers working with these heavy soils typically used terracotta field drains to help water pass to a system of drainage ditches at the field margins. These ditches, cut deeply into the clay, collect the water and help to move it by connecting with the stream systems; but, needless to say, in the winter months, with maximum saturation, surface soils are more often than not heavily waterlogged.

Consequently, drainage from the flat and fertile fields of Flanders is slow, and to describe the soils during wet periods as 'heavy going' is more than an understatement. Mud, in which soils lose their plasticity due to an increased level of water content, became the norm, and in military parlance could seemingly become 'bottomless'.[111] Canals, culverts, ponds and moated farms abound, and the local population has derived water from these natural and man-made features

Shell pocked battlefield of Third Ypres. The shell holes are filled with a combination of rainwater and undrained groundwater. The surface soils hold water as they sit on the impervious clay below; saturated from above and below, the shell holes brim with water.

for centuries. Here, at least, there would be opportunity to gain relief from the thirst that naturally accompanies physical exertion in the time of war.[112] But those supplies would soon be contaminated. As, to put it bluntly, 'when vast armies camped upon the plain in 1914 the water problem became aggravated, and especially so after the drainage washed the decaying bodies of the battlefield and passed into the water-bearing horizons'.[113]

The Third Battle of Ypres (1917) is perhaps the battle most commonly associated with the twin evils of unusual levels of rainfall and disrupted drainage. While there are assertions that Haig and his generals should have known there was to be heavy rainfall in the autumn, it seems a little hard to demand that their predictive powers extend to the view that August would be a particularly wet month. Yet total rainfall for August 1917 was to be almost twice the average for that would normally be expected for that summer month.[114] On 1 August, Field Marshal Sir Douglas Haig, Commander-in-Chief of the British Expeditionary Force, noted in his diary: 'A terrible day of rain. The ground is like a bog in this low-lying country!'[115] This would become a defining motif for the battle.

In fact, penetration of the water-bearing loamy soils through to the clay by heavy howitzer shells, can be considered as one the reasons for the development of the classically water-logged Flanders battlefields, with artesian water filling the shell holes in addition to the component supplied by rainfall[116]. This complexity of ground was not lost on at least one general, Friedrich 'Fritz' von Lossberg, mastermind of the German defence-in-depth strategy. Writing in 1939, he noted:

> The ground in Flanders consists of a very soft and fertile layer of humus [the soil] with a thickness of 1–3 metres. Under this layer of earth there is an impenetrable layer of clay about 1 metre thick. If this is perforated by artillery fire the groundwater oozes upwards into the shell craters and fills them to the brim. Virtually all created positions had to be constructed on top the humus layer which made them easily detectable for the enemy. During prolonged dry weather phases the humus layer hardens. In that case an attacker finds favourable conditions. After showers of rain, which in Flanders are a common occurrence, the humus layer is turned into a swamp-like pulp which gives an advantage to the defender.[117]

In such cases, without access to the normal means of removing surface water, even in dry months draining the deepest shell holes would have been largely impossible, their water content supplied from below, as well as above. However, this factor would very much depend upon the thickness of the sedimentary layers at any one point on the clay plain.

A wartime consideration of the geological maps of Belgium led, in October 1917 (while the Third Battle of Ypres was in full swing), to an assessment and classification of the nature of ground in Belgium with respect to drainage, subsoils, water content and surface. Carried out by the Geological Survey of Great Britain it examined the area at a small scale of 1/160,000. The report divided the region up into three types of 'country', and nine subtypes, labelled from 1–9. It recognised that the drainage of shell holes depended very much on these.[118] There would be: shell holes that would drain naturally (4 and 6, 5, 7 and 8 in part); shell holes in which water would lie until evaporated 1 and 2, 5, 7 and 8 in part); and, those where water would be permanent (3 and 9, 5 in part). This exercise in essence identified the water-logged conditions of the Polders, the capability of craters in 'blue clay' to hold water, and the fact that ground water would play a large part in recharging shell holes. This report was born out in practice – and is still evident today.

For example, at Hill 60 and the Caterpillar in Zillebeke, within the Ypres Salient, there are markedly different situations with regard to water filling craters left there by wartime mining activity. For while the main crater at Hill 60, blown

Results of the Geological Report on Country N. and E. of Passchendaele Ridge (GSGS, October 1917)

Clay Country	Sand Country	Sandy Clay Country
(1) Blue clay (a) of Roulers region. (b) of Dixmude region	(4) The Coastal Dunes	(7) Alluvials of the Lys Valley and of the Bruges and Ghent areas
(2) Clay W. of Eccloo and E of Bruges	(5) The Ypresian Sands (Water-bearing)	(8) High-level sandy clays of the Passchendaele Ridge and of the region between Thielt, Thorout and Bruges
(3) Clay of Polders, Nieuport to Ostend	(6) Dry Sands. (a) of top of Passchendaele Ridge and (b) of the forest region from Thielt and Thorout to Bruges	(9) Alternating patches of the sand and clay of the Polders east of Ostend and of the Dutch frontier

Source: Royal Engineers (1922a), *The Work of the Royal Engineers in the European War, 1914-19. Geological Work on the Western Front.* Mackay & Co, Chatham, pp. 35–37.

during the Battle of Messines on 7 June 1917, is dry, the crater at Caterpillar, just on the other wide of the railway cutting, is wet. The answer is that the caterpillar is supplied by groundwater (from the 'Kemmel Sands', discussed below), which sits in a clay bowl, while the Hill 60 crater is drained into the railway cutting.[119] This shows the complexity of the ground conditions.

There has been much discussion regarding the nature of the plain, and in particular whether or not it could have been 'reclaimed' from a 'bog-like' state. For example, author Lyn Macdonald expressed a commonly-held view in her popular 1978 book, *They Called it Passchendaele.*

Fig. 9.—Railway Cutting at Hill 60. Ypres Salient.
In Paniselian Sands. Dry above with Shelters; wet below Springs. Looking North-West.
Nov. 27th, 1918.

The Railway Cutting at Hill 60, showing drainage of the Kemmel Sands (as springs) into the cutting, lying on Ypres Clay. (Institute of Royal Engineers 1922a)

At some point in history the Flanders plain lay under the sea. It is reclaimed bogland, which it was only possible to inhabit and cultivate by constructing a complicated network of drainage ditches…In spite of the ditches, when there is heavy rain the land quickly becomes waterlogged, for there is no gravelly topsoil to filter away moisture, nothing but a yard or so of heavy clay…Beneath its covering of meadows and hopfields Flanders is a natural bog.[120]

It is worth comparing this view, worked into so many other popular accounts of the battle,[121] with that of the British Official Historian, Sir James Edmonds, writing in his long-delayed 1917 volume:

The battlefield, it was said, was 'a reclaimed swamp, which was only prevented [from] returning to its original condition of a soggy morass by an elaborate system of drainage'. A glance at [a map] will show that the scene of the struggle is the ridge on the eastern side of Ypres and the gentle slope leading up to it from the Yser Canal; it has never been a morass, except, perhaps, in Mesozoic times, and was drained by its natural slope and a number of small streams.

Mine craters at Hill 60 and The Caterpillar. The Caterpillar mine is water filled, maintained by groundwater from the underling 'Kemmel Sands', while the Hill 60 mine is dry, draining into the railway cutting. (P. Doyle)

Shell holes preserved in the battlefield terrain at the Hill 62 museum, in the Ypres Salient. They are developed in the Paniselian sands, but some are more easy to drain than others, due to local differences in the subsoil. (P. Doyle)

Moving across the surface of the wet Clay Plain was a challenge for men and animals.

The words quoted above apply to a district called 'Les Moeres, twenty miles away, near the coast between Furnes and Dunkirk'.[122]

Who is correct? For those participants who fought in the Salient in 1917, men who slogged through the mud of Flanders, such matters were somewhat arcane; the landscape *must* have been a swamp. For Pte Benn of the Loyal North Lancashire Regiment, the situation in front of Ypres was dire:

On the 30th July we tried to clean our rifles and ammunition, ready for the next day, but anyone who knows what Flanders mud is like on a wet day will realise the impossible task we had. The trench we were in was on a little slope, but before night it was beginning to flood. We couldn't do anything to prevent it, so we had to let it take its chance. We were still walking about the trench as we hadn't any cover, and through the trench being flooded it was impossible to get any sleep. We were past caring about anything now, dead beat and soaked to the skin for hours, and we thought next morning would finish us in the firing line. We thought it would have been impossible to drag ourselves through the mud, as every step sunk from 6 inches to a foot.[123]

And as Salient veteran Henry Williamson wrote, on his return to the then-healing landscape in 1925; 'The bombardments broke the *bekes*, or brooks, draining this land, which was once covered by the sea; and the pudding became porridge, a-swim with icy water.'[124]

In these descriptions, the geographical distinctions between the Polder Plain to the north and the Clay Plain of Flanders have been put aside, the complexity of the origins of the mud field that came to be associated with the Third Battle of Ypres in 1917 was blurred. For while water was everywhere, saturating the soils

British soldiers being engulfed by the clay plain; attempting to dig in at Ypres, late 1914.

of the Polders to depth; on the clay plain, such levels of saturation were not the norm. Here, it was usual for water to be drained by the natural slopes or by human artifice, but now it ponded on the clay surface, captured in shell holes that were not only fed by heavy rainfall, but also by groundwater. Sir Douglas Haig's despatch describing the battle tells it all:

> For four days, the rain continued without cessation, and for several days afterwards the weather remained stormy and unsettled. The low-lying, clayey soil, torn by shells and sodden with rain, turned to a succession of muddy pools. The valleys of the choked and overflowing streams were speedily transformed into long stretches of bog, impassable except by a few well-defined tracks, which became marks for the enemy's artillery. To leave these tracks was to risk death by drowning...[125]

For the soldiers who fought on this plain, life was hellish; for they found that they were fighting more enemies than they planned for:

> What did the infantry do at Ypres? Nine-tenths of the time they were fighting nature, the remainder they were fighting the Germans; and all the time that they were fighting nature the German from his vantage points on the high ground could look down into their very boot-tops, so the toll of life was high.[126]

THE 'SAND RIDGES'

Rising slowly up from the clay plain is a low range of hills that curve to the east of the city of Ypres. For American military geographer Douglas Johnson, the hills formed an arc surrounding Ypres that created a 'bastion' on the otherwise featureless plain.[127] This bastion stood in the way of armies advancing from the east across the plain, and was therefore to be protected and fortified in times of danger, an outer defence to support those city walls built by the master, Vauban, in the eighteenth century. With the low ridge system from Passchendaele to Messines falling into the hands of the Germans early in the war, defence of the city of Ypres became even more significant. With the high ground fortified by the Germans, Ypres was under constant observation. But holding Ypres was of the utmost importance, as only it stood in the way of a German advance on the channel ports – and the opening of an even greater threat to Britain.

These unassuming low hills gained such gigantic importance in the war. Occupied by the Germans from 1914, the ridges – and the German possession of them – became a thorn in the side of the British. For both sides, occupation of ridge tops and high ground meant the possibility of observing the daily activities of their enemies. Every movement and suspicious activity was logged – and shelled if necessary. With the Germans on the ridge tops from early-war the British would struggle under four years of direct observation by the Zeiss field-glasses of their opponents. As General Ludendorff commented, in his soldier's way:

> The high ground between Ypres and the Roulers–Menin line…affords a extensive view in both directions. These heights were also exceptionally important for us, as they afforded us ground observation posts and a certain amount of cover from hostile view.[128]

But the Germans did not have it all their own way. Fortunately for the British, Mont Kemmel remained in their hands for much, though not all, of the war (relinquished briefly in 1918, in the wake of the German assault). This allowed for an equivalent observation, in the other direction:

> Flemish Switzerland, Kemmel Hill, most prominent of all, [gave] the best observation we had for miles. It was developed into a maze of heavily built dug-outs containing various specialists, highly equipped engineers who spotted guns by flash and various methods in addition to the orthodox artillery observers who used plain eyesight plus glasses. But I doubt if the knowledge of all this helped the average infantryman as much as the mere sight of that considerable, and until late days, well-covered hill.[129]

Observed by officers of lower ranks than Ludendorff, British and Allied infantrymen who moved across the plain below suffered the disadvantage of doing so in plain sight – at least in daylight. This put severe strain on the troops who toiled in the Ypres Salient.

> Because the enemy could see every move on our part in the Salient all movements had to be carried out in the dark, and ammunition, rations, and building materials were carted up by night as far as the road went and then laboriously man-handled into the actual position. The work was bad enough in the summer, but when the whole of the ground was one sodden quagmire of trodden and re-trodden slimy mud, the task was appalling.[130]

Importantly, for farmer and soldier alike, the subtle but complex geological make-

View over the plain from Mt Kemmel. Kemmel was in British hands through most of the war.
(P. Doyle)

up of the ridges includes a substantial percentage of sand – a naturally more free draining material than the heavy soil of the clay plain below. Particularly are numerous streams – *bekes* – that break the profile of the ridge into distinctive spurs such as the Messines, Pilckem, Westhoek and Broodseinde ridges – names which would become indelibly engraved into the military history of the war by 1918. The Passchendaele and Messines ridges provide a range of panoramic viewpoints over what is otherwise a relatively featureless landscape – a landscape perfect for manoeuvring large bodies of troops.

The low ridges and hills were composed of sedimentary layers that had formed in a sea that covered northern Europe some fifty million years before. This was a distant geological past, and the sea levels had long since fallen to create a land surface that was transformed, with much of these layers removed, by the action of flowing rivers and the challenges of the Ice Age. Across Flanders, not just in Ypres, it is what geologists called the 'Paniselian sand complex' that formed the lying prominences. In fact the original Paniselian sediments were named after Mont Panisel near Mons, where they were first described in detail. The Paniselian sediments lie on the Ypres Clay, and were much studied by nineteenth century geologists and by others subsequently.[131] (Today, in common with the other geological layers of the clay plain, the Paniselian is now assigned by geologists to other named geological

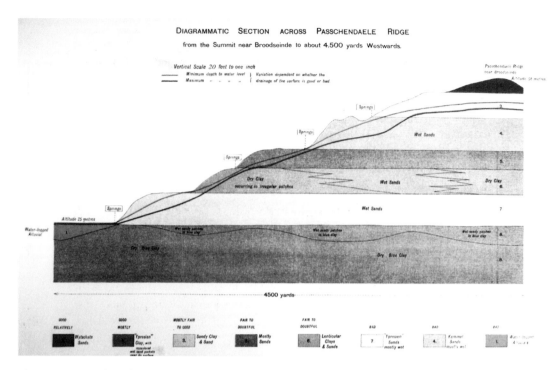

DIAGRAMMATIC SECTION ACROSS PASSCHENDAELE RIDGE

from the Summit near Broodseinde to about 4,500 yards Westwards.

Geological cross section (1917) across the Passchendaele Ridge, showing the water-bearing (blue shades), and water-excluding (red shades) layers of the Paniselian. Where these lie on clays, springs are formed. (The National Archives)

units – the Gent Formation and lower levels of the Tielt Formation.)[132] There are many subtle distinctions. For example, the Passchendaele Ridge is made up from mixed sand, clay and silt sedimentary layers, while Mont Kemmel is capped by geologically younger and startlingly orange, iron-rich, resistant sands.[133] In addition to the 'Paniselian' the ridges are also draped with soils, some of which reach great thickness. This is particularly the case in the southern and western slopes, towards the valleys of the Douve and the Lys, but applies anywhere there are flowing streams, depositing their own, wet, sediments.[134]

The rain that falls on Flanders, falls also upon the ridge tops. With sand layers closest to the very top, the rain soaks away into the land. This means that most of the groundwater in the Paniselian sands derives from downwards flow from rainwater.[135] The ridge surfaces were significant; not only did they create the hills and ridges, and absorb the rainwater that fell on them in abundance, they also provided a means of supplying the numerous streams and rivers that flow onto the plain below. Aubrey Strahan, Director of the British Geological Survey, was well aware of their importance:

As the Belgian Tertiary[136] basin is approached, the Paniselien Sand comes on in greater force. It forms the bold range of hills which surround Ypres on its southern and eastern sides, and which includes the site of the famous Hill 60. The Paniselien and Bruxellien sands absorb a large proportion of the rain that falls upon them, and give out the water as springs at their base, where they rest upon impervious clays or along and interbedded clay-band… Ypres was supplied by similar springs… but the gathering ground of the springs includes the scene of some of the most murderous fighting of the war.[137]

The greatest amount of groundwater flows downwards through the variable sands until it meets clay layers, where it 'perches', literally sits, upon them. Water can escape at the edges, were the sand layers meet the slopes of the ridges, and here natural spring lines are found.[138] This water content is clearly subject to seasonal variation, with the greatest rainfall in the winter months being typical; yet some layers were perpetually water-rich, such as the water-bearing Kemmel Sands that were identified, sandwiched between clay layers, by the British military geologists. These sands were first seen at Mont Kemmel, between the 60 and 70 metre contour, and they were encountered again on the Passchendaele Ridge.[139] Useful as a source for water, these sands were also a scourge of those attempting to dig through them, or into them, for trenches, tunnels and dug-outs.[140] In addition, the

Paniselian sands and surface soils at
Wytschaete. (P. Doyle)

Younger iron-rich sedimentary strata capping
Mont Kemmel. (P. Doyle)

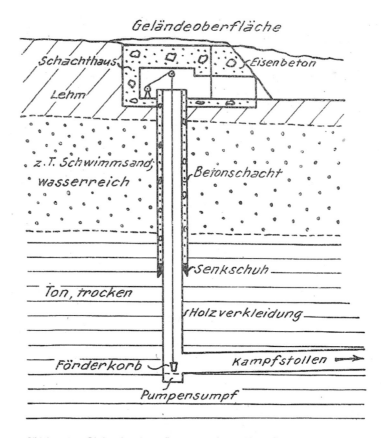

Abb. 58. Schachtabteufen durch nasses Gebirge in Flandern. (Nach Heyer.)

German section through the Passchendaele Ridge showing the strata and its difficulties. The Germans had to build a ferro-concrete (*Eisenbeton*) shaft house over a concrete shaft (*Betonschacht*), built to combat the water-rich sands. *Lehm* = loam; *Schwimmsand, wasserreich* = water-rich quicksands, known as the 'Kemmel Sands' to the British; *Ton, trocken* = dry clay. (v.Bulow et al. 1938)

ridges had more than one layer of clay, and it meant that there was more than one opportunity for water-logged conditions.

This was certainly the case for the Germans, occupying the ridge tops, and subject to a more complex geology beneath their feet than the British. Oberstleutnant Otto Füsslein, *Kommandeur des Mineure*, 4th German Army, was well aware of the difficulties.

Do you know the terrain of Flanders? The trench lines weaved their way over long and gently rolling ridges, through shallow depressions and across wide expanses of almost flat countryside. In the rich alluvial and sedimentary deposits forming the upper strata of earth and clay, water collected in the trenches, especially in the winter, and even more so in the mine galleries, initially only one or two metres below the surface and later four metres deep, progressively transforming them into quagmires.[141]

Such quagmires would be exacerbated by the existence of soils that covered both the plain and the ridges, often filling the valleys with wet, loose sediments that caused problems for any soldier determined to dig into the ground. While Kemmel remained in Allied hands for most of the war, it was the Passchendaele Ridge and its southern extension from Wytschaete to Messines that was to figure greatly in the story of the war – and would be the focus of attention from military miners. And for the Germans, perched on top of the ridges, there was much to contend with – a constant battle with waterlogged ground, *Schwimmsands* or swimming sands, being one of them.[142] Battling these sands meant creating concrete blockhouses, as the ground prevented dry dug-outs. Such blockhouses – pill-boxes as they became known – were built to withstand the assaults of both nature and men. The soldiers on the clay plain below were not the only ones to suffer the consequences of groundwater.

THE COAL BELT OF FRENCH FLANDERS

South of the Messines Ridge the ground descends from the Paniselian hills, first to the valley of the Douve, and then, farther south, to the Lys. These rivers flow over an extension of the clay plain so familiar to the soldiers of the Ypres Salient. As the frontline, established in 1914, snaked southwards, it passed by the French cities of Armentières and Bethune, before arriving in front of Lens, held by the Germans. Passing across this clay-rich landscape it would have been hard to perceive that at depth are older, chalk deposits except that they show white here and there in surface quarries. Farther south into French Flanders, coal deposits (of the much more ancient Carboniferous – the age of coal) are found closer to the surface, an accident of a great fracture known as the Marqueffles fault system. This is most associated with Vimy Ridge, a feature that was forced upwards by great earth movements to form what is known as a 'fault scarp', a steep slope created by fracture, and which now divides Flanders from Artois and Picardy.

The Lens Coalfield, now a world heritage site for its industrial features and history, extends along a line from the northeast to the southwest in front of Vimy,

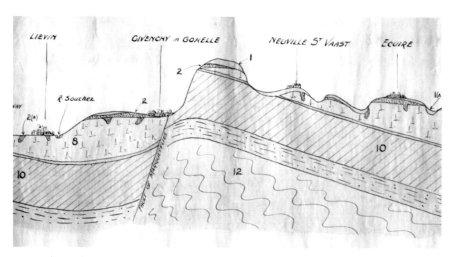

North-South geological section across the Marqueffles Fault Zone, the junction between French Flanders (left) and Artois (right), leading to the uplift of Vimy ridge. Prepared for the Second Army School of Sanitation in December 1916. Numbered strata are: 1, surface loam and 1b, alluvium; 2, clay with flints; 8, Upper Chalk with flints (sitting on a layer of fossiliferous chalk); 10, Middle Chalk (clayey), with Lower Chalk [11] beneath; 12, Devonian. The Coal-bearing strata of the Lens Coalfield (Carboniferous) occurs farther to the north.
(Myers Coplans Archive)

extending from Douai to Lens and on to Bethune. From a geological sense, the substructure of the various strata is complicated, as it is a westwards extension of the intensely folded and fractured region of the Ardennes, created during mountain building episodes some 300 million years ago. It was once one of the most important coal mining regions of France, and here the mines went deep underground in search of the coal seams, deep beneath the thick chalk layer above that creates the low rolling profile of the landscape, more akin to the downs of southern England – though scarred as if in the coal fields of more northerly counties.

Below surface, the geology is complex, with multiple slices of more ancient rocks separated by fractures – illustrative of the enormous pressures created during the formation of the Ardennes mountains.[143] These deep fractures repeat the sequence of coal-bearing rocks at depth, stacking several levels of productive coal – making the work of the miner here that bit more challenging, and dangerous. The most important of the fractures (known as 'faults' in geological parlance) is the *Grande Faille de Midi*, a feature that is usually buried but which effectively delimits the southern margin of the coalfield. It is these ancient, folded and fractured rocks that make up the Lens Coalfield complex, with many subsurface workings at depth (and explains why these works have been abandoned).[144] The coal-bearing rocks consist of typical sandstones, finer silts and coal seams, up to 1.6 m thick, that would have been familiar to any miner from the then numerous British coalfields – should they have found themselves in the mostly German-held mines during the war.[145]

The coal region was buried when sea levels rose during the Cretaceous period, some ninety million years ago. Then there were great volumes of chalk sediments deposited, the remains of teaming billions of minute sea creatures which blanketed the sea bed, and which in turn lay on clays and sands, all to a depth of c.200 metres.[146] Above the brilliant white chalk, variable in thickness, are the usual sedimentary layers of Flanders (but only to the north of the Coalfield), and the whole is covered by soils from the era of the Ice Age. As such, topographically, the Lens Coalfield would be indistinguishable from the Flanders lowland, but for the abundant physical evidence of mineworkings – remnants of industry long gone, the scars of man left on nature. Other, even deeper, scars would be left yet.

Mineworkings left behind today are the slag heaps and pitheads (*fosses,* together

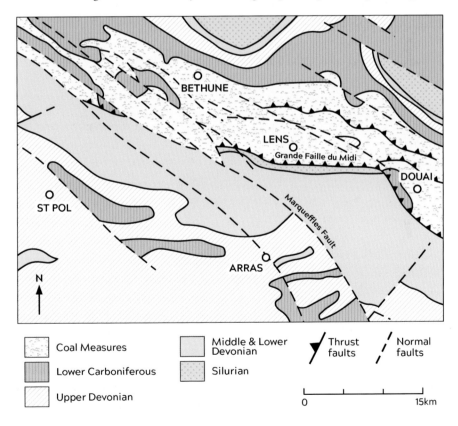

Geological map of the Lens Coalfield, showing the geological fractures.

The dour landscape of Loos, part of the Coal belt, marked by coal waste tips. (P. Doyle)

with shafts, or *puits*) and the huge, glowering piles of dark, non-reflective colliery wastes – known as *crassiers* – which provide evidence to the once feverish mining activity below ground. Clustered around these works were miners' cottages known as *corons*. During the war, these were active, the pithead gear and waste heaps bearing witness to the activity below ground; it was not a landscape that was universally admired at the time, and certainly not by the War Correspondent Phillip Gibbs, who witnessed the British Battle of Loos that was fought in this country in September 1915:

> It was a hideous territory, this Black Country between Lens and Hulluch. From the flat country below the distant ridges of Notre Dame de Lorette and Vimy there rose a number of high, black cones made by the refuse of the coal mines, which were called *Fosses*. Around those black mounds there was great slaughter.[147]

To the south of Loos, the flat chalk grounds were thrust upwards by titanic geological pressures to create the upland of the Artois plateau, a plateau that has as its northern margin the immense natural break of the Marqueffles Fault that both uplifted Vimy Ridge and nearby Notre Dame de Lorette (the site of commemoration of French military endeavour), while depressing the wet Flanders

Evidence of the coal workings at depth; the head gear near Loos known as 'Tower Bridge' to the British.

plain north of Lens. It is this very discordance between pastoral chalk landscape and industrial wasteland that helps define the region like no other, creating a division between the Flanders plain and the killing fields of Artois and the Somme beyond.

THE CHALK UPLAND OF ARTOIS AND PICARDY

Beyond Flanders, the Artois region exposes chalk which has been flexed by immense geological forces into a broad, domed, structure, known as an anticline, which is an extension of the Weald in southern England – a feature created by the mountain building events that created the Alps. Yet, though uplifted, it forms a simple, rolling chalk plain cut through by streams and rivers. A connection of Artois and Picardy to the lands to the north, it is picked out by remnants of sedimentary layers that link to the Paniselian, and the whole region covered by that thick blanket of soils which were created during the Ice Age – some of them unique to this region, a function of the weathering down of the chalk hills, others allied to sediments created during those glacial times. This landscape was represented in some of the most significant battlegrounds of the war, at Arras and Vimy Ridge, at Cambrai, and, farther to the southeast, the battleground of the Somme. Though it is very different ground from that of Flanders, once again the invading Germans of 1914 were quick to exploit its strengths.

> The battlefields of the Somme differed vastly from the muddy plains of Flanders. Here were ranges of chalk hills and ridges, the one most immediately important being that which formed the watershed between the Somme valley and the basins of the Scarpe and the Scheldt. This undulating ridge, which effectively commanded the lower country to the west, had been seized by the Germans in the miscalled 'Race to the Sea' in October 1914, and held firmly ever since.[148]

Despite the prevalence of the chalk, for the most part it is not naturally exposed at the surface – unless in rivers or road cuttings – and this made the cutting of trenches through the landscape all the more startling. The scars of those trenches are still readily seen from the air when the there are no crops, preserved as infilled white trench lines that criss-cross the chalk hills of Picardy. Seen now as ghosts in the fields, they were once bright white snaking lines and chalky spoil parapets that were obvious sights for aerial observers, who were able to pick out mining activity, new trenches or all manner of engineering works by the appearance of new, white, works. For the soldiers toiling through such landscapes, ever conscious of the aviators above, one approach was to dig deep communication tunnels. This was achieved in the Artois region, with exceptionally long subways constructed below the city of Arras, linking ancient quarries and passageways (*souterrains*, or *boves*) cut during mediaeval times.

The chalk upland block Artois and Picardy has, in contrast with the deep rocks

The healed, pastoral, landscape of the Somme. (P. Doyle)

of the Lens Coalfield, a relatively simple structure below ground. The chalk strata appear to be near enough horizontal, parallel with the surface of the Earth, so that while the men of the trenches were digging down through successive layers of chalk, in effect they were also digging down through successive layers of the sea floor that formed during the Cretaceous period. Though seemingly flat, these layers have actually been gently folded by the Alpine earth movements to create a series of flexures in the rock, flexures that line up in a northwest-southeast direction. These, in turn, align with similar flexures in the chalk rocks of southern England – a reminder once again of the closeness in geological terms of the two countries. All these features help to create the distinctive topography of the Somme, the rolling chalk downland (again so similar to that in southern England) disturbed here and there by woods and ravines. The 6th West Yorkshire Regiment arrived on the Somme in February 1916, and took stock of the landscape before them:

> [Thiepval] had all the characteristics of Picardy, being hill, well-wooded, with a series of long irregular spurs and deep depressions which ran in a S. and S.W. direction to the main valley of the Somme River. In one of the deep depressions the River Ancre ran past Miraumont, Grandcourt, Beaumont Hamel, Albert…till it reached the Somme near Corbie. The German trenches were sited very skilfully on the high ground at the crest

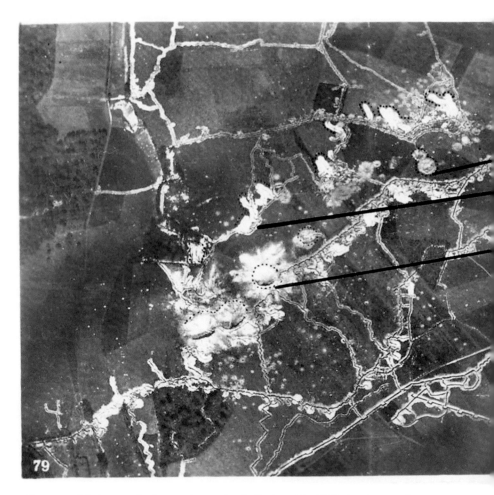

German aerial photographs from an instruction leaflet issued in 1917, showing trenches dug in chalk, mine craters (*Minensprengungen*) and mine works (*Minierarbeiten*). The new mine works are detected by the presence of white chalk spoil. (R. Schäfer)

of the Ancre, and from a defensive point of view had every advantage of position. It will be easily understood that the effect on the morale of the British troops of being compelled to cling painfully to the western slope of positions dominated by the enemy was not good.[149]

For the British, these ravines, spurs and woods would be some of the toughest nuts to crack when they assaulted the Somme in 1916. The Germans had exploited their natural power, doing so in accordance with the insistent instructions of their 1916

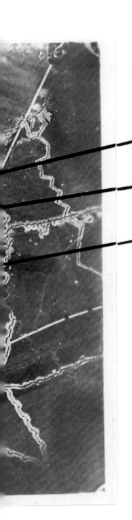

7.)

Minensprengungen.

Minierarbeiten.

Den auffallenden Stel-
len gegenüber Spreng-
trichter.

military manual, *Stellungsbau:* 'Every suitable spot must be utilized for defence and be prepared beforehand for this purpose. Such places are called strongpoints (large defended areas including villages, copses, etc, which may often be closed)'.[150] These features, many of them a function of the chalk ground and its soil cover, were built into the German line on the Somme with grim determination – and would be significant when the drumfire stopped and the battle opened, 1 July 1916.

With the geological structure of the region matching that across the English Channel, it is not surprising that the chalk of the Somme and Artois is equivalent to that of southern England, and like it, comprises three broad divisions: a lower, more clay-rich part (*les marnes crayeuses*), a middle, flint-bearing level (*la craie grise à gros silex cornus*, overlain by *craie blanche à silex*), and an upper, pure white, flint-poor part (*craies blanche*).[151] Overall all these chalks (and their flints) were

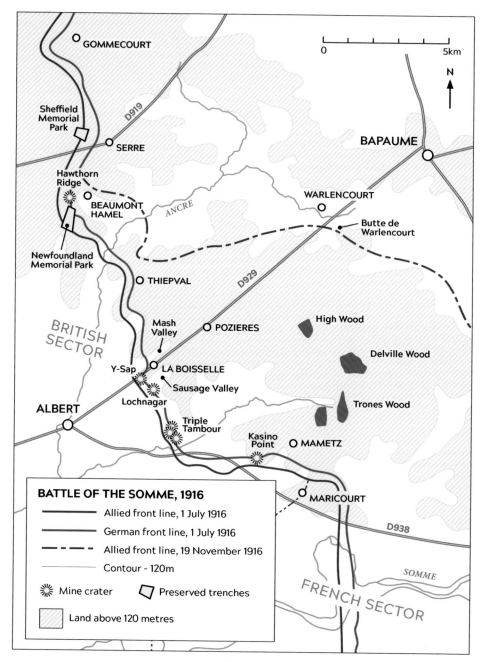

Map of the Somme battlefield; the central ridge consists of chalk overlain by Ice Age soils.

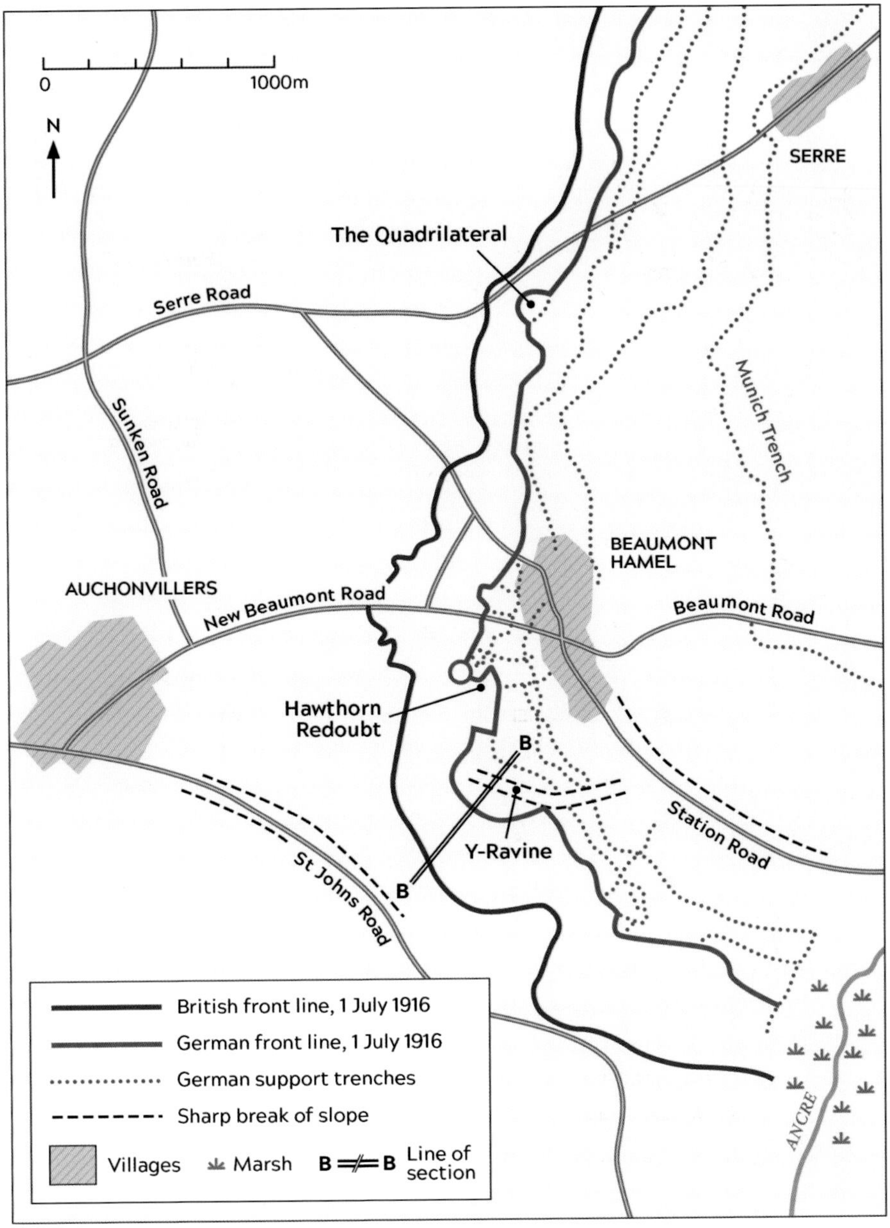

0
1000m
N
SERRE
The Quadrilateral
Serre Road
Munich Trench
Sunken Road
BEAUMONT
HAMEL
AUCHONVILLERS
New Beaumont Road
Beaumont Road
Hawthorn
Redoubt
B
Y-Ravine
Station Road
St Johns Road
B
ANCRE
British front line, 1 July 1916
German front line, 1 July 1916
German support trenches
Sharp break of slope
Villages
Marsh
B B Line of section

Map of the German defences at Beaumont Hamel. In line with the instructions of the German manual, *Stellungsbau* (1916), strong points, fortified villages and natural features (the dry, steep valley known as Y-Ravine) have been built into the system. See cross section B-B on page 86.

formed by the accumulation of countless billions of sub-microscopic plankton with tiny lime or silica shells. This accumulation created an enormous reserve of limy sediments on the sea floor, raining out of the warm seas at a time when the oceans were at their deepest. Flints, occurring as strange splintery nodules or thin dark layers in the white chalk were formed from the silica-rich shells of intricate single-celled organisms, the silica remobilised to fill in cavities. While these matters were probably furthest away from the minds of the average soldier on the Western Front, what would have concerned them was the way that flints, if struck by a pick or entrenching tool, would have given out an alarming ring into the night sky – or along the gallery of any tunnel – enough to alert the enemy.

The oldest chalks are clay-bearing, greyer in appearance that the ones above – and traditionally called '*les bleues*' by French miners. Some others are phosphatised, reinforced by calcium phosphate and harder and darker in appearance. It was the clayey chalks had the greatest bearing on the movement of water through the otherwise lime-rich rock. Chalk has fine pores that allow some water to pass through them, but the major part of its permeability – permitting the passage of water – is due to its abundance of fractures, joints and other features that create the typical block-work look of an average chalk face. The presence of clay particles and clayey layers in the lower chalks thus impedes the flow of water, by forming impermeable layers, which in turn become the base for groundwater; the downwards flow of rainwater, for example, being impeded by such layers. Knowing the level of the clayey chalks was of great importance to the British military; as a consequence many boreholes were drilled in search of it.[152] Not only was the location of the clay important for water supply – where it had been thrown up by the Marqueffles Fault, there was the possibility that it could have been used as a medium for mining.[153]

The water content of the chalk is of great importance, as groundwater provides much of the water to the local population, up to sixty percent of supplies.[154] The boundary between the clay-rich chalks and the flint-bearing chalks above is of the greatest significance in this respect, and determining the boundary of the two for water supply purposes was of significance to the military geologists.[155] Geologist Lt (later Capt) W.B.R. King RE was originally taken on to carry out a study of this flow, which was highly influential in assisting the army in its search for groundwater supplies.[156] As such, King mapped out the surface of the clay bearing rocks with the aid of boring machines over a large tract of France.[157] The difference between the water-rich upper chalks and the water-poor lower chalks was startling. In the clay-chalks water extraction could be of the order of 1000 gallons hourly, while where water was found in the upper, clay-poor upper chalks, the extraction

Craie blanche à silex – while chalks with scattered layers of flints, near Beaumont Hamel on the Somme. (P. Doyle)

was greatly increased, up to a level of 12,000 gallons hourly.[158] This really mattered to an army that required large volumes of water to sustain its millions of men and pack animals.

The chalk is mostly frost shattered in its upper part, because though Ice Age glaciers did not reach this part, their influence was strongly felt. Here, during the glacial interval, the ground was frozen as permafrost, then seasonally thawed, and the growth of ice crystals in rock pores soon broke down the strength of the chalk.

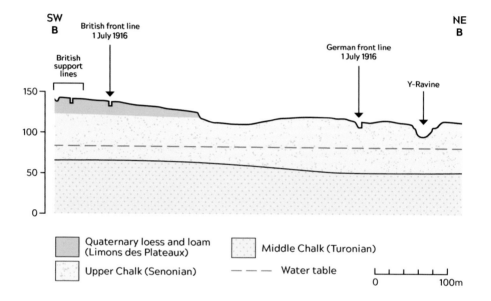

Geological cross section in the Newfoundland Memorial Park, Beaumont Hamel, showing the German defences and the situation of the British lines in the *Limon*. The German lines were well drained and lay in the chalk; the British lines, subject to flooding in the winter. Location of section B-B indicated on map on page 83.

Other evidence of the Ice Age on the Somme is provided by the soil layers that lie above the white chalk. Typically there are four separate layers: clay-with-flints, loess, loam and alluvium, although not all will be present at any given location.

In many ways, it was these soils that would have the most effect on the trench-dwelling soldiers, as it was through them the soldiers dug, and it was within them that the soldiers lived. Wind-blown loess caps the clay-with-flints and is in turn covered by a clay-rich sand or loam. The loess and loam are often classified together

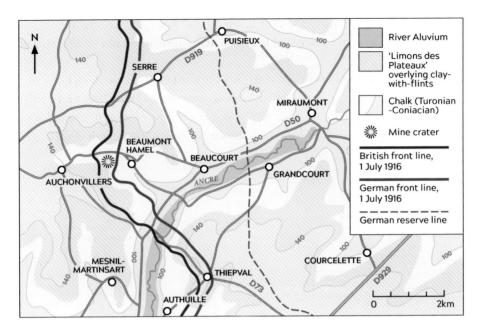

Geological map of the Beaumont Hamel–Thiepval Ridge, and the valley of the Ancre.

on French maps as *Limons de Plateaux* – a fine covering on the upland areas, but sometimes reach a thickness of up to 10 metres. It forms a cap to the hill-tops and slopes, and helps to fill the valleys. It was the *Limons* that perhaps had the greatest effect on the movement of men and materiel in the winter months.

Aubrey Strahan, Director of the Geological Survey of Great Britain, commented on this set of deposits in 1917, 'this is the deposit with which our men are generally in contact in trenches and dug-outs, and which is in evidence on the clothes of those returning from the Front'. The contrary nature of the deposit, at one time thick mud, at other, choking dust, did not escape Strahan's notice, either.

> In dry weather the *limon* readily returns to a condition of dust; in wet weather it forms a mud unlimited in quantity and obstructiveness. But as a material in which trenches and dug-outs can be excavated with the minimum of labour it seems to have found some use.[160]

The clay-with-flints (*Argile à Silex*) is a product of weathering of the limey chalk, leaving a residue of clay minerals mixed with hard flints behind. The thickness of this deposit is variable, ranging from less than a metre to up to 10 metres, and the other

Limons – Ice Age soils overlying frost-shattered chalks on the Somme. (P. Doyle)

Ice Age deposits are known to lie above this distinctive clay layer. Where clay-with-flints caps the chalk, water is retained leaving a heavy soil that is often uncultivated, except for forestry. The clay layer was also to create a difficult barrier for those troops committed to 'digging in' on the Somme. Leutnant Kurt Trautner, a Saxon schoolteacher with geological training, was soon to recognise the difficulties.

> Hacking oneself into the earth was an exhausting business as the heavy pick continuously hit large lumps of flint which meant there was hardly any progress. The ground consists of clay – clay mixed with an exceptional quantity of flint nodules. The French geologist knows them as '*Argile à Silex*'. It is basically a by product of weathering. The surrounding chalk weathers away while the harder flint resists...[161]

The presence of the flints also created a greater hazard, as the brittle nodules shattered under shellfire.

The mud of the Somme: German trenches developed in the *Limon*, on the River Ancre.
(P. Reed)

The whole morning I continued working in the hole with my small spade and tried to throw the debris out with my bare hands - by then the first shell splinters mixed with stones where whizzing through the trench (...) After the work was done [..my right hand] was torn bloody by the sharp edged pieces of flint.[162]

The clay-with-flints bed is also impervious to the passage of water and acts like so many local layers in this part of the Western Front to impede the downwards movement of groundwater, exacerbating the problems of mud formation in the Somme region. Despite the apparent dryness of the chalk, it is this overlying clay, and the propensity of the *Limon* above to liquidise, that created a mud like no other. For John Masefield, the slopes of Montauban formed 'an expanse of smoothish tilted slopes...No doubt there are places in the English chalk counties which resemble this sweep of country, but I know none so bare or featureless. The ground is of the reddish earth which makes such bad mud...'[163] Other battlefield travellers would comment on the mud, too:

The mud of the Somme battlefields was of a very different quality from that remembered with equal abhorrence in the Ypres sector. The mud on

Sunken Lane at Beaumont Hamel: this had an important role as a natural trench on the First Day of the Battle of the Somme, 1 July 1916. (P. Doyle)

the Somme sucked like quicksand. It was sticky as treacle: it appeared to be bottomless. The familiar 'duck tracks,' long wooden laths covered as is a bath mat, of the northern sectors were useless on the Somme. Stand anywhere between Les Boeufs and Rancourt, and the feet will rest on soil into which men sank waist, even breast, deep beneath the surface of oozing mud, trenches were water-logged, a pitiless rain descended.[164]

Many of the wooded areas of the Somme battlefield lie in soils developed in clay-with-flints, with the chalk forming most of the valleys in the region, with the loess and loam capping the hills and forming the intermediate slopes. Also common over the landscape of the Somme are 'sunken lanes' – as typical of this part of France as they are in the same tracts of country in England.[165] Produced by the act of countless generations of carts and wheeled traffic wearing down through the soft chalk, the lanes leave embankments floored with white chalk, yet with walls of crumbly Ice Age sediments above. Such natural trenches were not neglected by the armies who lived amongst them – and one example that was close to the British frontline in July 1916 became infamous.

The deep part, which is like a very deep, broad, natural trench, was known to our men as the Sunken Road. The banks of this sunken part are

'Sarsen stone' found near 'The Pimple' at Vimy Ridge; such hard rocks were valuable as road stones. (Institute of Royal Engineers, 1922a).

perpendicular. Until recently, they were grown over with a scrub of dwarf beech, ash, and sturdy saplings, now mostly razed by fire. In the road itself our men built up walls of sandbags to limit the effects of enemy shell fire.[166]

In some places, residual sands, equivalent in geological age to the Paniselian strata of Flanders, are known to cap the chalk, lying below the Ice Age soils described. These sands were sometimes encountered as 'sarsen stones'; remnants of a level that was once widespread. The stones are incredibly durable (having been strongly cemented with silica), and for that reason, wherever possible, sarsens were harvested hungrily for use in road stones.[167]

Several rivers cut the plain and many dry valleys, some of them deeply incised, are also found within the area. Dry valleys are very typical of chalk downland, as water only flows over the surface when the permeable chalk is waterlogged (or capped with impermeable layers). In most cases the water disappears below surface, running through the cracks and fractures, and in many cases helping to create caves as the water dissolves the chalk away. This is the reason why the chalk upland is effectively starved of surface water, and as a result, on the chalk land a large number of small hamlets formed as clusters of houses around wells and other groundwater supplies. This contrasts with the more scattered and isolated farms in Flanders, where surface water is much more plentiful.[168] Nevertheless, the rivers that do cross the plain display a strong parallel alignment, obviously controlled by the underlying form and structure of the chalk. These rivers would become well known as the site of battle: the Somme itself, and the Ancre. Beautifully clear chalk streams feed these rivers today – but beautiful as they are, they were soon choked with debris during those terrible years of war.

4 GEOLOGY AND TRENCH WARFARE

The line of trenches runs nearly everywhere through low-lying ground, intersected with watery ditches and small streams; the land is so level, and the atmosphere so heavy, that, as a rule, the eye ranges little further than the rifle bullet will carry.[169]

A well-revetted German trench on the Western Front, c. 1916

The Great War *is* trench warfare to many, yet it has a much longer history. In modern warfare, trenches all too often appeared due to the offensive capability of advanced weapons, with desire asserting itself to stop the war of movement by 'digging in' – thereby protecting the infantry and preserving their opportunity to attack again. But the use of trenches has a long history in siege warfare. Dating back to at least the seventeenth century, siege trenches were dug by an attacker in an attempt to protect their camp and works. Trenches and saps were thus built as a fortification to face a fortification, and were known as the 'lines of circumvallation'.[170] The recreation of the trench lines in late 1914 therefore owed much to at least two and a half centuries of application and development of the art of the military siege, rather than a new innovation, and produced parallel fortresses that were exceptionally difficult to destroy, and which in turn required powerful 'siege weapons' to attempt to do so. New 'siege engines' would be called upon in this age of industrial warfare.[171]

Trenches may have reappeared often in history, but one thing was certain: that not all trenches were equal in value and effectiveness. Trenches could suffer enfilade fire – the opportunity for an enemy to fire along their length – which was in part due to the method of construction, and the position relative to topography. They could be exposed to observation and vulnerable for the same reason. Trenches could be perennially wet; they could be subject to collapse, or they could be exceptionally difficult to dig. These factors were to a large part controlled by the nature of ground, of the underlying geology. And if the armies that fought in the Great War had not expected trench warfare, then they would need to learn quickly how best to use it – and this would mean reaching out to the new science of geology in order to mitigate the various problems that presented themselves. It was as if Walter Kranz's prediction of the importance of soldiers who *really* understood ground had come true.

Things had changed since the 'investment' of fortifications by the construction of the lines of circumvallation. Now the defensive value of trenches, often hurriedly dug, was magnified in the face of the increased efficiency and accuracy of artillery and machine gun fire. Such trenches reduced the effectiveness of offensive action by infantry, especially where deployed in direct frontal assault, and increased the importance of defensive positions. This was, again, not a new phenomenon; the development of trench lines in the later stages of the American Civil War, for example, provided an inkling of things to come. With huge losses of life in the opening stages of the war, as Napoleonic tactics were used with rifled weapons, it was not surprising that Civil War soldiers were happier to dig in and fire from trench positions, rather than face their enemy on the open field of combat.[172]

Perhaps echoing this sentiment, the military manual *Military Engineering (Part 1) Field Defences* (1908), the most up-to-date account of the subject in the British army at the outbreak of war, viewed trenches purely as a shelter from fire, rather than a means of winning a war:

> When two forces armed with modern weapons are opposing each other in the field, the object of intrenchments, which may be used by either side or by both, is to give cover from the enemy's fire, rather than to offer an obstacle to his assault.[173]

For the early nineteenth century Prussian military theorist, Carl von Clausewitz, writing in his classic book *On War* (1832), 'The object of a strong position is to make the force there stationed in point of fact unattackable, and by that means, either really to cover a certain space directly, or only the troops which occupy that space in order then, through them, in another way to effect the covering of the country indirectly.'[174] This was certainly true of the First World War, and it was especially so of the trenches constructed by his twentieth century countrymen.

Trench warfare was therefore, ultimately defensive; and sitting in trenches deep in the earth was unlikely to bring about a decisive victory. For Marshal Foch, writing a decade before the Great War:

> Defensive battle never brings about the destruction of enemy forces; it never allows one to conquer the ground held by the enemy (which after all is the only external sign of victory), therefore it is unable to create victory... Any defensive battle must, then, end in an offensive action, in a thrust, in a successful counter-attack, otherwise there is no result.[175]

Waiting in trenches was an inadequate response to warfare, unless of course, the strategic objective was to remain on the defensive. And this, after all, is largely what the German High Command was committed to doing after the failure of the Schlieffen Plan. They did it well, holding the Allies and committing them to attritional warfare in 1915–17. Their one major experiment in offensive action – the attack at Verdun in February 1916 – planned as a means of 'bleeding the French army white' – backfired. The French proved here that the Germans could also bleed.[176] But for the most part, they were content to wait, until the war in the East was won, or until one side or other sued for a separate peace.[177] Nevertheless standing on the defensive will always tempt the enemy to end the siege with decisive action.

Once trench warfare had come to stay, the average Great War soldier's intimate

Trench routine; here a sentry keeps an eye on activity in a barricaded trench. Shared trenches became a fact of life in some sectors.

view of terrain was simply observed from the bottom of a trench upwards. Occupied there on trench duty, repairing the trench sides, its parapet or barbed wire, soldiers were challenged to see anything other than the small slit of sky. Most men busied themselves with the improvement of their lot, in their appointed piece of line. Even for the average soldier in the trenches, the reliance on ground was obvious, so intimately did he engage with the earth itself. He lived there, fought there, and ultimately died there. Though times would vary, the soldier on the Western Front could expect to spend at least half of his time 'in the trenches' in some way or another. Expected to dig them into the unrelenting soil, he would also shelter there from the elements and from the rain of shells, observing the world from the bottom of his ditch.

We were not supposed to sleep, and we hadn't time anyway as we were digging and consolidating trenches; it was nothing new to see the pick or shovel fall and the man after it. We were absolutely beat and were falling asleep standing, sitting, or anywhere. If anyone had got this part of the trench finished, they could have slept, but no one could get finished, as none of us had the strength to do so. Even if we could have slept our only beds would have been the trench bottom, or on the fire-step…[178]

Digging out trenches in the Ypres Salient; combatting the elements was typical of both sides of No Man's Land.

Digging became as much of the daily life of the soldier as the expectation of death and wounding from random shells or spent bullets – the very things the men were seeking to escape. It soon entered the language of the average soldier:

I confess that we are getting 'fed up' with digging. The men sing about it as they march – to the tune of a well known hymn – 'Digging, digging, digging: always b– well digging.' They write about it in their letters home: they talk about it. Yesterday, I saw, worked on the parapet in pieces of chalk (the material through which we are digging), the following simple inscription – '1st C. Gds–Navvies.'[179]

Yet while their men dug, and stared nervously skywards, commanders struggled with the options to dislodge their enemies. With the defensive lines in place, and getting ever stronger, once more the concept that the war could be distilled into a struggle for topographic position asserted itself. Disposition of high ground, the relative incision of valleys, and the presence of wooded areas were of paramount importance to both attacker and defender; while the nature of the ground conditions controlled the effectiveness with which defensive trench positions could be constructed. This meant that geology, which not only ultimately controls topography, but also commands the nature of ground conditions, became one of the most important factors in the outcome of the siege warfare waged on the Western Front. This conclusion would, perhaps, have come as no surprise to Clausewitz.

Though trench warfare was becoming a much more professional business by 1916, it is still important to understand that the situation and condition of Allied trench systems was often greatly influenced by their General Staff's offensive policies, and a general unwillingness to yield ground, in its early days at least. The Allies were fighting on French and Belgian soil and were on the tactical defensive, a situation that could only be reversed by a sustained tactical offensive – in line with Foch's doctrine from 1903. For them, the concept of building strong defensive positions was anathema; an admittance of defeat if only at ground level. In simple, practical terms this equated with an unwillingness, in the early parts of the war at least, of the Allies to construct permanent and sophisticated positions that would provide safe accommodation for the troops, and of an inability to actively select in advance the best tactical position for trench lines. For the General Staff there was a constant fear that trench warfare would engender a defeatist attitude, an 'unhealthy' dependence on shelter or safety.

> The attack on…a system of defences demands in all ranks dash and gallantry of a very high order…At the same time, the state of comparative inactivity, which is the normal condition of life in the trenches, is very unfavourable to the development of these qualities in officers and men. There is an insidious tendency to lapse into a passive and lethargic attitude, against which officers of all ranks have to be on their guard, and the fostering of the offensive spirit, under such unfavourable conditions, calls for incessant attention.[180]

The Germans, on the other hand, had gained ground early in the war and were able to retain their position, through the maintenance of an overall defensive attitude. There was no squeamishness about maintaining strong positions. Their field manual, *Stellungsbau* (1916), made clear the principal considerations – and the commitment to attrition:

> Field positions when constructed afford considerable advantages to the defence. The important points to be borne in mind by the *defence* in a *war of positions* are:
>
> Economy for forces.
>
> Diminution of losses and increase of enemy losses.
>
> Utilization of ground so that conditions favourable for combat are obtained, while they are made unfavourable to the enemy.[181]

As a result, deep shelters designed to protect troops from direct shellfire were mostly a feature of German defensive positions, while Allied positions had mostly small excavations in trench walls, or, later, cut and cover shelters using corrugated iron and sandbags. All in all this meant in many cases that Allied lines were poorly situated with respect to topography and ground conditions, while German policy allowed for strategic withdrawal to carefully prepared and suitably located positions. For example, at Loos, in September 1915, the British became aware of the strength of the German positions in chalk ground. On his arrival at the front, James Norman Hall observed the German dug-outs for himself:

> Under a clayish surface soil there was a stratum of solid chalk. Advantage of this had been taken by the German engineers who must have planned and

German deep dugout – kitted out for a long occupation.

supervised the work. Many of the shell-proof dug-outs were fifteen and even twenty feet below the surface of the ground. Stairways just large enough to permit the passage of a man's body led down to them. The roofs were reinforced with heavy timbers.[182]

The British and their allies would have to catch up after the Somme, when the strength of German dug-outs were seen to be proof against the heaviest bombardment yet amassed against them. The British would once again encounter deep dug-outs and fortified positions, and when the Germans were seen to retreat to a yet stronger line of fortifications, the *Siegfried Stellung* – known to the British as the Hindenburg Line – there would be great need of the 'offensive spirit'.

The two lines that stretched across Europe became two great, opposing, linear fortresses, packed with men and stood on the defensive. The siege that ensued was the greatest in history, and the potential for breakthrough was much reduced. The location of trench systems with respect to the topography directly influenced their safety – with High Commands struggling against the exposure of troops to direct observation and therefore to effective artillery or small arms fire. The nature of ground conditions was also influential in any attempt to end the siege: it influenced the effective use of the 'siege engines' such as high angle howitzer artillery and mortar fire (forced to shelter from counter-battery fire), gas warfare (dependent on topography as well as atmospheric conditions) and tanks (and their ability to freely manoeuvre across a landscape). In all cases, accurate knowledge of topography and ground conditions was essential – if an adequate attempt at break through was so desired.

TRENCHES

In their simplest sense, the trenches of the Great War were linear excavations of variable depth that were mostly open to the sky, but were sometimes roofed for concealment purposes, usually with close-boarded timber.[183] The stated purpose of the trenches was, of course, to provide protection to the front line troops and their supporting arms in the face of 'small arms' fire (rifles, machine guns and the like) and artillery. Despite their simplicity, the function of trenches varied and as the war progressed, with no absolute sign of a break in the deadlock, more and more types were developed. The pace of change was so rapid that the third edition of *The Royal Engineers Field Service Pocket-Book* (1916) contained only blank pages for field defences, accompanied by the statement: 'Owing to the constant changes taking place in Field Defences it has been decided… to omit this section which will be rewritten after the war…'[184] However, in the main there were two consistent types: fire trenches, which formed the front lines, and communication trenches, which joined them.

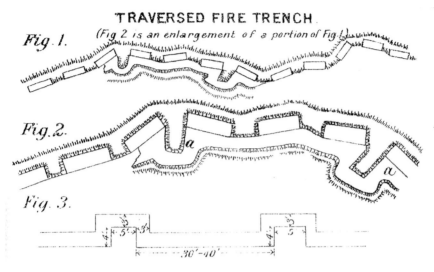

Plan for a traversed fire trench, from the *British Manual of Field Defences* (1908).

Traversed fire trench preserved in Paniselian sediments at the Hill 62 trench Museum, near Ypres. (P. Doyle)

Fire trenches (i.e. fighting trenches) were divided into a regular pattern of fire bays (facing the front, and occupied by soldiers on guard) and traverses (which linked the bays). This system meant that no soldier could walk in a straight line for long, without having to switch back on himself. Such movement was intended to limit the effects of shellfire exploding in the trenches, or from the possibility of enfilade rifle and machine gun fire along the length of a trench – with inevitable consequences.

British and German fire trenches were alike in this respect; French versions varied, some had a more leisurely, curved, zigzag – but all calculated to reduce the impact of explosions and enfilade fire.[185] In fact French military engineering was the inspiration for much of trench warfare, and French terms were commonly applied. Thus, the spoil removed in digging a trench was used to form a *parapet* – a mound of earth in front of the trench on the enemy side, intended to stop bullets, and a *parados* – a slightly higher mound at the rear, which would interrupt the movement of bullets and reduce the impact of exploding shells, and prevent soldiers' heads from being silhouetted against the skyline. Firesteps were constructed to allow the infantry to fire over or through the parapet. Facing the front, loopholes were provided to observe the enemy with greater safety; found as steel plates with a hole big enough to admit a rifle, they were often targeted by snipers. Because of this, blankets and other coverings were used to create darkness behind them – though snipers were adept at finding them.[186]

Communication trenches (or CTs) varied in length. Running from the rear areas and connecting all the forward trenches up to the front line, they offered protection for supply and troop movements from the rear. They were usually dug in a zig-zag or wavy pattern and in Flanders, where the geological conditions meant that revetment – officially defined as 'any artificial material used for retaining earth at a steeper angle that it would normally assume'[187] – was essential, CTs had similar dimensions to a fire trench. In the coastal strip at Nieuport, communication trenches of French construction were close boarded and roofed by timber, and referred to as *boyaux couverts*.[188]

In the ideal situation, each fire trench was approximately two metres deep, and 0.6 metres wide at the bottom, usually widening to two metres at its top, but depths varied according to topography and the depth to permanent water saturation. Trench width at floor level was around 0.8 metres, and at the top, given the appropriate regulation 'batter' or slope, up to three metres. In areas where groundwater was close to surface, 'borrow pits' were dug on either side of the trench to supply extra earth needed to build up a sufficient height to protect the troops. In some cases sandbag 'breastworks' were constructed where ground

Communication trench preserved in Paniselian sediments at the Hill 62 trench Museum, near Ypres. (P. Doyle)

conditions prevented even the most rudimentary trench lines. Captain F.C. Hitchcock of the Leinster Regiment described his ideal trenches in the clay-ground near Armentières, in 1915:

> Our trenches appeared to be very formidable; they were duckboarded, and the parapets and *paradoses* were completely revetted with sand-bags. The parapets were 6 feet high, and the wooden fire steps being 1½ feet in height, gave a fire position of 4½ feet. Owing to the low-lying nature of the terrain the trenches were breastworks.[189]

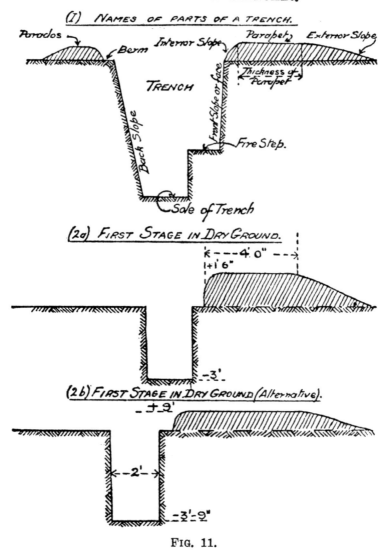

SECTIONS OF FIRE TRENCHES.

(1) NAMES OF PARTS OF A TRENCH.

(2a) FIRST STAGE IN DRY GROUND.

(2b) FIRST STAGE IN DRY GROUND (Alternative).

FIG. 11.

Standard trench dimensions and nomenclature.

Such breastworks, known as 'high command' trenches, in contrast with their normal 'low command' cousins,[190] were common in the Ypres Salient, for as the men dug down through the wet soils that lay on top of the clay, they soon hit that impervious layer. Digging down further would simply create a void, lined with

FIG.I.   SECTION. OF BREASTWORK IN WET SOIL.

[Diagram: Section of breastwork in wet soil, with labels:]

+4'·6" — 4'·0" · +4'·6" · Min 6'·9" · 9'·0" · 3'·0"

+3'·0"   Parapet.   Slope 1 in 2

±0   ±0   ±0

BORROW-PIT
Sloped outwards.

X PM   X.P.M.Panel or Gabion.

−3'   X.P.M. Panel salved
corrugated iron and boarding or   Hidden Barbed Wire.
brushwood.

Note:- Depth of bottom to vary according to ground. Set frames as low as possible
to save breastwork. Drainage at grade of 1/60 to lower ground essential.

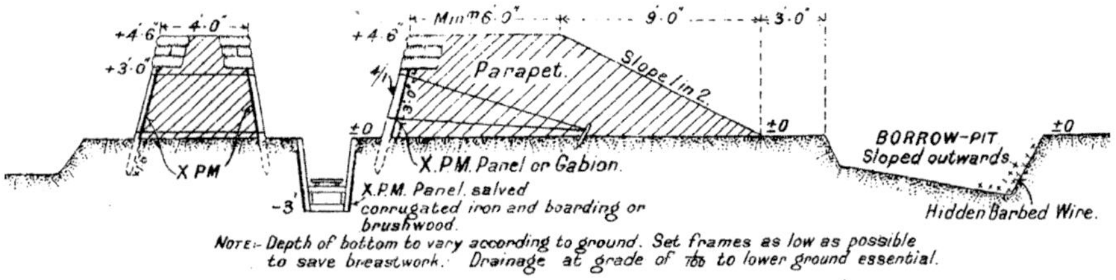

Breastworks in wet ground; this system, developed in 1916, uses specially prepared 'A' frames.
(*Manual of Field Works*, 1921)

impervious clay, that would soon be filled with water, and which would require pumping against both groundwater and rainfall. There would be no end to it.

Most trenches were 'floored' with wooden duckboards (also sometimes called 'trench boards'), which were built up to allow drainage beneath – in fact it was common for successive levels of duckboards to be laid one on top of another to combat the difficult conditions encountered. British duckboards were built to a standard specification, allowing them to be laid such that the forward part fitted within the outer spars of the next prepared duckboard track.[191] German trench lines by contrast, often employed timber planks that were run along the line of the trenches.[192] In rare cases, bricks and rubble were used, when trench lines snaked through the destroyed villages and houses.[193] 2nd Lt A.D. Gillespie wrote home from the Salient in March 1915 to praise the benefits of adequate flooring in this way: 'We are in a real trench this time, one of the few, I suppose, which has survived the wet weather. It's really very luxurious, for the bottom is all paved with brick, or boarded over; and naturally there is still a deal of mud in places, we are quite happy…'[194]

With the possibility of troops standing in cold water in undrained or water-logged trenches, came the probability of 'trench feet'. Field Marshal Sir John French, commanding the British Expeditionary Force, was to encounter this condition in the course of the First Battle of Ypres.

It was at this time, the third week of November, 1914, that the serious evil known as 'Trench Feet' first made its appearance in the Army in France. The condition is caused by prolonged immersion in water…It is seldom caused unless the immersion is as long as 24 hours, but the cooler the water, the less is the time to produce it…The only *real* preventative is to arrange that the men do not remain deep in mud or cold water for prolonged periods. If this is not possible, cases of 'trench feet' are inevitable.[195]

Sir John French estimated casualties from 'Trench Feet' to be somewhere in the region of 20,000 men in the winter of 1914–15. In his view, 'with good trenches and proper care 'trench feet' should be of rare occurrence';[196] it was the duty of engineers and geologists to ensure that it was. By 1916, advice of the *Notes for Infantry Officers on Trench Warfare* was that drains of 'adequate capacity' should be engineered into the floor of the trench as it was being built, sturdy and 'boxed in' to prevent collapse; but noted:

> In the case of trenches dug in the presence of the enemy the above methods cannot be applied. Drainage is a very difficult problem in these circumstances, even when the ground is not practically flat. Trenches on a forward slope cannot be drained except to the front, and it will seldom be practical to dig drains leading forward from the trench. Practically all that remains possible as a means of getting rid of water and keeping trenches reasonably dry and clean is constant pumping and putting down some sort of paving or flooring.[197]

Pumping wet trenches; this solution, fighting against the lie of the land or of groundwater issues, was never anything more than temporary.

Ensuring the trench was adequately drained and floored was clearly essential, if the men were not to suffer from the elements, as well as the constant shell-fire. While men hoping that waters would subside inside a trench, this factor was at the mercy of ground conditions. As the British post-war *Manual of Field Works (All Arms)* was quick to point out: 'sumps or soakage pits should not be relied upon unless natural drainage is possible... unless the sump reaches a permeable stratum, it must be pumped or baled out....'[198]

As had been suggested by Walter Kranz, drainage of field fortifications was likely to be a role for engineers and their geological advisors. The German manual, *Stellungsbau* (1916), noted sagely 'If the water level in the country is high, special measures to deal with it may be necessary.'[199] Never a truer word was written about the clay soils of Flanders. In this respect, the German army was ahead of the game, and became expert in the drainage of trenches as the war progressed. This was only to be expected; one of the most significant roles for *Kriegsgeologen* identified by Kranz was the drainage of waters likely to cause a problem in trenches.[200] A British manual, *Summary of Recent Information Regarding the German Army and its Methods*, issued in January 1917, summarised the German approach, emphasising its reliance on expertise:

> Great attention is paid to drainage of trenches, as on the success or non-success of the measures taken may depend whether this position can or cannot be held in the wet season. It is laid down that the drainage must be done on a definite plan which must be carried out in good time. Drainage engineers and geologists are to be consulted, and use made of existing maps and plans. Wherever possible, the drainage water is to be led in the direction of the enemy, pipes being put through the parapet for this purpose.[201]

Brushwood revetment in a German trench system.

Corrugated sheeting revetment in a British trench.

Sandbag revetment in a British trench; sandbags were not considered the best choice, as they were quick to rot. (Library of Congress)

Timber board revetment in a German trench, with loopholes.

Drainage was significant, but so was the need to keep trenches in good condition in poor weather. With trench sides (known as slopes) cut at a higher angle than the soils could support naturally, to prevent collapse, they were supported or 'revetted' with whatever was available, sometimes wattle, often corrugated sheeting and expanded metal (XPM), sometimes chicken wire, or even timber boards if they could be salvaged. 'Brushwood' and 'well-built sods' were also recommended and used.[202] Timber was often used to hold these materials in place, as were angle iron posts anchored deep into the earth; and layers of bonded sandbags strengthened the whole. The military manuals laid down the parameters:

> The side of trenches which have to be occupied for a long time, and particularly in wet weather on a damp site, must be revetted. Hurdles or rabbit netting held up by stout stakes securely wired to short pickets firmly anchored in the parapet or *parados*, form a useful type of revetment for this purpose. Sandbags are not so suitable. In the winter in Flanders some really solid form of revetment, such as planks or timber, or expanded metal sheets, is necessary.[203]

To assist with the construction of trenches in 'soft ground', 'trench frames' were recommended in British use. These were published in the December 1916 revision to the earlier British manual *Notes for Infantry Officers on Trench Warfare,* drawn up in March of that year. Such frames were an inverted 'A', the cross of which

REVETMENTS.

TRENCH FRAMES FOR USE IN SOFT GROUND.

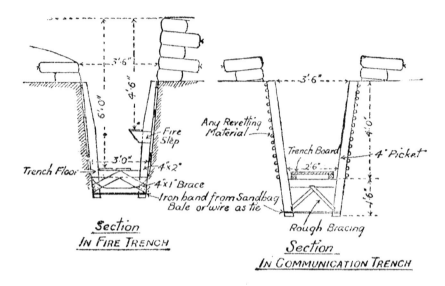

A-Frames for wet ground, as specified in Notes for Infantry Officers on Trench Warfare, 1917

provided an elevated foundation for a duckboard track, and the main line of the 'A' providing a support for both the trench revetment, and the sandbag walls of a breastwork.[204] Major W.E. Buckingham RE, Assistant Inspector of Mines, was equally impressed with them when he encountered the frames in a communication trench in 1917:

> I was very struck with this trench which is the most elaborate trench I have seen. It was made in accordance with recent E in C's [Engineer in Chief] plates with expanded metal revetment held in place by [inverted A] frames about 3' or 4' above duck board level & then a flat ledge, & unrevetted sides above.[205]

Both the trench frames and the revised manual saw much use in the Ypres Salient, and elsewhere, with the frames constructed and ready for use by the autumn at least. Captain F.C. Hitchcock of the Leinster Regiment received examples in September 1917, though the appearance of such large items in the trenches was not without problems:

…one [shell] went slap into the CT called Uhlan Alley, and made a devilish mess of the duckboard, 'A' frames, and corrugated iron sheets, which were revetting the parapets. It was really quite funny, as the sappers had only laid down the 'A' frames that morning as a pattern for us to copy![206]

For the most part, similar trench systems were employed by the main protagonists on the Western Front, directed by their high commands, but influenced by experience on the ground. For example, a British, commercially-produced, manual *Knowledge for War* published in 1916, gives a list of the typical components of a trench system at this mid point in the war; a complex arrangement of lines used by both sides to give the maximum confidence of 'defence in depth.'

> The following summary will give a good general idea of the means taken to prepare a defensive front in trench warfare:–
>
> 1. Obstacles–generally barbed wire–in front of first line trench, concealed if possible from artillery observation.
> 2. Listening posts, look-out posts, machine guns.
> 3. Fire trenches, recessed and traversed.
> 4. Communication trenches to the rear, linking up the whole system.
> 5. Shelters and dug-outs. These should be immediately behind the first line fire trenches, with easy communication to them.
> 6. Support trenches–traversed–from 25 to 100 yards in rear of fire trenches.
> 7. Dressing stations, kitchen, etc., branching from communication trenches.
> 8. Second line trenches. Fire trenches, machine guns, etc., similar to organisation of first line.
> 9. Supporting points, behind second line, well defended by parties of 20 to 40 men, serve to hold up enemy assault on first and second line; such points should be entirely surrounded by barbed wire.[207]

In ideal circumstances, trenches were to be planned, laid out and traced across ground so as to take in its natural characteristics and use them to advantage. The British *Field Defences* manual of 1908 recommended: 'The ideal site for trenches is one from which the best fire effect can be obtained, in combination with complete concealment of the trenches… As such positions will rarely be found, the best compromise must be sought for'.[208] For the German High Command, committed

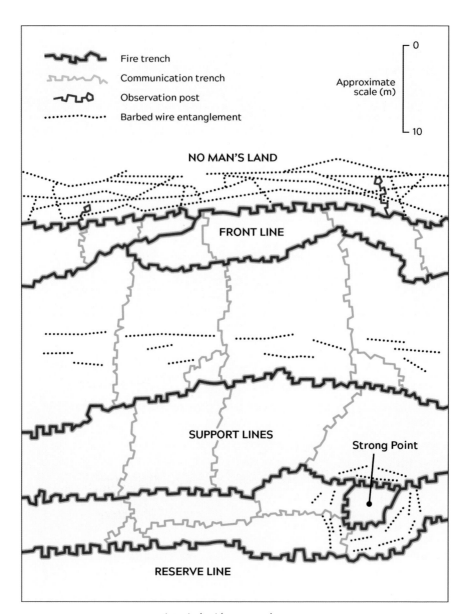

Fire trench
Communication trench
Observation post
Barbed wire entanglement

0

Approximate
scale (m)

10

NO MAN'S LAND

FRONT LINE

SUPPORT LINES

Strong Point

RESERVE LINE

A typical mid-war trench system.

to ensuring their trench lines were the strongest, the use of natural features as strongpoints was the most important factor.

Great use has been made by the Germans of natural strong points, such as villages, farms, and woods. In the villages, the borders and interior have been strongly organised, generally for all round defence, and a particularly desperate resistance has been offered in them. The normal procedure now, when taking up a new position, is to fix on a general line of natural strong points, and to prepare these for defence first and then to join them up by fire trenches, without much regard to the field of fire of the latter.[209]

Nevertheless, fire trenches on both sides were usually arranged in successive parallel rows, with the front line, support line and reserve line all connected by the communication trenches, which were the main thoroughfares of trench warfare. In well-established trench systems the front line consisted of a fire trench and ancillary supervision trench with deeper dug-outs providing accommodation for the troops. In his despatch of 23 December 1916, Sir Douglas Haig described the defences the Germans had prepared well in advance of the Somme battle.

> During nearly two years' preparation he [the enemy] had spared no pains to render these defences impregnable. The first and second systems each consisted of several lines of deep trenches, well-provided with bomb-proof shelters with numerous communications trenches connecting them…The woods and villages in between these systems of defence had been turned into veritable fortresses…The existing cellars were supplemented by elaborate dug-outs, sometimes in two storeys, and these were connected up by passages as much as thirty feet below the surface of the ground.[210]

This ideal represented the idea of 'defence in depth'; as the war progressed beyond 1916 so the increasingly the front became more fluid, especially as the front line was obviously most often targeted by the enemy artillery. Late war, frontlines became outposts; few men served in these; instead there was a small garrison intended to interrupt the initial assault and to brave the shells.[211]

Trench construction was usually carried out by the infantry themselves, and training was given in the use of both the pick and shovel – as their individual entrenching tool was there mostly for

USE OF SHOVEL.

Training infantrymen how to dig was an important consideration in trench warfare (*Manual of Field Works*, 1921)

emergencies. But under the orders of the Royal Engineers, fatigue parties and later labour battalions had mostly to dig their trenches rapidly under the cover of darkness, generally with men spaced between two to three paces apart. For the Germans, there were explicit instructions that the construction of trenches was to be entrusted to those men who would, at least at first, be occupying them, again under the control of engineers.[213]

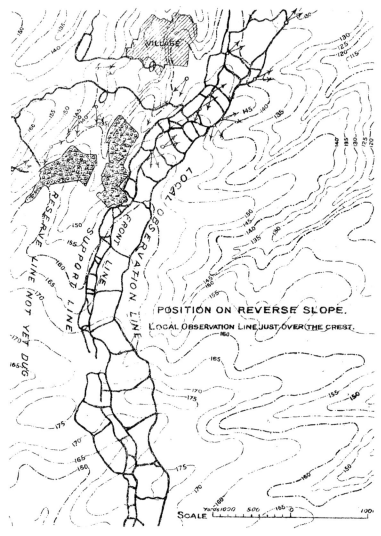

Siting of trenches topographically to maximise defence required great skill; here the trenches follow the contours, thereby drawing in the enemy into a hail of enfilading fire.
(*Manual of Field Works*, 1921)

Speed of digging was directly influenced by ground conditions, prevailing weather, and the nature of the troops. With, in most cases, the Germans dictating the line of the opposing trenches, more often than not the trace of the British defences was unfavourable, but it is hard to generalise. For the British at least, there was little chance to reference the nature of the local geology. For the Germans the ideal was to have two types of geologist to advise: 'the trained ones who are of use in the field before and after the battle', and 'the officer on the front during battle'.[214] The implication here was that *all* officers should have geological training to assist their men.

Position relative to slope was an important factor to be considered in the construction of trenches. Basic principles for entrenchment were laid down which emphasised theoretical aspects of position in relation to forward and reverse slopes, valleys and spurs, and topographical height. These aspects were considered important in order to allow effective observation of opposing trench positions, to prevent enemy observation of forward and reserve trenches, and to provide necessary supportive arcs of fire for small arms. Ideally, the trench lines were to be designed to contour hills and valleys, particularly important in providing 'mutual enfilade' fire in valleys, the assaulting troops being attacked from both sides of the valley, and on the slopes of spurs by the defenders.[215]

In all cases, the positioning relative to slope was to maximise observation of the enemy to direct artillery and machine gun fire. In the Ypres area, the British trench lines were positioned either at the foot of or, on the reverse slopes of, the sand ridges overlooking the clay plain. This made artillery observation difficult, and provided ample opportunity for accurate offensive fire from the German artillery. In the rolling chalk upland of the Somme, British positions were more variably positioned, and more able to follow the guidelines laid down by the official regulations. But again, for the most part, the German lines were more formidably sited.

The front line trenches of the opposing armies were separated by a belt of contested ground known as 'No Man's Land', usually extensively pitted by shell holes and mine craters. In some cases, only mine craters lay between the two lines, and guidance on capturing and strengthening craters was given in all the manuals.[216] No Man's Land was bordered by belts of barbed wire entanglements which were renewed by wiring parties working under the cover of darkness. The compexity of the barbed wire obstacles intensified during the war. An intelligence summary of German defences from from 1916 ruefully commented 'One of the most distinctive features of the German defences is the labour expended on constructing thoroughly good and effective wire entanglements ' – all evidence of the German determination to hold the defensive.[217]

No Man's Land at Vimy Ridge, formed from a series of mine craters blown in the chalk subsoils. (P. Doyle)

Behind the frontline, some 10 to 30 metres, were the support and reserve lines, trenches that were still 'organised for fire', with the intention of holding back the enemy if a break-through of the frontline had been achieved. Most important was the support line, as it was here that the major part of the trench garrison was housed, with a smaller number of sentries in the frontline itself. Farther back were the reserve lines, housing men who had been cycled out of the frontline, taking their turn before they were removed from the line completely for a period of rest. The whole system could be encapsulated within a zone of 50 to 150 metres width, and access from the rear areas to each of the trenches in turn was through communication trenches, which traversed the ground between the lines of fire trenches. In some cases, particularly where the enemy controlled the high ground, tunnels or subways were constructed to allow safe passage of troops to the front from the rear areas. This became a feature of the trench war in 1917.

Trench warfare evolved as the war progressed; from shallow scrapes to engineered slopes. Sitting in his trenches, Leutnant Eugen Röcker wrote home about the evolution of the trench lines.

I have witnessed the development of trench-warfare for more than a year. One year ago the art of building trenches was still in its infancy. Today its done in a far bigger style. Our communication trenches stretch for kilometres, the ground is covered with boardwalk. Each Musketeer has his own secure dug-out, a year ago only the officers had them. The advances in armament forced us to dig deeper into the earth. The conflict is slowly turning into an underground war. A sophisticated war full of horrors. Its strange that mobile warfare lacks that kind of sophistication and is far less dangerous. In sophisticated war you sit comfortably, in a well furnished dug-out, but you can be dead from one second to next. In mobile warfare you sleep on wet ground under an open sky, in all kinds of weather, wet and freezing. Hard to choose what's better. I wonder if I will ever see another year so full of good and bad, of joy and sorrow, of deprivation and indulgence.[218]

Uniquely placed to observe this were the aviators of both sides, who would contribute materially to the battle through their detailed observation of positions, and the taking of photographs.[219] As Röcker would find, when he transferred to

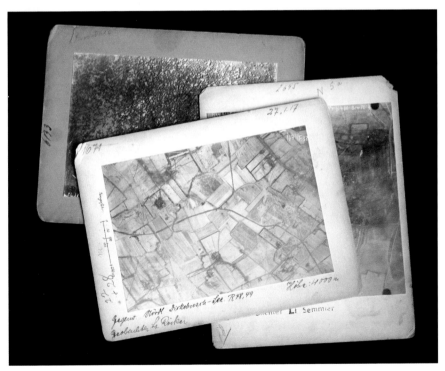

Aerial photographs of the British lines taken by Lt Eugen Röcker.

become a pilot, trench lines were particularly vulnerable to aerial observation, and flyers would patrol the front in order to discern any changes, take photographs for map construction, or spot for the artillery.[220] Lt Cecil Lewis was to take aerial photographs on his first duties over France with the Royal Flying Corps in 1916 – he found the ground difficult to read from the clouds.

> My first real job [was] to photograph the enemy second line trenches. The lines, from the air, had none of the significance they had from the ground, mainly because all contours were non-existent. The local undulations, valleys, ravines, ditches, hillsides, which gave advantage to one side or another, were flattened out. All you saw was two more or less parallel sets of trenches, clearer in some places than in others according to the colour of the earth thrown up in making them.[221]

The documentation of the trench war was like no other that had gone before. From 1914–15, there were reports, surveys, plans and even simple letters home; and then there were superbly detailed trench maps, regularly updated through aerial photography. The use of aerial photographs became a high art, with the 'exquisite definition with which they show all trenches and military works' being of 'enormous help… to both sides'.[222] These and other documents have left a legacy of archival materials that allow us to understand how the war developed and evolved. And over the last twenty years, detailed archaeology has contributed to our understanding, and has permitted us to see, in some ways, what the soldiers saw in 1914–1918.[223] The following examples illustrate just how dependent those trenches were on 'ground'.

Boesinghe: examples of trenches and dug-outs on the clay plain of Ypres

The entrenchments at Boesinghe comprise both trenches and deep mined dug-outs. The trench/dug-out system is located close to the Yser Canal to the north of Ypres, close to the end of the British line in the Salient.

These British trenches were constructed in late 1915, after the German offensive of spring 1915. At this stage in the war the system of trenches was constructed with standard front, support and reserve lines, connected by communication trenches. In 1992 the area was being cleared as part of the development for an industrial park north of the prosperous city of Ypres. During these works, a trench system was uncovered with an associated deep mined dug-out; this had a maximum depth of approximately 10 metres, and is thought to have been been constructed by the 173rd Tunnelling Company (RE). This dug-out served as the headquarters of the

Amateur archaeological investigations of British trench lines from c. 1916–17, excavated into silts and sands overlying the Ypres Clay at Boesinghe; duck boards in position, with upright timbers (part of a 'A frame' construction) to hold the revetment in place. Here the A frames were used to build up breastworks in this wet soil. (P. Doyle)

13th and 16th Royal Welsh Fusiliers in the Third Battle of Ypres.[224] Development proceeded while local amateur archaeologists excavated the site, examining the trench system and, poignantly, uncovering the remains of 155 soldiers – British, French and German – who had been buried in No Man's Land, casualties associated with both the Second and Third Battles of Ypres, in 1915 and subsequently, in

1917. Part of the site is now preserved in concrete, and signposted as 'Yorkshire Trench' after its original trench name.[225]

The trench system exposed by the 1992 excavations was shallow; it had been developed in a thin layer (up to 2.2 metres thick, according to the contemporary geological maps) of Ice Age soils, sands and silty clays that sit on the Ypres Clay plain. Situated east of the Yser Canal, cut deeply into the Ypres Clay, the British line had the canal to the rear, its embankment raised up from the clay forming a significant position for the construction of dug-outs and other shelters. The trench line lies on approximately the 15 m contour line, and faced a German line that sits close to the 20 m contour, the westwards extension of the Pilckem Ridge. The difference in heights also represents differences in geology – the Germans squarely upon the sands that sit on the clay, the British at its feather-edge.[226]

Here, a German strong point, the Caesar's Nose, pointed belligerently towards the British line using a low-lying spur as its point of reference. This work had, in fact been part of a contested system of trenches, with both sides effectively sharing the line in 1915.[227] The 6th West Yorkshire Regiment arrived in the line in July 1916, and found it to be favourable, and dry, but these conditions were not to last.

> When the battalion first took over the line, the trenches had not fallen in. The precautions which began to be adopted on a big scale in 1916 to preserve trenches from collapsing in the winter months (such as 'A' frames and other systems of revetting) had not been taken in the Salient. The Division [49th] arrived too late to organise draining and revetting on a sufficiently elaborate basis. The result was disastrous. When the Autumn rains began in August, the trenches disappeared, or became canals… The line could only be held by a system of detached posts, where men were prisoned till nightfall, up to the knees in water day and night… Tremendous efforts were made throughout the Division to combat the most serious danger of water-logged trenches – 'trench feet'…[228]

The trench system had to be considerably improved, in line with the advice provided by *Notes on Trench Warfare for Infantry Officers*, and in particular the use of A-frames as illustrated in its revised diagrams.[229] By mid 1916, these 'A' frames were in use – Lt Grover of the King's Shropshire Light Infantry recalled their function in this sector:

> I spend a lot of time in the Salient, where the water level is just below the surface, and when it rains the whole thing is just one field of mud, so all the

defences have to be built up. Which means you not only have to build them up with sandbags, you have to revet them very strongly. We had things called 'A Frames', in the form of an inverted A with a trace across to allow a drain below, and that was the inside of the trench, these were fitted in and were revetted inside.[230]

These trenches were therefore constructed using breastworks, and the archaeological work demonstrated the presence of the inverted 'A' frame structures intended to

Detail of the 'A frame' construction type uncovered in the trenches at Boesinghe; duck boards are laid upon the horizontal spar of the inverted 'A'. Breastworks were then built up to create sufficient head cover; due to the shallowness of the sands overlying the clay, this would have been a necessity. (P. Doyle)

support the revetments and breastworks of sandbags. Examining the site carefully, it is possible to see that the trenches themselves were about a metre in depth to the duckboard surface, with up to another metre beneath this to the level of water saturation. This is consistent with a position for the trench, just overlying the impervious Ypres Clay. Other, more simply constructed trenches, earlier versions, were also found in this area. In at least one part of the trench the presence of several successive layers of duckboarding suggests attempts to raise trench floor level above the saturated ground before the 'A' frames were installed.

Importantly, associated with the trenches and opening from them, is a deep mined dug-out with an inclined and close-boarded entrance descending from the trenches. These are organised into galleries of standard dimensions, with separate chambers as appropriate. The dug-out is constructed within the clay, but clearly required constant pumping, especially as the overlying permeable sands allowed the migration of water into the dug-out entrances. The open entrance, once covered by gas-proof curtains, would have been inviting to any collected waters, flowing down the steps to the void below.

Close-boarded entrance incline into a British deep dugout at Boesinghe. Ingress of water from trench level would have meant that pumping from sumps would have been necessary. (P. Doyle)

GAS-PROOF CURTAINS.

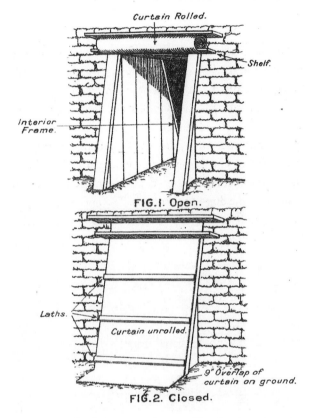

Gas proof curtains were used to help prevent ingress of heavier-than-air gas into the dugout.
(*Manual of Field Works*, 1921)

Forward Cottage and Cross Roads Farm, Ypres Salient

In 2005, another part of the British front line trench system in the northern limb of the Ypres Salient between Boesinghe and Wieltje, was excavated. The system lay along the trajectory of the proposed A19 motorway extension, and the archaeological investigations were carried out in order to make an asessment of their archaeological value.[231] The site was found to be in such good order that the road extension was never built.[232]

The site, situated east of Yorkshire Trench, formed part of the front that existed from 1915–1917 – when the line was pushed forwards during the Third Battle of Ypres. Consisting of a front line trench system between the destroyed farms of

'Forward Collage' and 'Cross Roads Farm', the line of the trenches faced a road known as 'Admiral's Road', with the cross roads being formed by 'Buffs Road'. Such terms were common aspects of British trench naming.[233] As at Boesinghe, this area figured in both Second Ypres (1915), and Third Ypres (1917) battles, and once again the front line lies on a spur of the Pilkem Ridge, an extension of the Passchendaele–Messines Ridge complex, a rise barely discernable but nevertheless significant. Here the front is parallel to the 25 metre contour, with a slight dip occupied by Admiral's Road in the middle of No Man's Land. The German trenches opposite – some 200 metres away at Forward Cottage, facing 'Canadian trench', and 450 metres at Cross Roads Farm, there facing 'Caliban Trench' – are at approximately the same level, also sitting on the 25 metre contour. Here the lower levels of the Paniselian sands are seen, lying as would be expected, upon the Ypres Clay.

Though seemingly insignificant, the slight height advantage of the German trenches was enough to cause issues, and in many cases there was an interchange of frontlines, heavily fought over.

> Certain trenches... were much overlooked by High Command Redoubt, some 150 yards away. The Germans throughout the 19th April [1916] heavily bombarded these trenches, and succeeded in seizing them at night... The Brigadier-General therefore decided to bombard them steadily throughout the 21st, and recapture them on the night 21st/22ndApril. It was found that the enemy had dug good new trenches in several places, and equipped them with steel loop-hole plates, and these were occupied thankfully by our men. The general state of the trenches, commanded as they were by the enemy's positions, in the water-logged Ypres Salient during the winter of 1915-1916 defies description, and all praise must be given to the regimental officers and men for their hard work and cheerfulness under most depressing conditions.[234]

Two of the 2005 excavation sites – one at Forward Cottage and the other at Cross Roads Farm – show differences in trench architecture associated for the most part with the underlying geology. At Forward Cottage, both German and British frontlines were exposed, but while the German trenches were undistinguished, it was the detail of the British trenches that was most rewarding. The trenches excavated displayed the standard trench architecture and were well preserved, dug through soils into the Paniselian sands, and sitting at the level of the Ypres Clay.[235]

At Forward Cottage the British trenches, dating from 1917, were constructed

Well-preserved trenches at the Forward Cottage archaeological site. Here well-constructed and sturdy inverted A frames were found in-situ together with their corrugated iron revetment sheets. The site has a greater thickness of Paniselian sands and silts than at Boesinghe, and consequently the trenches are deeper. However, water can be seen sitting on the clays at the foot of the trench.

(P. Doyle)

Evidence of the differing construction methods at Forward Cottage archaeological site. Here is the same inverted A frame construction, sitting at the level of the 'blue clay' below the Paniselian sands. Intersecting this is what is considered to be an earlier trench line, with trench boards laid directly onto the sedimentary layers, without the opportunity for drainage afforded by the A frames.
(P. Doyle)

using state-of-the art inverted 'A' trench frames, the frames being used to hold back the corrugated iron sheeting that served as a trench revetment. Both were in remarkably good condition, preserved to a depth of ~1 m. As at Boesinghe, the purpose of the 'A' frames was to allow for the construction of elevated 'duck-board' walkways above a drainage channel, necessary as water was not free-draining. The limbs of the frames also served as firm supports for the corrugated iron revetments. The lower portion of the 'A' frame was in contact with the remarkably blue-coloured Ypres Clay, while the revetment and trench frames were in contact with the Paniselian sediments, mostly fine sands and silts – and therefore likely to be wet during the winter months. This explains the need for such trench frames here, for though the trench line was deeper than that at Boesinghe, the ever present situation of the Ypres Clay at its foundation meant that the site was still likely to pool water. With Third Ypres characterised by heavy rainfall and a waterlogged battlefield, it is hardly surprising they were needed.

At Cross Roads Farm, the site displayed trenches that dated from the period 1915–1917. Here the 1915 trenches displayed duck boards laid directly upon the level of the clay, with blue clay being displayed beneath the boards. These trenches would have been wet; the permeable Paniselian sands allowed the water to flow freely, which would then have ponded on the clay. This situation would have been the same for the Germans, and in both cases, the trench lines would have quickly filled with water, requiring elaborate drainage, pumping and even bailing of the trench lines. Trench feet – that dread result of standing in wet conditions with feet constricted in boots and puttees – would be the result. In an attempt to raise the level of the trench floor, these early trenches have duckboard sections stacked one on the other. Once again, the preferred revetment was that of corrugated iron sheets, held in place by angle iron or timber stakes. The trenches here were almost within the regulation depth; but to improve the lot of the average soldier would have required the use of inverted A trench frames, as at Forward Cottage.

Also on site here is a small ammunition storage chamber, a small deep, dug-out that was found with a perfectly preserved water pump and fire hose intact. With the storage chamber below the level of the clay-sand interface, the pump would have seen almost constant use, once again indicative of the waterlogged conditions in this part of the front line.

If these trenches were typical of British trench architecture of 1915–17 in the northern sector of the Ypres Salient, comparison with German lines would be instructive. German front-line trenches at Messines at the southern extremity of the Ypres Salient (south of St Eloi) were excavated in 2012–13 as part of a major replacement of water mains in the region.[236]

In situ stacked duckboards provides evidence of attempts to build up the trench floor at Cross Roads Farm in order to escape flooding. Here the Paniselian and other porous soils lie directly on top of the Ypres Clay. Under winter conditions, and without adequate means of drainage, these trenches would have become waterlogged and hazardous. (P. Doyle)

Messines: German trenches of the defensive system

The excavation site uncovered a German trench system that was located on the slopes of the Messines Ridge, just above the valley of the Douve, surrounding the town of Messines itself. Messines sits on a spur of the main ridge system east of Ypres, and forms part of a wider plateau with Wytschaete to the northwest, and Messines to the south. This plateau had seen hard fighting in 1914, and had stabilised in its position in 1915, becoming a dominant fortress, comprising a system of strongpoints that were designed to break up any attempt to take the ridge top by frontal assault. With the Germans occupying the high ground, with every spur

In situ preserved pump and fire hose leading to an underground chamber at Cross Roads Farm. As can be seen from the water in the chamber, pumping would have been necessary. (P. Doyle)

and building built into the line as a fortress (as laid down in *Stellungsbau*),[237] the British were forced to build trenches that were effectively 10 metres lower, facing the forward slopes of the ridge.[238]

Capping the ridge top at Wytschaete are the driest sands known to the British (not surprisingly) as the 'Wytschaete Sands'.[239] But for the most part, the rest of the ridge is composed of the various levels of the 'Paniselian', overlying, as always, the Ypres Clay. Here are found the water-logged Kemmel Sands, sandwiched between the clay-rich layers, and there were even wetter 'alluvial' soils, that thicken to considerable depth in the valley of the Douve at the foot of the ridge. To the west, in the distance, was the British held high point of Mont Kemmel, with the valleys of the Steenbeek (flowing to the south) and Haringbeek (flowing to the north) between them – again filled with wet alluvial soils.

The trench system was constructed as a strongpoint in the German front line. In fact the excavations disturbed what was the German second line in the defensive system constructed here. In the archaeologists' excavation trenches were exposed in turn the details of the German Great War trenches, incredibly well preserved. Here was *Eckert Graben* (known as 'Uhlan Support' to the British) a second line position organised as a firetrench; a machine-gun position; and a communication trench, *Blauer Graben*. To the south of Messines, on the slopes facing the Douve, was exposed *Emil Graben* ('Uhlan Avenue') a line to the rear of the Second line.[240]

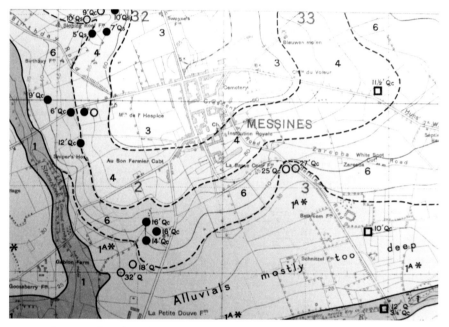

Extract from British geological map indicating 'Suitability for dugouts', showing the location of the water bearing Kemmel Sands (4). Above the sands are drier sediments (unit 3, draining into the layer below), and below them are silty clays (unit 6). The valley of the Douve is filled with wet alluvial sediments. The line of the German trenches cuts across the junction between units 4 and 6; this means that they would have been liable to flooding. (The National Archives)

By fate, the the German lines here almost exactly follow the junction of the Kemmel Sands, between the 50 and 60 metre contours. While the centre of Messines sits on drier ground, the trenches constructed in front of the village sit squarely within the outcrop of the water-rich Kemmel Sands, and once again there was the threat of flooding from the ever-present impervious clay beneath.[241] Not only that; the valley of the Douve was filled with water-rich alluvium, sediments that had been built up by the flow and overflow of the river to an extent that it was ninety feet thick at its deepest. This wet ground would cause problems for the tunnelling companies that were trying to undermine the German defences here, it also meant that as the British and German trench lines breasted the ridge and moved down into the valley on to Ploegsteert and beyond, there was increasingly difficult, wet and water-logged conditions for both sides.[242]

Evidence of periodic flooding from the sands is provided by successive layers and levels of timber flooring and duckboarding – this is not unsurprising given the geological situation here. On top of the typical long trench boards are timbers

German trench boards in situ at Messines, together with crumpled corrugated iron revetment. In places these boards have British-style duckboards stacked on top of them, evidently to escape flooding. Here the Paniselian is thick, but waterlogged at depth. The sediments get darker in colour at the base of the excavation, this indicates permanent dampness or saturation, with the greenish clay minerals not being oxidised. (P. Doyle)

laid so that they resemble duck boards of the British type. It is probable that these trenches were drained using the German system, that 'wherever possible, the fall of drainage should be towards the enemy'.[243] This approach was facilitated by the simple fact that the German lines lay on the slope above the British.

Duckboards and timber revetment in the German trenches at Messines. Revetment is from reclaimed timber; a green timber door has been used in this case. (P. Doyle)

Exposed in the archaeological investigations at Messines were narrow trenches that were boarded throughout, and that were revetted with a variety of means. This included the rescue of doors and other timbers from damaged and destroyed buildings in the village. Timber used in trenches in this way was potentially dangerous – it could provide splinters that would add to the problems of men tightly packed in the line. Also, *in situ* brushwood hurdling that is commonly seen in German trenches. This type of revetment was the preferred means of protection – but was difficult to replace in the shell-blasted landscape of Flanders. The manual *Stellungsbau* was clear on this point:

The sides of trenches must not be revetted with any material that may make traffic in the trench impossible or even difficult after bombardment. Planks

Brushwood hurdle revetment in place at Messines. (P. Doyle)

and timber should not be used if possible. Hurdles are not so objectionable. The best revetting material is sods or thin loose brushwood.[244]

Here and there the revetment shows the impact of British shelling; left frozen in time, the fuze of a shell lodged in the disturbed timbers of the German line. Such revetment was held in place by timbers, some of them cut branches rather than shaped timber, and the trenches are uniformly cut through the water-rich silts and sands of the Paniselian.

The German trench system also included a concrete shelter with room for six or seven men, located at the termination of *Eckert Graben*. This was cast *in situ*, and must have been a response to the damp conditions. The water-rich *Scwimmsande* into which the trenches were dug, meant that there was no hope of a mined dug-out here. Concrete was the solution. This dug-out gave access to the Second Line, through a revetted and planked trench, and was fully equipped[245] with an internal pump. From its entrance was a carefully prepared rifle rack and a recess with hinged lid that contained German stick-grenades, found as they had been left by the last German occupants in June 1917.

Four shallow mined tunnels were also uncovered in the excavations.[246] At a depth of just 2–3 metres, the protection given to them from howitzer shells was likely to have been limited headcover, though it appears that there is a rubble

Concrete infantry shelter at Messines. As the ground here is too wet to support deep dugouts, this shelter was cast in situ within the Kemmel Sands. (P. Doyle)

Grenade recess in the trench side at Messines. (P. Doyle)

'burster course' of building waste, suggesting that the tunnels were constructed as 'cut-and cover'. Each tunnel had been constructed using a 'mining case' timber revetment, supported by bridle joints and pegs. Most likely the purpose of these tunnels was for storage and concealment, rather than protection from artillery *per se*. The tunnels have no inclines – just simple adit entrances from the trench line to the south of Messines. The tunnels sit between the 45 and 50 metre contours, in Paniselian sandy-clays that underly the difficult and water logged Kemmel Sands[247] – a factor that suggests that, in winter at least, these tunnels had to be drained effectively, either by drains running downslope, or by pumping.

German shallow adit tunnel at Messines, constructed from mining cases. It no doubt provided concealment from the enemy and may have been drained down slope. (P. Doyle)

Timbers with bridle joints from the mined gallery at Messines. (P. Doyle)

German mining tools found in situ; short handled pick and shovel. (P. Doyle)

La Boisselle: trenches in chalk

Moving to Picardy, the opportunity to observe excavated trenches has been provided by research at La Boisselle. Here, in 2011–12, one of the last remaining pieces of original extant battle terrain on the Somme battlefield was excavated by the La Boisselle Study Group.[248] Situated in the village of La Boisselle, the terrain captures a snapshot of the Allied (British) and German frontline trenches dug into chalk from the period 1914–1916. Here, at a farm known to the French as 'Ilôt' and the Germans 'Granathof', the French stopped the German advance on the Somme on 14 September 1914. With the village firmly held by the Germans, this part of the frontline was exploited by underground warfare, with numerous attempts to dislodge the enemy using mines, commencing in December 1914 and continuing until the British occupied the front line in August 1915. From this point on the British took over the tunnelling activity, deepening the system from around 12 metres to 24–30 metres below ground.[249] These mines, forming craters at the surface, were part of No Man's Land – just 45 metres apart – up to the opening days of the Battle of the Somme.

The nature of these very trenches were recorded by Charles Douie, an officer in the Dorsetshire Regiment, who served in them in 1916:

I learned something of the reputation of the La Boisselle trenches. They were among the most notorious in the British lines. For a considerable distance the opposing lines were divided only by the breadth of the mine craters: the British posts lay in the lips of the craters protected by thin layers of sandbags and within bombing distance of the German posts; the approaches to the posts were shallow and waterlogged trenches below the level of the German lines, and therefore under continuous observation and accurate fire by snipers.[250]

With No Man's Land so challenging, and with the need to maintain the offensive, mining activity here was extensive – and had been so since late 1914.[251] La Boisselle was captured by the British on 4 July 1916, and the notorious trench system and its mines were left behind.

The trenches excavated by the La Boisselle Study Group expose a small system facing the mine craters and supporting a number of adits that lead underground.[252] As described by Charles Douie, the trenches were relatively shallow here, dug directly into the chalk and therefore directly visible from the air. Here, there are only relatively thin surface soils compared to other parts of the Somme;[253] though the chalk is extensively shattered. No doubt some of that shattering could be attributed to the effects of the almost continuous bombardment, but it is more likely that this a by-product of freezing and thawing of water droplets within the chalk during the Ice Age, and to the growth of larger ice bodies within the ground – permafrost – which broke up the integrity of the chalk strata.[254] Lying above this layer is a thin level of soil, consisting of clay or loess with chalk blocks.[255]

'Scone Street', one of the main trenches excavated, has access to the extensive underground workings. With weakened chalk for much of its trench slopes, this trench would have required revetment, and there are remains of timber there to support this. The level of weak chalk is variable, and at the mid party and base of the trenches there is much stronger, robust, chalk. Flint levels are evident *in situ* – and these would have provided an extra hazard, the brittle flints providing sharp shards if hit by explosives. The presence of the flints shows that the chalk here is from the second of the three main chalk units within the region, of *la craie blanche à silex*. Accessing the slope into the underground mine workings, the solid chalk is present, again with flint lines, and exposing the bright white of this distinctive rock, here and there stained black by soot from the miners' candles.

Given that the clay-rich chalk is at depth, the Tunnelling Companies here found that the water level was at least 100 feet beneath the surface[257] – typical of the chalks at an upper level, at least in summer, with ground waters percolating

'Scone Street': a trench line cut through fractured chalk at La Boisselle, Somme. (P. Doyle)

Trenches in fractured chalk with scattered flints at La Boisselle. (P. Doyle)

Above: Incline through white chalk at La Boisselle, permitting access to the underground workings. The chalk is sound and required little support, though slab or block failure was possible. Below: Soot from miners' candles below ground at La Boisselle; flint nodules can be seen. These would have been a hazard to silent underground working. (P. Doyle)

downwards through the various fractures and levels that characterises the 'block-work' nature of this pure lime rock. It was for this reason that the tunnellers of two specialist Royal Engineer Tunnelling Companies, the 179th and 185th, were able to work below ground to lay their offensive mines. This contrasts with the depiction of 'waterlogged trenches' by Charles Douie – but his experiences surely belong to winter conditions, when the water saturation levels were highest – as well as to local conditions, where the surface soils prevented water drainage.

DUG-OUTS

Dug-outs on the Western Front were underground shelters intended for a variety of uses, and not surprisingly, their usefulness was largely controlled by local geology.[258] Dug-outs came in a diverse range of types, with their design and position mostly dependent upon local requirements for protection against artillery and, to a lesser extent, gas. They may also be classified according to the depth to which they penetrate. The principle was known as 'degrees of protection' in the contemporary engineering manuals:

> Protection is given in three degrees.
> i. Splinter-proof: against penetration by splinters of shells of all calibres.
> ii. Medium shell-proof: against direct hits by shells of all calibres up to 6-inch
> iii. Shell-proof: against direct hits by shells of all calibres and aeroplane bombs.[259]

Achieving these levels of protection required one simple factor – the deeper the dug-out, the better. With sufficient headroom came the ability of a dug-out to withstand a bombardment of the heaviest calibres. And with this there was the need to understand the geology of the ground into which the dug-outs had been excavated. Geology would once more play a major role in the lives of the average soldier on the Western Front.

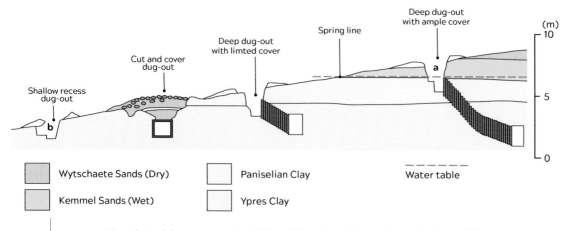

Hypothetical dug-out types in the Ypres Salient, in relation to the typical strata. The water-logged Kemmel Sands present a problem to the otherwise dry dug out at (a). The shallow recess at (b), floored by clay, would present problems due to water pooling.

The nature of dug-outs in relation to geology was outlined by the American chief military geologist Alfred Brooks, based upon the combined wisdom of the Allies to that point. In simple terms there are three basic types of dug-out: shallow excavated shelters, often hastily cut by soldiers seeking some form of shelter; 'cut-and-cover' dug-outs, which employed a specially 'engineered' roof intended to protect the occupants; and deeper, mined, dug-outs that were to provide a more healthy head cover of undisturbed geology. However, many other structures, including surface 'pillboxes' and other concrete features, were known as 'dug-outs' during the war (and are often marked as such on contemporary plans and maps).

The use of shallow shelters was common early on, as men sought shelter in what were known as 'funk-holes' – recesses cut into the slopes of trenches that provide

'Funk holes' cut into trench sides by British soldiers on the Somme; these have been cut into the sands and silts of the *Limon*, overlying the chalk and clay with flints.

only rudimentary protection from spent bullets or shrapnel balls. They were easy to dig in the surface soils of Flanders and Picardy – and were a feature of early trench systems, like that described by infantryman H.S. Clapham, serving in the Ypres Salient in January 1915:

> We held a front-line trench which had only recently been dug by the Engineers and is supposed to be one of the best around here. It is comparatively dry, and there are a fair number of dug-outs, little cubby-

holes in the *parados*, into which two or three men can just curl themselves. Although we were about 80 yards from the Huns, we could see nothing of them but a mound of earth and sandbags.[261]

The degree of protection of such shallow scrapes was very low, and in many cases, this protection was illusory – providing just an opportunity for soldiers to at least seek shelter in the earth from the rain. More often than not, however, the weakening of trench sides in this way meant that collapse was inevitable. As the war

'Funk hole' exposed in the *Limon* complex in the sunken Lane at Beaumont Hamel, Somme.
(P. Doyle)

German shallow shelter in a reserve trench; this would not afford much protection.

progressed, so this type of shelter was strictly frowned upon. As *Notes for Infantry Officers on Trench Warfare* put it: 'The first instinct of the men is to improve the protection afforded by the trench by burrowing out for themselves hollows in the front face, under the parapet ('undercutting'). This practice must be absolutely prohibited.'[262]

As artillery power increased, so the 'degree of protection' needed increased too. So-called 'cut-and-cover' shelters gave a little more protection – achieving, where they could, 'medium splinter-proof', levels of protection. Starting with an open excavation, sometimes roofed with a curved prefabricated corrugated steel 'elephant' sections,[263] a range of layers was added to improve protection to these shallow excavations, including steel beams, concrete, bricks rubble and timber carefully arranged to counter the effects of artillery.[264] These had the advantage of providing extra depth and an opportunity to apply additional layers of diverse materials intended to deflect or dissipate blast energy of an artillery shell. Different construction methods were compared to assess their reactions to every conceivable kind of shell burst. They also had the advantage that layers could be added to the roof of a dug-out to enhance their protection – and make up for any deficiencies of the local geology. Cut-and-cover provided the quickest method for constructing 'deeper' shelters, but only up to a depth of four metres or so; beyond this the deep mined dug-out was by far the safest and most economical structure, and by mid-1916 this had become recognised as providing the best form of protection for troops.

Steel 'elephant iron' sections for use in dug outs; they formed the basis for cut and cover constructions in many cases.

Cover/mined dugout depth, relative to soil type, to provide minimum protection shell penetration by howitzer and mortar fire

Soil type	Mining Notes (1916)	Mining Notes (1917)	Depth in RE (1925)	Depth in IRE (1927)
Made earth	–	–	10.7m (35ft)	–
Soft soil	5.5m (18 ft)	6.5m (21ft)	–	6.7m (22ft)
Hard soil	2.7–3.7m (9–12ft)	5m (16.5ft)	–	5.2m (17ft)
Masonry	–	–	–	2.1m (7ft)
Concrete (plain)	–	–	–	1.5m(5ft)
Concrete (reinforced)	–	–	–	1.0m (3.25ft)
Clay	–	–	9.1m (30ft)	–
Gravel	–	–	7.6m (25ft)	–
Chalk	2.7–3.7m (9–12ft)	4.6m (15ft)	7.6m (25ft)	4.6m (15ft)
Hard rock	–	–	4.6m (15ft)	–

Sources: Mining Notes for 1916 and 1917, manuscripts in Royal Engineers Library; Royal Engineers (1925), Chapter XIV; Institution of Royal Engineers (1927, p.157).

DISPUTED EARTH

Deep mined dug-outs were substantial underground excavations, and their construction became more sophisticated as the war progressed. Captain G.M. Brown of the Suffolk Regiment described a spacious example on the Somme in 1918:

> Let me describe our dug-out: a window frame some three feet square in the chalk in the side of the trench, a steep dark flight of steps, and one reaches the outer tunnel…From this open little rooms about five feet square where Officers' Orderlies sleep; from this a lower tunnel of the same dimensions, reached by a similar window and shorter flight of steps, and one comes to our living room; a six by two shelf serves as a table, at which, if one is sitting at it, no one can pass…On the shelf or table is an oil lamp, some bottles, glasses, tinned milk, butter and jam, yesterday's newspapers and all one's possessions that go for a trip into the line.[265]

Drawing of the interior of a British shallow dugout.

The excavation of such large subterranean features was controlled by ground conditions,[266] and innovative methods were devised to deal with local geological difficulties. In the Ypres area, satisfactory deep shelters could be constructed at depth in the clay. What was necessary here was the prevention of water pouring from trench level down the steep incline necessary to allow entrance to the dugout. Here, sumps and pumps were necessary.[267]

Other difficulties lurked beneath ground. For example, in the sand dune belt of the Belgian Coast construction of underground chambers was hindered by 'running'

Dug-out shelters in the dunes near Nieuport; with the water table at the base of the dune, the shelters are all in loose sands above, and required close timbering.

sands, i.e. loose, water-saturated sand with little strength and a propensity to flow. This led to an innovative method of sinking pre-fabricated steel shelters some seven to eight metres to connect with tunnelled galleries. If this wasn't enough, on the slopes of the Passchendaele and Messines ridges, water-bearing sands of the Paniselian – the Kemmel Sands so often identified on British plans – were apt to flow and were incapable of retaining the form of the dug-out void, even if a tunnel could be cut to excavate it. Intersecting either of these water-rich layers was a major issue for soldiers and geologists alike.

There are four main geological factors that were to be taken into consideration by the armies in France and Flanders in the construction of deep dug-outs:[269] the level of water saturation and its fluctuation; the stability of the roof and walls; the prevention of deep shell penetration, and; the intended use for the dug-out and its position relative to the frontline. All of these fell within the domain of the military geologists – all of them outlined by Walter Kranz in his original definitions of *Militärgeologie*.

Water was this one factor that would have the greatest impact on the situation of dug-outs, for, placing them badly, intercepting water-bearing layers, could mean that the dug-out would very soon become uninhabitable. Alfred H. Brooks, the Chief US Military Geologist despatched to the Western Front, was amongst the first to write about this in a technical journal, when he contributed his paper 'The Use of Geology on the Western Front' to the US Geological Survey in 1920.[270] Dealing with groundwater was not always an easy task, and certainly not easy to predict – as Brooks was to explain to his specialist readership:

> No problem is of greater difficulty to the military geologist than the accurate determination of underground-water conditions. Even after the general law controlling the ground-water table in any particular province has been determined by field examinations, there may be sufficient local variations from this law to invalidate its application to a certain locality.[271]

As we have seen, in Flanders, the presence of the 100-metre-thick Ypres Clay leaves the overlying Paniselian sands often saturated with the water that percolates down from ground level. Away from the slopes of the Passchendaele Ridge, with its variable geology, there was the opportunity to dig down into the clay. This clay is relatively stiff and produces the firm ground optimum for tunnelling, although field experience of dug-out excavation demonstrated that swelling of the clays did periodically occur away from its more heterogeneous top, crushing and bursting supporting timbers.[272] But at least they could be kept relatively dry – so long as surface water was not allowed to flood down into dug-outs along their inclined stairways; even then pumping was a solution, with water held in sumps designed ready to be pumped. But all too often, as the Germans would find, the vagaries of the water-bearing or water-excluding layers of the ridge slopes meant that dug-out construction was challenging. A stoical view often had to prevail – as expressed by 2nd Lt Arthur Stanley-Clarke, of the Dorsetshire Regiment, writing (with his tongue firmly in cheek) of the Ypres Salient in 1915.

> Instructions for making a dug-out – find a suitable spot, for preference at the bottom of a hill, so that any spare water will run in your direction. Dig a hole 6 ft by 4 ft by 4 ft high and don't be discouraged if it fills with water – bail it out – or invent some means of getting the water to run up hill – next, get a door and lay it across the pit, leaving room enough to get in, bearing in mind however that a Field Officer may want to enter, so allow a little more, otherwise your dug-out may be torn to pieces. Next get earth, or if not

available, mud and throw it over the door to a depth of about two feet. If a lot of this falls into the dug-out, never mind it is the fortune of war! Then get straw, don't bother whether it is wet or dry, the dry soon gets wet and make yourself a floor of this then lie down to look up at the roof you have constructed and count the number of places it leaks in. This if it does not drive you off your head will it will prove a pleasant afternoon's occupation. At night you can put more earth on top to stop the water and then watch the whole thing cave in. Nobody with a weak heart should try the above.[273]

However, help was at hand. By 1917, in the Salient at least, the British had abandoned their lacklustre and laissez-faire approach to dug-out construction, and the Tunnelling Companies that once were concentrated on offensive mining, were, in the aftermath of Messines, now turning to dug-out work.[274] A series of special geological maps were produced by the British, based largely on extensive boreholes, which indicated that successful deep dug-outs could only be excavated in the Ypres

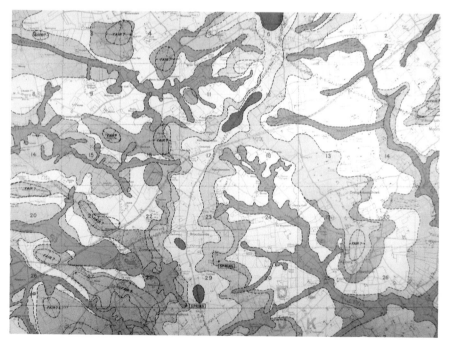

Extract from the special 1;10,000 geological map Zonnebeke produced by Lt Col Edgeworth David as a guide to dugout suitability, based on borehole data provided by Lt Loftus Hills. These maps were produced for the variable Ypres Salient. The extract shows the Passchendaele Ridge, with Zonnebeke centre of the map. The deeper the red, the drier the strata; this is a 1917 edition, later, 1918 editions had more subdued colours. (The National Archives)

Clay.[275] These maps were produced between November 1917 and June 1918, and were arguably the first of their kind – geological maps with the sole purpose of guiding engineers with their work.[276] For their part, the Germans also produced maps – *Mineurgeologsich Karten* – that were designed to aid in the prosecution of mine warfare. For example, a map produced of *Doppelhöhe 60* (Hill 60 and the Caterpillar to the British) as part of a specialist report on mine warfare shows the location of mine galleries relative to dry and wet sands of the Paniselian.[277]

Nevertheless, the British dug-out suitability maps can claim to be the only systematic set of specialist military geology maps to be produced in the war. They were focussed on that part of the Ypres Salient that needed the most attention – the Passchendaele–Wytschaete ridge system, displaying the greatest geological variability at depth. The maps were an innovation; twelve map sheets at a large scale of 1:10,000 were produced to cover the ridge, and were tinted with quite startling colours that made a clear statement as to their suitability for use in dug-out construction: the deeper the red, the dryer the strata; while more intense blues indicated more troubles from water.[278] In this way the maps were capable of being read by anyone – not just a trained geologist.

If water was a problem, then the greatest threat to dug-outs was undoubtedly from howitzer shells, heavy trench mortars (*Minenwerfer*), and heavy shells from larger artillery pieces such as land-based naval guns. The first two weapons fired shells with a steep trajectory which were capable of considerable ground penetration; the latter had a shallower trajectory but a high velocity and was equally destructive to dug-outs particularly when used there was a concentrated barrage of mortar shells. Specifically to destroy such underground shelters, shells were also fitted with delayed action fuses in order to penetrate as deep as necessary before detonating, rather than bursting on impact with the surface. How deeply a shell could penetrate depended upon several factors: the angle of penetration, with high trajectory shells being the most efficient and; the nature of the ground, reflecting the geological strata through which a shell had to pass, and within which a shell would burst.

Wartime and immediate post-war opinions of the minimum head cover required to withstand bombardment from large calibre shells varied, dependent on a number of geological materials. At least 4.6 metres of solid geology were needed, rising to 9.1 metres for softer soils. Additional protection could be afforded by a so-called 'burster course' of solid or broken masonry. This had two functions: firstly the masonry pieces might deflect the direct trajectory of the shell, and secondly they may cause it to explode sooner, thus dissipating the destructive effect.[279] Cut-and-cover dug-outs usually employed a multiple layer approach in their construction,

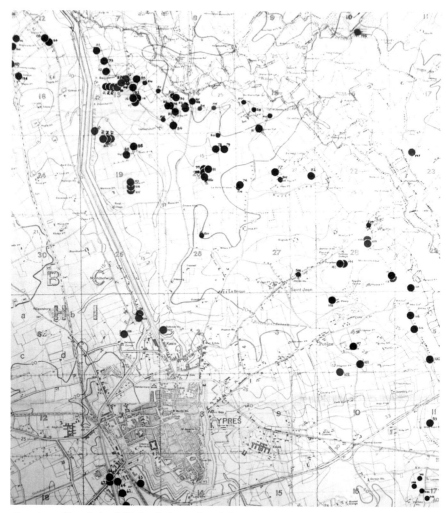

Location of boreholes drilled to help produced the dugout suitability maps in 1917; blue dots 'bad' (wet), red dots 'good' (dry). (The National Archives)

a process that was also used above the more vulnerable sections of deep dug-outs: stairways, inclines and shaft heads. This approach involved layers of earth, a brick/ stone burster course, earth or rubble in sandbags, logs and corrugated iron and heavy steel rails, a 'distribution' course to spread the effect of a successfully encouraged premature detonation, and sometimes air spaces between layers to further cushion the effects of a direct hit.[280]

Deep mined dug-outs, the type most desired by the troops, were intended to withstand direct hits, and therefore needed adequate head cover, i.e., sufficient depth of earth and other material between dug-out roof and the surface to arrest the progress and detonation of the shell at a point where the dug-out would remain undamaged. German engineers were first to realise the potential of deep dug-outs; it was not until October 1916 that the British Army began standardisation of design, and within two months dimensions, overall design, general size and arrangement of galleries, ventilation, etc. had all been standardised. There were between 8–10 model types; the Inspector of Mines, Colonel R.S.G. Stokes RE, was to state that: 'there is no reason why deep dug-outs should not be as completely and as advantageously standardised as huts'.[281]

The British commenced extensive mined dug-out construction in the Ypres Salient in late 1916, and the locations of over 350 underground structures have been recorded to date.[282] Initially these were mostly constructed near the front lines for headquarters use, but from mid-1917 after the Battle of Messines Ridge and later following the Third Battle of Ypres, the Tunnelling Companies, with the

Entrance to a deep German dugout (in this case a kitchen) with added roof protection.

assistance of Field Company and Pioneer Battalion personnel were redeployed to urgently excavate a wider range of accommodation in newly captured terrain.[283]

Dug-outs were further categorised under two headings by the British: 'permanent' and 'battle'. Permanent dug-outs were built in the front and support lines, as well as the rear of these positions, and catered largely for Battalion and Company headquarters (HQ), together with and accommodation for platoons. Battle dug-outs were located in the rear lines with Divisional, Brigade, Battalion and Company HQ, and dug-outs to house platoons and companies. Both types of dug-out were used for troop accommodation, aid posts, headquarters, communications, hospitals, and observation posts, amongst other functions. All dug-outs had separated accommodation for officers, NCO's and other ranks, and larger examples often incorporated cookhouses, latrines and drying rooms, with electric lighting and ventilation being installed throughout. Excavation of dug-outs increased in intensity as the war progressed and as surface life became more untenable with the proliferation of artillery and the use of gas shells.

Dug-out systems could vary from simple galleries with a few chambers intended to accommodate a small number of occupants, to large complexes capable of housing thousands of men in parallel bunked linear 'dormitories'. Construction of dug-outs was generally carried out according to standard plans, and employed a range of standard sized pre-cut, and sometimes pre-formed, materials. For example, in British excavations, internal gallery dimensions for typical timber frames (known as 'setts') from which all dug-outs were built, were 6 feet by 3 feet for a standard gallery, and 6 feet by 6 feet for a gallery containing bunking. Chambers for officers, offices, and kitchens were usually wider. Depths varied, with the majority in Flanders lying within a range of depth between 4 to 15 metres. Shallow examples providing a head cover of just 2–3 metres are rare, and probably pre-date mid-1916 examples. Materials used for construction are equally variable. Judging by archaeological evidence most dug-outs were supported by softwoods, although one was found almost entirely constructed in oak; some also incorporated steel, notably the use of rolled steel joists to increase structural strength. Occasional examples used whole or halved tree trunks.[284]

Famously, the Germans made extensive use of deep dug-outs cut into the chalk ground of the Somme, often amply supplied with 'home comforts'. Captain G.M. Brown described one such shelter, captured from the Germans, in 1916:

> The dug-out that has been allotted to me for next week is an old divisional HQ of the German Army, fitted as though it were impregnable, arm-chairs, bureaus, cabinets, framed pictures and electric lights, and upstairs with

double and single bedrooms, more like a week-end cottage than a dug-out, but further details later. The main disadvantage is the atmosphere, for the place is littered with German dead.[285]

With the German strategy of remaining on the defensive, making full use of the capability of chalk to be dug easily, and for its capability of maintaining a void space without much additional support. As American military geologist Lt Col A.H. Brooks noted: 'The chalk formation was the most favorable for dug-outs, as it could usually be mined without blasting and required little timber'.[286] These advantages would later be put to good use in the construction and enlargement of ancient tunnels and *souterraines* in Artois and Picardy. Lt. V.F. Eberle, an engineer officer with the 48th (East Midland) Division, experienced a *souterraine* in the village of Fonquevillers, behind Gommecourt, on the Somme in the winter of 1915.

> We were still under orders that everyone in Fonquevillers should sleep below ground-level. We had intended transferring all our sappers to certain subterranean grottoes under the cemetery. Their origin was stated to be quarrying for stone, when the church adjoining was built. When the French earlier in the war made a local attack here, they made a wide sloping entrance, and used them for assembling a large number of troops prior to the attack. To provide ventilation and more light, they construced an open shaft, with heavily timbered sides and about 7 feet square, from the cemetery level to the grotto, where it was supported by strong props.[287]

Excavating purpose-built dug-outs in chalk was not without its draw-backs, however. Military geographer D.W. Johnson examined a hypotherical situation of dug-out construction on the Somme, in his book *Battlefields of the World War* (1921): 'Trenches, dug-outs and tunnels will be dry and habitable if excavated in the right formation; but if ignorance of the geological structure of the battlefield leads to excavations in the wrong formations, an army may find the waters beneath the earth more dangerous than the fire above'.[288]

Johnson was refering inevitably to the complex of soils that lie on top of the chalk surface: clay-with flints, loess and loam. On the Somme, deep dug-out construction was limited by the depth to saturated chalk, which varied according to season and maximum rainfall. The depth to the surface of this saturated 'water table' was estimated through a programme of borings that were carried out under the direction of the British military geologists. What most soldiers knew was that shallow excavations could be cut into capping soils, the *Limons de Plateaux*, just

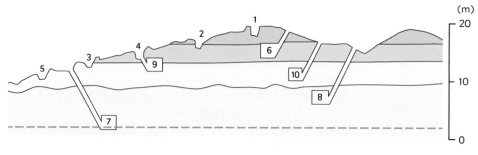

OPTIMUM POSITIONS		POOR POSITIONS	
2	Trenches drained by loess	1	Trench in impermeable loam
4	Trenches drained by loess	3	Trench floored by impermeable clay
6	Dug-out roofed by loam and drained by loess	5	Trench floored by impermeable clay
8	Deep dug-out in dry chalk	7	Dug-out in zone of saturated chalk
10	Deep dug-out in clay	9	Dug-out roofed by permeable loess and floored by clay

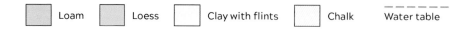

Loam   Loess   Clay with flints   Chalk   Water table

Poor and optimum positions for dugouts and trenches in the chalk and overlying sediments of the clay with flints, and the overlying loess and loam of the *Limon* complex.
(Based on Johnson 1921)

so long as they did not disturb the boundary between water-bearing chalk and the overlying clay. With so much fluctuation in the winter, such shelters became untenable, the mud devilishly intractable. Nevertheless, such infantry 'funk-holes' were dug against regulation into the trench sides, directly into the *Limon*, would only give the illusion of safety – and were strictly against regulations in 1916.[289] While deeper dug-outs in the chalk itself would be dry (protected by the clay layer above its surface), shallower dug outs that did not penetrate beneath this clay layer could be liable to flooding.[290] Needless to say, such shallow dug-outs would naturally be at the mercy of the heavy shellfire on the Somme, with such limited roof thickness to render them dangerous.

Evidence of dug-outs lurking beneath the former battlefields, their supporting timbers now decaying, is provided by the opening of surface 'crown-holes' – sure indications of open voids at depth. This is particularly the case in Flanders,[291] but similar issues are likely also to occur in chalk ground.[292] The chances of future dug-out failures are strong as they move towards collapse; it is fortunate, then, that some have been studied in detail archaeologically, chambers giving up their details of life underground, often with their artefacts intact, just as they were abandoned.[293] Such chambers also provide detailed clues on their construction,

'Crown-hole' that opened in front of a farm building on the Passchendaele Ridge; this indicated the presence of a dugout beneath the farm. (Johan Vandewalle)

and of the difficulties of dealing with the local geological conditions. Beecham dug-out, near to the crest of the Passchendaele Ridge, and close indeed to the largest Commonwealth War Graves Commission Cemetery, Tyne Cot, was one such dug-out to reveal its secrets.[294]

Beecham dug-out

Beecham is a mined dug-out of German origin on the slopes of the Passchendaele Ridge. Situated near to the village of Zonnebeke, surprisingly it was dug with little pretence for the greatest 'degree of protection' with, in places just 1.2–2.0 metres of overhead cover, though reaching an average total depth including the gallery, of 4 metres.[295] Beecham was a mined dug-out rather than a cut-and-cover construction, its mined origin is suggested by the presence of relatively undisturbed strata above the roof timbers, and the absence of the typical materials used in cut and cover dug-outs, including sandbags and rails. A stratum of broken masonry was identified at 0.25 metres, below a surface of made-ground consisting of mixed sands and debris; it is likely that this represents the debris of the original farm rather than a military-derived, shell bursting course.

That the dug-out is German in origin is shown by details of its timber lining, and by the simple fact that it was in German-held territory – taken in the final stages of the Third Battle of Ypres (the Battle of Passchendaele) in 1917. Beecham was then re-used by Canadian troops, and there is ample evidence of their occupancy after the capture of the Passchendaele Ridge in the autumn of 1917. It is likely that this dug-out was constructed relatively early, from 1916 or even earlier.[296] The shelter was investigated following collapse of the roof and the development of

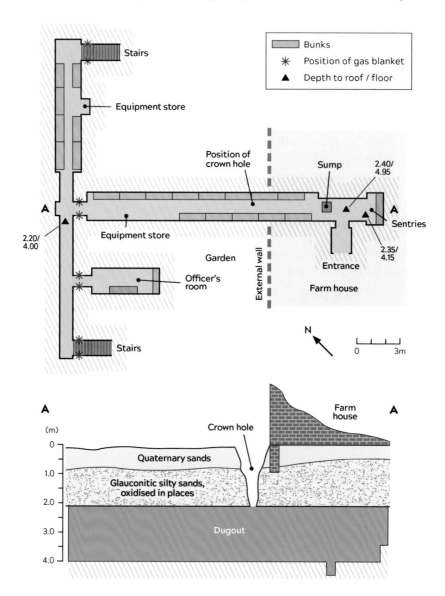

Plan of Beecham Dugout (top) and its location relative to the geology (bottom)

a 'crownhole' in 2000–2001;[297] with the dug-out in danger of total failure – and therefore a direct threat to the farm above it – the void has now been filled with expanding concrete. The dug-out had been excavated in a relatively uniform green silty-sand horizon (although this has been subject to considerable oxidisation),[298] sitting in the lower part of the Paniselian, in clayey levels recognisable in a number of contemporary boreholes drilled for the British Army.[299] The British military map drawn up for 'dug-out suitability' in 1917–18 shows that Beecham sits squarely in a geological unit that was only 'fair to doubtful' for dug-out construction.[300] Soil cover consists of 0.7 metres of brown sands with thin seams of flint pebbles.

Entrance to Beecham dug-out, showing close timbered supports. (Johan Vandewalle)

Beecham conforms to a basic T-shape, the main gallery trending northwest–southeast (effectively parallel to the present roadway in front of the farm), running from beneath the present farm building to the northwest. The dug-out was close-timbered throughout; bunks provided accommodation for up to 70 men. A sump, 0.75 m deeper than the base of the dug-out, had been installed to pump out accumulated water. Duckboards with non-slip protection of rabbit wire were discovered covering the floor of the completed construction. Stepped, inclined entrances and gallery junctions were equipped with inclined frames enabling impregnated cloth or dampened blankets to be rolled down and dampened as a precaution against gas attack.[301]

Bunk gallery at Beecham, close timbered. (Johan Vandewalle)

Officers' room, Beecham dug-out. (Johan Vandewalle)

Clues to the failure of the dug-out roof; the timbers have rotted due to exposure to the air. The fact that the stairway was constantly wet is illustrated by the retention of the green colouration to the sediments below the steps; elsewhere the silts have oxidised brown. (Johan Vandewalle)

Water filling the dug-out on first inspection could either have come from groundwater, or from water percolating down from the ground surface. Oxidisation of the silts – from bright green to brownish – to the level of the base of the gallery suggests that the water table was originally at the level of the base of the gallery itself, so typical of the Ypres Salient. Closest to the timber of the dug-out walls, and beneath the steps of the entrance inclines, the glauconitic sediments are not oxidised; this shows that the timbers retained water and prevented the green silts from becoming the brownish oxidised versions, even when the dug-out was pumped dry.

It is not known why this dug-out was relatively shallow (and in danger of destruction from heavy artillery shelling); it is not imagined that this could have provided total 'shell-proof' protection for its occupants. But as it relatively behind the front lines in 1916, the primary purpose of the dug-out may have simply been concealment of men, rather than their protection. On that basis, the problem of the ground conditions that so affected the Germans (even with their superior vantage point), and which led to the adoption of concrete shelters, rather than dug-outs, left the engineers with little choice but to dig the shelter to such shallow depths.

Vampir dug-out

While Beecham is a shallow German dug-out, in levels of the Paniselian, Vampir is an example of a British deep dug-out cut directly into the clay plain, situated between Ypres and Zonnebeke. While Zonnebeke itself sits quite close to the crest of the Passchendaele Ridge, and the road way therefore tracks up from the clay to the typical Paniselian silts and sands, the dug-out was dug directly into the clay itself – in the wide valley of the Hannebeek stream, flowing northwards to the coast. The dug-out was discovered by archaeologists of the Association of Battlefield Archaeology and Conservation (ABAC), and Glasgow University (GUARD), in 2007–8.[302] Other similar dug-outs have been investigated when they have been threatened by destruction or development,[303] but Vampir provides an excellent example of a dug-out chamber in clay, with all the benefits and limitations.

The dug-out was deep–mined, found to be thirteen metres below the surface (and thereby providing a shell-proof shelter), with two long galleries (one wider to be used for bunks), and with entrance inclines filled with clay.[304] It is identified as having been cut by members of the 171 Tunnelling Company RE (assisted by infantry labour from the 9th Highland Light Infantry) over a period of four months, first occupied in April 1918.[305] Serving initially as a Headquarters for the 100th Brigade (33rd Division), it was captured during the German advance during the battle of the Lys later in April 1918; it was again recaptured in September.

Entrance to Vampir dug-out. This was cut through clay, but was liable to permit water to flow down the steps into the chamber. Pumping would be necessary. (Tony Pollard).

The original dug-out was intended for 50 soldiers, but due to the fact that it was captured so soon after its completion, it was never fitted out with bunks and other features indicating its use and long-term occupation. Found intact within the dug-out – still capable of operating – was a pump, indicative of the need to remove

surface water that undoubtedly made its way into the chamber via the entrance inclines.[306]

Intact pump in Vampir dug-out, essential to deal with water ingress down the entrance inclines. (Tony Pollard)

Excavated at depth, it lies entirely within clay, with no Paniselian cover in this part of the Salient. Thin soils are present, but the inclined entrance cuts directly though them into the Ypres Clay below. This was of course the perfect situation; allowing access to the greatest degree of protection, then sorely needed. But with it came issues – the swelling pressures of the clay were extreme, leading to the possibility of collapse through the crushing of timbers.

A study of the pressures suffered by such dug-outs at shallower depths (of 28–

30 feet) was carried out by the British military geologists – in order to examine the cause and the solution, essential if they were to give the 'degree of protection' required, and no present a problem to the men who occupied such chambers.[307] Pressure on the timber cases used to support the void spaces was indeed seen to be a function of the swelling of clay minerals, absorbing water, and affecting the side timbers, but that the failure of the supports was also down to pressure of the clay above bearing down on the timbers, distorting them sideways, and weakening

Steel beams and railway lines required to deal with the excessive swelling pressures in the clay at depth. Corrugated sheeting is used between the beams. (Tony Pollard)

them. The conclusion was that supports should have gaps between then – thereby allowing some release of pressure as clay was forced through the spaces – and that the side sections of the 'mine sets' should be made as beams. This would allow a greater degree of pressure to be supported, more than twice in fact.[308]

In Vampir, revetment of the dug-out was entirely from steel beams and salvaged railway lines backed by corrugated iron; obviously requiring more than the usual soft-wood mining frames (setts) seen in many other dug-outs. The steel beams resisted the top pressure; the gaps between them (covered by corrugated iron sheeting), the side pressure. Vampir dug-out was built to last; today, it has disappeared below ground, filled with water to preserve it.

Maison Blanche *Souterraine*

Dug-outs (as opposed to tunnels) in the chalk of Artois and Picardy are less well known today – though larger interconnected systems are known at Vimy, Loos and Arras, and many others surely still exist underground, undiscovered. Situated to the west of Vimy Ridge, Maison Blanche is one of eight known *souterraines* in the region – underground caverns that have some antiquity, serving as quarries,

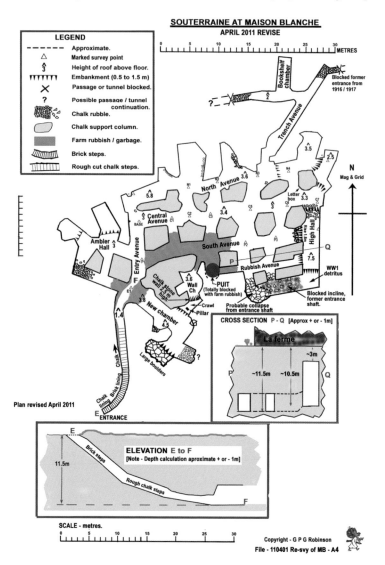

Maison Blanche *souterraine*, Neuville St Vaast, showing the pillar and stall excavation method. (Phillip Robinson/Durand Group)

shelters or storehouses for the local population – that were pressed into service in time of war. Cut into the chalk just south of Neuville St Vaast, Maison Blanche has been investigated by the Durand Group, who have carried out an extensive survey of its construction and survey of the direct evidence of wartime occupation.[309]

Cut into the chalk strata, the *souterraine* was first brought into use as an underground military shelter behind the reserve line by Canadian soldiers. These men, deep underground, passed the time by carving – in often intricate detail – regimental badges in the soft chalk, or in covering the walls with copy-pencil graffitti. The original excavation was by a traditional 'pillar and stall' method – in which the pillars support the roof, allowing the chambers ('stalls') to be excavated for stone removal. There was little or no need for further revetment or support, though shoring was required where there were weaknesses in the rock. The chalk is largely flintless – making its further excavation simpler; and is therefore prone

One of the chambers in Maison Blanche. (P. Doyle)

to be dry, its floor above the level of seasonal fluctuation in the water table that is typical of the chalk. The strength of the *souterraine* was that it had been cut into solid rock, and could be extended to give greater occupancy if needed. There would be no issues with swelling pressures here, though at times the air would be damp, and the roof would give a good hope of a decent 'degree of protection'.

The Maison Blanche *souterraine* was indeed enlarged and new entrances put in place by Tunnelling Companies. The 15th battalion CEF (48th Highlanders of Canada) was one of its most prominent occupants – there is plenty of evidence of its occupancy in what would have provided a 'shell proof' shelter for many men:

Soldiers worked the soft chalk, carving badges in particular; this to the 48th Highlanders of Canada. (P. Doyle)

Most of the men were on working parties each night, labouring in the front line, supports, and in tunnels being built behind the frontline. These, in later days, saved hundreds of men who sat deep and laughed as concussions shook the shoring and earth trickled down. They slept in the bad air of the Maison Blanche Caves during the day.[311]

TUNNELS AND SUBWAYS

While dug-outs represent chambers that provide safe shelter below ground for the occupancy of multiples of men, there other excavations that are intended to provide some means of escaping the artillery battle that raged above, an exploitation of 'underground terrain' for shelter and troop movements.[312]

Tunnels were constructed for offensive and defensive purposes. Offensive tunnels were used primarily for both the placement of explosive charges beneath selected enemy positions. Where it was possible, such tunnels were constructed at depth, usually to follow the most favourable geological strata – in the Ypres Salient, mostly the clays – but sometimes, by necessity they were cut through unsatisfactory layers to permit the interception of enemy tunnellers.[313] All so often this was the situation that presented itself to the Germans who occupied the ridge tops in the Ypres Salient.[314]

But there were other tunnels too, their primary purpose to permit the movement of men underground, getting them closer to the frontline without having to present a target to an enemy who might seek to prevent that movement through artillery fire. In many ways, these tunnels were the logical underground development of the surface communication trench that became such a feature of the standard trench system on the Western Front. As with all tunnelling activity, the success of such tunnels and subways had a lot to do with the nature of the strata through which they were driven, and it was the lot of specialist tunnelling companies and equivalent groups of military engineers to make sure they were excavated and supported to the required standards.

By July 1916 the British had standardised the interior dimensions of all their workings to just three sizes, in order to maximise the rate of forward drive of the galleries while ensuring the strength of their tunnels: ordinary galleries (offensive or defensive mines): 1.30 m (4 ft 3 in) by 0.69 m (2 ft 3 in); galleries near the shaft bottom or for the first 75–100 metres: 1.52 m (5 ft 0 in) by 0.76 m (2 ft 6 in); and, galleries (tunnels) for the movement of men underground: 183 cm (6 ft 0 in) by 0.91 cm (3 ft 0 in).[315]

While tunnels for offensive purposes were made as small as possible, it is obvious that to permit fully-equipped men to move freely, greater dimensions would be necessary. Such galleries were 6 feet high and 3 feet wide, with at least the capability of men to move along the tunnels ready for action, of emerging into the sunlight fully equipped. There were other types too; shallow tunnels intended to provide access to No Man's Land that would be converted to communication trenches by breaking through the roof, to be used on the Somme in 1916:

> It had been proved conclusively that the right to retain any ground won depended upon the capacity to defend it. At St Eloi, for example, the initial advantages had been neutralised by our inability to construct and maintain communication trenches to the newly-won position… Keen brains analysed the tactical difficulties, and eventually evolved the ingenious plan of constructing the necessary communications across No Man's Land *before* the attack commenced.[316]

Named 'Russian Saps', these shallow tunnels were excavated in some number during the dry months through the *Limon* complex of soils that capped the chalk over much of the Somme – in advance of the battle on 1 July 1916. Though a great many of them were dug, their use was limited, even though their use might have allowed men to move with safely into forward positions, an act that might well have saved lives.[317] Nevertheless, whether Russian Saps or subways, all would be subject to the same geological constraints that were applied to the construction of dug-out chambers (and indeed of offensive mining); namely that of depth to saturated water, the strength of the tunnels and need for support and revetment, and the capability of and ease of the engineers and tunnellers to cut them in time for their intended use.

Such subways would provide great assistance to the men in preparation for offensives in 1917, at Arras and Vimy in April for example, and at Nieuport in the late summer.

Nieuport: Polder plain and dune field tunnels
Nieuport is situated on the Flemish coastal plain, at the hub of a system of five waterways which serve the whole of Flanders, controlled by locks and sluices from the Yser River. The town lies at the junction of the dune field and the Polder plain, and is influenced by the geological conditions of both areas. It is the location of Nieuport at the head of its waterways and commanding the Yser that made it strategically important. Opening of the sluices in 1914 led to the flooding of a large tract of land along the line of the Yser from Nieuport to Dixmude, halting the German advance.[318] From 1914 to the end of the war Belgian engineers controlled the sluices to retain these inundations, while the French army occupied the short strip of dry land from Nieuport to the sea.

From June 1917 the British army relieved French forces and occupied Nieuport and the adjacent coastal towns of Nieuport-Bains and Oost-Dunkerke until mid-November, when the French returned. The British were there in preparation for Field Marshal Sir Douglas Haig's planned invasion of the German occupied Belgian coast, a component of his overall strategy for the offensive in Flanders in the second half of 1917. The plan was dependent on success in Third Ypres, and would allow the Allies to clear the threat of submarine warfare from Belgian ports, while linking with the 'push' at Ypres.[319] With its strategic importance, Nieuport and its surrounding villages was a frequent target for long-range German artillery fire, with shells projected into the streets of the town, so close as it was to the frontline. It was here also that other innovations, such as varieties and new types of gas were tried out in advance of their wider distribution. It made sense, then, that for the defenders of the town there should be tunnels and subways constructed.[320]

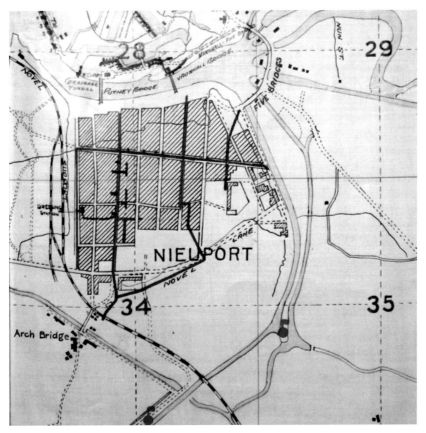

Plan of subways beneath the streets of Nieuport. The main galleries follow the streets.
(The National Archives)

As such, in just a few short months, British and Australian tunnelling companies excavated many kilometres of tunnels and dug-outs beneath the streets of the town – and in the nearby dune fields – that varied in depth from shallow cut-and-cover types (*boyaux couverts*) to deeper mined subways (*boyaux enterées*), many of which were interlinked to cellars of ruined houses.[321]

The viability of these tunnels was due to a large extent to the ground conditions, and particularly to ground water; seasonal fluctuation in the level of water-saturated ground was a significant problem. Depth to the fully water saturated ground varies, but is generally near to ground surface since the elevation of the coastal plain at Nieuport is close to sea level. Dug in summer, however, these tunnels were dry; but winter saw the tunnels flooded (the French having previously used surface cut-and-cover tunnels to combat this).[322] Trial borings to test ground were made for the British Army in 1917, which showed that the Ypres Clay was struck at around thirty metres.[323] The sediments above were considered as two basic units: a lower coarser sand unit with marine fossils, and a upper finer sand unit with thin seams of polder clays.[324] Contemporary geological maps also demonstrate the presence of yellow marine sands similar to that of the coastal dune fields.[325]

The principal tunnels dug beneath the ruined town underlie the main streets of Langestraat, Astridlaan, Hoogstraat, St Jacobstraat/Schipstraat and Slachthuisstraat.[326] The tunnels run centrally down these streets, with inclined

Failure of a house at Nieuport, attributed to a failing subway at depth. (P. Doyle)

access tunnels connected to cellars of existing houses, which also served as shelters. The main tunnels are connected by a number of shorter ones beneath houses in Recolletenstraat, Hoogstraat, Kokstraat and Astridlaan. Finally, extensive *boyaux couverts* follow the line of original eighteenth century fortifications to the south of the town.

The long tunnel beneath Hoogstraat varied from its shallowest depth of under one metre, to some 5 metres depth of cover beneath the centre of the street.[327] The tunnels themselves were of the order of two metres high and 1.5 metres wide. They were close timbered with wooden 'setts' due to the weak ground. In the Hoogstraat tunnel, Major W.E. Buckingham, the Assistant Inspector of Mines, reported water in the gallery at least 0.15 metres deep, suggesting a depth to the water table of at least two metres.[328]

Away from Nieuport itself, in the dune fields of the coastal strip, extensive tunnels, dug-outs and shelters were dug by British and Australian tunnelling companies.[329] The dunes are predominantly composed of loose sand; when saturated with water their strength is very low, and easily loses integrity to form a slurry of 'running' sand.

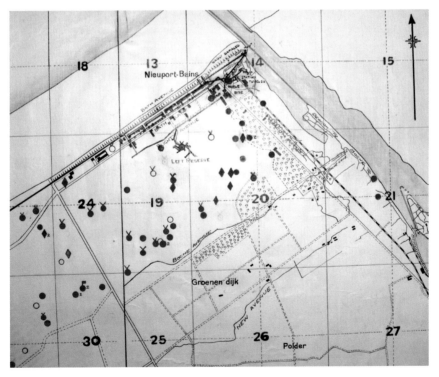

Location of dugouts in the dune field at Nieuport Bains. The red dots correspond with shelters of differing types. (The National Archives)

As noted by Major Buckingham, 'Mining is impossible in the hollows between the dunes owing to water being to [sic] close to the surface'[330] – so tunnelling was restricted to the sand hills themselves. Operating in such mobile sand was made possible through a close boarding technique known as 'spiling' (driving inclined timbers ahead of the working face), and by sinking prefabricated corrugated iron shelter segments into position.[331] Taking into consideration the depth to fully saturated ground, and the minimum thickness of cover needed for adequate protection against artillery shells and mortars, tunnelling was feasible provided the dunes reached a minimum altitude of ten metres above sea level, and could provide at least six metres of head cover. Contemporary maps demonstrate the extent of this tunnelling between June and November 1917, providing accommodation space for many thousands of men.[332] Though not connected underground to the tunnels under the town, they provided a significant 'degree of protection' for the men who massed for the attack on the coast in 1917 – an attack that was never brought to fruition as the offensive near Ypres came to a halt on the muddy plain and ridges.

Vimy Ridge and Arras: chalk tunnels

Subways and tunnels became very much a component of the war in 1917, with opportunities taken to provide a safe system of delivering men to the front wherever the ground would permit it. Topography and geology was such that the opportunity to dig tunnels for use as subways was limited to the sector away from the clay plain of Flanders. This was especially the case in the dry chalk ground of Artois, where the decision was taken to dig a sytem of tunnels and subways in preparation for the Battle of Arras – and the associated assault on Vimy Ridge by the Canadian Corps – that would take place on 9 April 1917. Field Marshal Sir Douglas Haig would make special mention of this in his *Despatches*:

> Very extensive mining and tunnelling operations were carried out. In particular, advantage was taken of the existence of a large system of underground quarries and cellars in Arras and its suburbs to provide safe quarters for a great number of troops. Electric light was installed in these caves and cellars, which were linked together by tunnels, and the whole connected by long subways with our trench system east of the town.[333]

Mining at Vimy Ridge and Arras meant exploiting the chalk; beneath the the ice-shattered levels and the capping of the *Limon* complex (overlying remnants of sands the same geological age as the Paniselian, farther north). The chalk here is

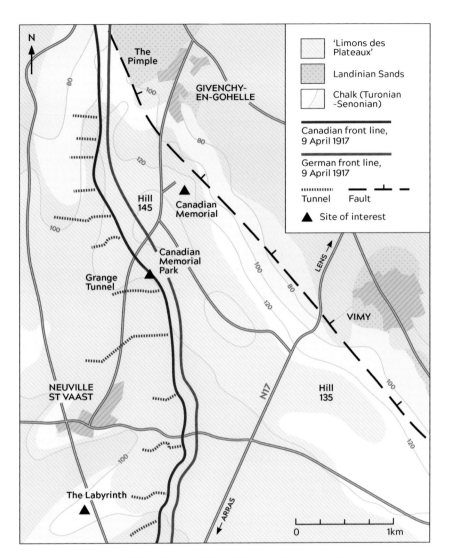

Map of the subways at Vimy Ridge in relation to geology

Craie blanche – white chalks with rarer flints, overlying clay-rich layers.[334] At Vimy Ridge, there were five tunnelling companies (172nd, 175th, 176th, 182nd and 185th TC) engaged in digging both offensive mines, and subways.[335] In all some eight offensive mines were also laid – though only two were used – and twelve infantry subways were constructed than ran from the reserves to the frontline.[336] These subways were spacious; the chalk easy to work and capable of maintaining its gallery shape. As with all chalk, the presence of fractures and distinct layers meant that there was the possibility of periodic failure of the roof, as slabs defined by these natural features collapsed. There were also unpredicable fractures created during the geological uplift of the ridge itself, and the periodic movement of the Marqueffles Fault.[337] To avoid failures along these lines, and spaced out to ensure a regular support, there were mine setts, but unlike the demands of the Ypres Clay there was no need to compensate for swelling pressures. Though the chalk is

The Grange subway at Vimy, taken in low light. Timber supports are spaced out; the gallery holds its shape, but support of the roof is necessary to prevent slab failure. (P. Doyle)

porous, its lime minerals were not prone to swelling. Instead, its high permeability means that water will descend to the level of saturated ground, and as the mines were developed in the upper units of the chalk, that water table was at some depth.

The subways at Vimy were intended, like most military subways in the region, to provide access to the front without the need to subject soldiers to artillery attack. There were numerous entrances and exits that were prepared ready to be broken out, using bored 'Wombat' charges,[338] for the attacking troops. The galleries were also provided with a range of ancillary chambers and facilities, including dug-outs and assembly chambers, dressing stations, mortar, bomb and ration stores, and, with water at depth there were wells to provide access to supply water points where soldiers could fill their water bottles with clean groundwater. There were signal cables, and tramways. Considering the level of safety, the subways took only three and a half months of construct. If nothing else, they were a haven from the war above:

> The troops housed in the Subways were able to rest in a safe, warm and dry place, up to the time of the attack. The Subways proved throughout proof against bombardment, the only damage done being to some of the exits. These were easily and quickly repaired…It is estimated that in one Subway alone the traffic amounted to 9700 [soldiers] between the 5th and 11th of April [1917].[339]

The city of Arras was considerably farther away from the front line than at Vimy. Under the ancient city were chalk 'caves' structures, like the *souterraines* of other parts of Artois that had supplied stone for facing the city's ancient buildings. In time of war, these underground quarries would be pressed into use for an altogether different purpose. Dating back at least to the seventeenth century, these large underground cavities – at depths of 20–60 ft – were beneath the city's southeastern suburbs (with some cellars or *boves* in the city centre), and were, like other *souterraines*, supported by the classic 'pillar and stall' design, working on one plane *in situ* so that a floor and roof of intact chalk were created. The stone pillars left held up the roof, and the galleries cut around them supplied the stone. There were flint levels – as these tunnels were cut through layers of pure white *la craie blanche à silex* that are well developed across this region, as its name suggests, containing a number of hard flint levels.[340] Cutting through the chalk would inevitably mean that picks would ring on the hard flint nodules.

British troops arrived in the city from March 1916, and following their arrival, the underground chambers were surveyed and by the end of the year were being

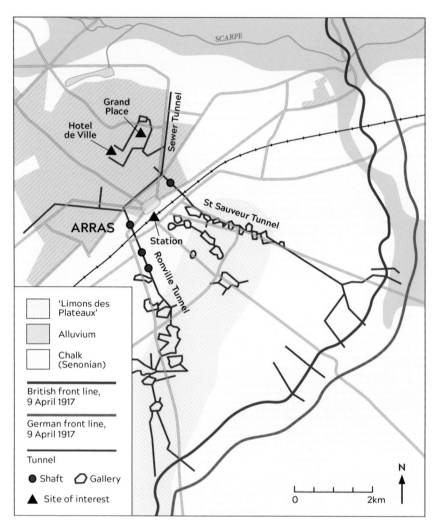

Arras subways and caves in relation to geology.

extended by the New Zealand Tunnelling Company. The New Zealanders worked systematically to link up the numerous chambers with tunnels, allowing both access and providing a drive towards the front line to the east of the city. Slab failures were once again a real possibility, so the New Zealand tunnellers assessed weak points and supported them with stout timbers cut from the forest at nearby Le Cauroy. The tunnel galleries cut by the tunnellers were large, measuring 6.6 ft high and 4 ft wide,[341] in line with their purpose as infantry subways. Excavations were commenced in January 1917, and completed in March, in time for the Battle of Arras on 9 April 1917.[342] As one tunneller recorded:

There was the unvarying routine for many months, eight full hours hard slogging in the solid chalk and flints till relieved at three, eleven or seven o'clock, then a good hour's plod back to billets along the trench, a rum ration, a hot meal and to sleep till time for next shift, each day of week or month exactly alike…[343]

As with Vimy, these tunnels accessed water at depth, providing wells for the numerous men who served here. The system became vast, capable of housing some 20,000 men, the main tunnel galleries (St Saveur and Ronville), running beneath main roads at the surface, linking the city centre *boves* to the trench lines.[344] The galleries linked cavernous chambers named after New Zealand cities, or those of England and Scotland, each capable of holding thousands of men. The whole system became an underground city, with chambers for sleep, kitchens, water

Exit 10 from the Wellington Quarry, one of the ancient underground chalk chambers linked by the Ronville Tunnel to the south of the city of Arras. Each chamber along this tunnel was named after New Zealand towns and cities by the NZ Tunnelling Company. (Ei Shany/CC-BY-SA-4.0)

points, latrines and a full dressing station. The tunnels would also serve their primary purpose. At the termination of each main tunnel were offensive mines dug by 'wombat' drilling machines, packed with explosives; these were more 'Russian saps' that would create communication trenches to link with the captured German lines. Then 'at Zero Hour', 05.30 on 9th April 1917, the mines were blown and the attack swept forward, leaving the tunnel entrances behind them'.[345] The attacks on the first day were a great success; geology had favoured the attackers, and the tunnellers, working against the clock, had learned how to use it.

5 BREAKING THE SIEGE: ARTILLERY, MINING, GAS AND TANKS

All night long the bombardment had continued, but at 6.25 a.m. The final intense bombardment started. Until 7.15 a.m. observation was practically impossible owing to the eddies of mist, rising smoke, flashes of bursting shells, and all one could see was the blurred outline of some miles of what appeared to be volcanoes in eruption. At 7.20 a.m. rows of steel helmets and glitter of bayonets were to be seen all along the front line.[346]

With the trench lines intact from late 1914, all the characteristics of a siege had set in on the Western Front. At Ypres, with the first offensive over by 22 November, the British observed the trench lines being strengthened and improved: 'for nearly three weeks, the exhaustion of both sides, coupled with bad weather. Led to a lull in operations…the enemy near Ypres was quiescent and observed to be digging a series of lines of defence, and to be erecting more and more wire.'[347]

" Daily Mail " WAR PICTURES

62. BRITISH MACHINE GUNNERS WEARING GAS HELMETS.

OFFICIAL PHOTOGRAPH, CROWN COPYRIGHT RESERVED.

British machine gunners wearing gas helmets; trench warfare was an extended siege, kept in place by defensive weapons such as the Vickers machine gun; breaking it needed new approaches, including gas.

Though there would be an attempt, in April 1915, to break out of the Ypres Salient, and an all-out assault on the French lines at Verdun in February 1916, the line became set. And with the Germans holding a mostly defensive line – their Western Front – from the Swiss Frontier to the North Sea, they had hopes for a negotiated settlement in the west, while defeating the Russians in the east. For the Allies, there was no question of negotiation; facing the German linear fortress meant the concept of 'investment': the German supply lines interrupted at sea by the British blockade, the German trenches broken down by latter-day 'siege engines'. Not that the Allies had it all their own way, as at times those siege weapons were turned towards their lines. At all levels, innovation and competitive advantage was the defining concept, underground, on land, and in the air.[348]

For men in those trenches there was a material truth, that 'the defence was so strong that each offensive action was brought to a standstill'.[349] Breaking these defensive lines meant the destruction of the opposing trenches – or more specifically, the destruction of the men who manned them. Writing in 1920, tank pioneer Col. J.F.C. Fuller identified three pivotal moments, and three modern technologies deployed, when things hung in the balance 'in the trenches':

> Three definite solutions were attempted – the first, artillery; the second, gas; and the third, tanks – each of which is a definite answer to our problem if the conditions are favourable for its use. Thus, at the Battle of the Dunjec, in the spring of 1915, the fire of Mackensen's massed artillery smashed the Russian front...At the Second Battle of Ypres the German surprise attack succeeded because the British and French possessed no antidote. At the First Battle of Cambrai, the use of tanks on good firm ground proved an overwhelming success...[350]

To this can be added a more ancient art, that of military mining, a centuries-old siege tactic that was to have specific success at the Battle of Messines in June 1917. Significant to all of these is the value, importance and nature of *ground*.

Artillery was the first of the wonder weapons wielded against the opposing trenches. Early war, it was really a question of deploying field guns firing over open sights as an anti-personnel weapon. Highly mobile, these field pieces were brought into battle by horse teams, just as they had always done. Though the terrain was rough, it was as yet not cut up; and the heroic defence of the guns in retirement was always something that would stir the public, just as it had at Colenso against the Boers in 1899, when Victoria Crosses had been awarded for just that act. But with the trenches firmly in place, there had to be much more to artillery than its use as

Field gun artillery shells. Shrapnel, an anti-personnel weapon, was perfect when deployed against an enemy in the open. High trajectory, high explosive shells fired from howitzers were required against trenches.

a simple anti-personnel weapon; now a more advanced scientific approach to the destruction of fortifications was needed. The British manual *Military Engineering (Part 1) Field Defences* (1908) included this prescient statement:

> Field gun shells are not intended to destroy earthworks. Against deep trenches, with low, flat parapets, field artillery has but little effect. The tendency of the shell to glance on striking an earth parapet is specially marked in the case where the latter is made of sand and light soil.[351]

There would be requirement to deploy higher trajectory weaponry; howitzers capable of destroying entrenched positions, but which are, by nature, more static in position – and which therefore require a more secure emplacement. Gunners would also require more detailed maps, better survey, and altogether a more scientific approach to their shoots as the war progressed.[352] Thus by the end of the war, to be effective, artillerymen had a list of basic requirements: good maps; their own position accurately located; the position of enemy guns accurately located; and, a means of laying their guns accurately on these targets without registration.[353]

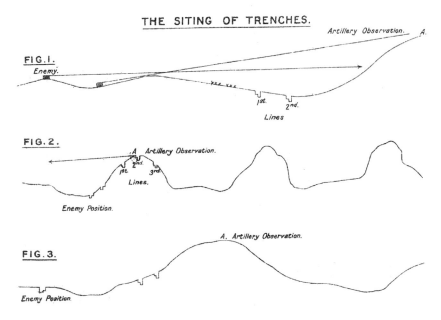

Artillery observers were necessary to support the artillery pieces behind the front lines. The position of the observer varied according to topography and 'siting of trenches'.
(*Manual of Field Works* 1921)

With the development on heavy siege weaponry (as these artillery pieces were still called), came the need to have prepared positions in the rear, away from the front. Artillery pieces thus withdrew from sight, and relied on Forward Observation Officers (FOO) in Observation Posts (OP). With trenches located on the forward slope, such officers would serve with the infantry in the trenches (or in forward 'saps' in the rarer occasions when trenches or prepared positions were on the reverse of a slope), it would be down to the FOO to communicate with the gunners in their positions, directing their fire on the targets.[354] With the observations of such officers – often braving the dangers of No Man's Land – and with cooperation of aviators and observers in static balloons, the desired effect of more accurate gunfire, for the British at least, was achieved in 1917–18.[355]

Protection of the guns against counter-battery fire meant the construction of more sophisticated field fortifications, 'measures for protection…defences suitable for position warfare'.[356] Those defences meant concealment and cover, as well as a suitable base that would aid in the correct laying and sighting of guns. In 1917–18, this meant greater toil for the gunners. For example, in 1917, at Hill 60, the gunners worked to construct tunnels to house their battery personnel in tunnels, and to adequately support and conceal their weapons and ammunition. It was a physical affair:

> The gunners had been engaged on the construction of a new battle position higher up still, right on Hill 60. Here, night after night, they toiled with picks and shovels under the direction of Engineer officers, the work being frequently interrupted by heavy shell-fire and gas-bombardments…days of ceaseless rain had churned the whole place into a morass, digging parties returned in the early morning unrecognisable in their plastering of yellow clay.[357]

Battles thus became bigger and better artillery 'shoots', an arena of artillerymen fighting engineers, gunners fighting gunners. Stuck in the middle, their bayonets fixed, were the infantry – as always the boots on the ground would still have to take the forward trenches when the gunnery was done. New tactics and approaches, creeping and box barrages for example, would assist these men; but all too often it came down to the number of artillery pieces per unit area, and the number of shells per unit gun. With the tactics of 'destruction' the guns were aimed the defenders, and the defenders' terrain; this meant, at Vimy Ridge in 1917 for example, that while objectives were achieved, 'the consequences of 'destruction' were a devastated terrain and a wrecked road system that hampered exploitation.'[358] Artillery was not the total answer – though ultimately, scientifically worked, it would provide some of the means of winning the war. But there were other weapons of the siege war that would assist in breaking down the enemy – and his fortifications.

OFFENSIVE MINING

With the establishment of trench warfare, it followed that military mining, the traditional approach to siege breaking, would be employed. While mining also provided a means of permitting men to move about undetected, deep underground, it was the opportunities presented to break down the walls of fortresses by undermining that perhaps has a longer history in warfare. In the Great War, the first attempts at breaking the siege through mining was developed in December

1914, with engineer companies waking to the need to destroy strong points, or to break the line through cratering at the surface.[359] This was in line with doctrine laid down in military manuals, that 'in all kinds of fortress warfare of which we have hitherto had experience, it has frequently happened that the besieger has had to carry on his advance below the ground'.[360] And just as there was the eruption of trench warfare in the Russo-Japanese War of 1904–5, so there was the resumption of the ancient art of military mining, particularly so as 'neither the Japanese nor the Russians had an adequate armament of modern siege artillery.'[361] As it was for these opponents, so it was for the armies of the Western Front in 1914 – the ancient art of mining was to reappear, and there would need to be personnel to support it.

The British army had no organisation for mining, although all officers and the majority of men of the Royal Engineers received a short training in military mining… After the First Battles of Ypres 1914 operations were evidently developing into siege warfare, and it was equally evident that the RE Field and Siege Companies had far too much other work in hand to provide personnel for mining…In February 1915, after some discussion, it was definitely decided to create eight Tunnelling Companies…[362]

Mine crater in Flanders. Often capturing the mine crater was an important aspect of trench fighting, providing a temporary topographical advantage to those who could capture it. All too often, in Flanders the mine crater would fill with water due to both groundwater flow and rainfall, depending on the geological situation.

DEFENCE OF CRATERS.
NEAR LIP DEFENDED.

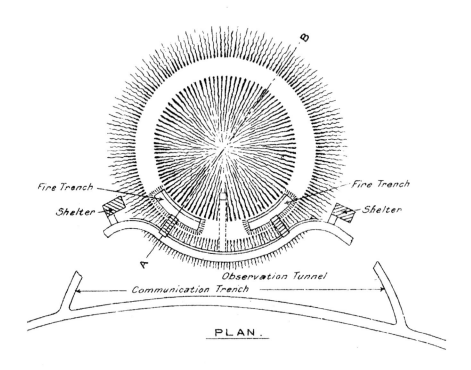

PLAN.

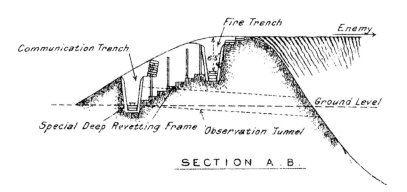

SECTION A.B.

Mine craters were valuable additions to the defensive schemes, and it was important to capture and hold them immediately after they had been 'blown'. (*Manual of Field Works* 1921)

Military mines are any underground system that was intended for offensive action through explosion, or indeed of defensive action to counter enemy mining. Throughout the war, from 1914 onwards, mining and tunnelling was carried out by specialist mining units on both sides, with increasing sophistication – though the re-establishment of mobile warfare in 1918 saw a decreasing relevance in underground fighting.[363] Nevertheless, mining operations were significant, with heavily fought over sectors in France and Flanders – such as the Bluff and Hill 60 in Flanders, the Hohenzollern Redoubt in the coal belt, the mines of Artois and Vimy Ridge, and the Somme. Mining in Flanders was largely concentrated in the area to the north and east of Ypres known as the Ypres Salient, with a significant density of mining in and around the villages of Hooge, Zillebeke, Wytschaete and Messines from 1915–1917.[364] Complex systems of defensive tunnels were built on many levels for listening and interception purposes. The concept of listening and countermining galleries was almost as old as offensive mining itself,[365] and as the war progressed, so it soon developed a level of sophistication on the Western Front too. Justly, the most famous of all mine systems was the use of mines to dislodge the Germans from the Messines–Wytschaete Ridge in June 1917. The Battle of Messines would mark the apex of mine warfare; two years in the planning, it would not be repeated. In all cases, Messines included, the purpose of the mine was to remove an obstruction, to destroy a redoubt or fortification.

In France and Flanders, mining was inhibited by the nature of the chalk, clays and sands that determined the topography and landscape of the region. Surrounding Ypres, arguably the most successful mining was that which exploited the Ypres Clay, or of other clay layers within the Paniselian that lay above the clay plain. For many miners, seeking out the striking 'blue clay' was the opportunity to reach a medium that gave the best possible results. For Captain Cecil Cropper of the British 250th Tunnelling Company, writing in late 1915 'The crux of the matter… was that we should be able to get down into the Ypresian Clay Bed, [the] blue clay formation, in which we could carry on mining operations'.[366] It was in this medium that the approach known as 'clay-kicking', a specialist technique that allowed miners to work rapidly and drive galleries through the clay without recourse to picks and shovels – which in a war that employed men to listen intently for their enemies workings was essential. Brigadier J.A.C. Pennycuick, Royal Engineers, described its use:

171 Tunnelling Company had been specially raised and had recruited 'clay kickers' – a new RE trade. The 'clay-kicker' lay on his back at the head of the mine gallery, with a sandbag behind his shoulders. He worked a spade

MINING TOOLS.

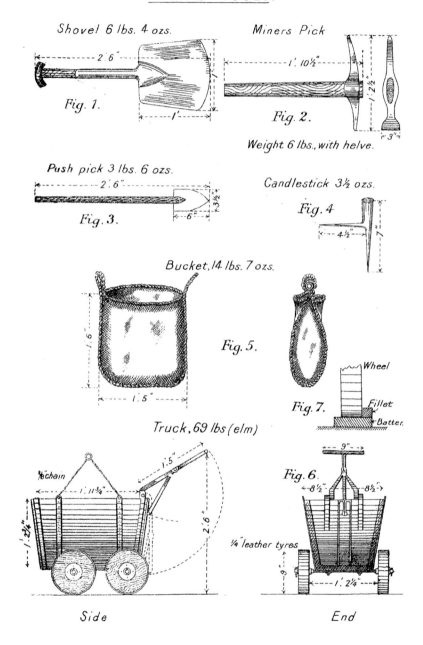

Shovel 6 lbs. 4 ozs.

Fig. 1.

Miners Pick

Fig. 2.

Weight 6 lbs., with helve.

Push pick 3 lbs. 6 ozs.

Fig. 3.

Candlestick 3½ ozs.

Fig. 4.

Bucket, 14 lbs. 7 ozs.

Fig. 5.

Wheel
Fillet
Batter.

Fig. 7.

Truck, 69 lbs (elm)

⅛ chain

Fig. 6.

¼" leather tyres

Side

End

Mining tools; military mining has a long history, and use of the correct tools, those making the least noise, were essential. In clay, 'push picks' and 'grafting tools' were used by the clay-kickers; in chalk, traditional picks and shovels were used (War Office, 1910)

with a long narrow blade, with his feet and hands, to bring down the spoil from the face of the gallery. Two other miners removed the spoil and a small team brought up and fitted the close timbering. As the galleries were only 5ft by 4ft (sometimes 3ft by 2 ft) the work was exacting and skilled.[367]

Looking down a deep shaft in the mine system at La Boisselle, Somme. The water level here is at depth. (P. Doyle)

Looking back along the entrance incline to the tunnel system at La Boisselle, Somme. Cutting
through chalk with brittle flints, this created noise that was likely to travel a distance.
(P. Doyle)

As with all military mining, position relative to water level is significant. This
affected Artois and Picardy just as much as it did in the wet levels that lay above
the clay. As Standish Ball, British Assistant Inspector of Mines was to comment,
'a complete knowledge of the geological nature of the ground to be worked in was
essential, particularly as regards water level, it being found in some parts of the
chalk country that the difference between summer and winter water level varied
as much as 30 ft.'[368] While it was the 'blue' Ypres Clay that was the target for

the clay kickers, on the Somme, and in Artois, successful mining operations were largely restricted by the height of the water table within the chalk. This level varied according to topography, and according to season, and consequently, a knowledge of its height was essential, not only for the tunnellers, but also for those seeking out the water itself. On the Somme and in Artois, British military geologist Lt W.B.R.

Locating the Line of March of the Human Mole

Contemporary artist's impression of an officer using a 'geophone' location device to locate enemy working by sound.

King was to map out the level of water saturation in the chalk, and determine its fluctuation – of inestimable value to both efforts.[369]

On the Somme, clay kicking was not possible (except, perhaps, in the surface soils overlying the chalk), and here the miners used short handled picks and shovels – and those listening heard their vibrations passing through the strata underground. Here tunnelled galleries hewn with picks in the traditional way were self-supporting, with added timber being only necessary to prevent 'slabbing' – the collapse of sections of roof. But with this strength came relative hardness; each strike of the pick invited a ring, particularly where the metal tools found the intermittent lines of tough flints so characteristic in chalk strata. To dig silently in chalk was impossible, and totally clandestine work was only achievable by driving galleries at great depths where it was hoped the enemy might not have a listening presence, a tactic which could never be guaranteed; or by being painstakingly careful in the excavation and digging at rates which might be so slow that the whole project was rendered ineffectual. Such techniques were essential though, as sound was known to travel great distances underground, and that it varied according to geology. Thus, the use of a pick in chalk galleries could be detected, two and a half times further than the use of the same tool in sandy-clay – and the use of the clay-kicker's 'push-pick' was a fraction of that.[370] With the evolution of new techniques – including the development of 'Geophones' capable of detecting and accurately locating enemy galleries underground – stealth was essential.

The Somme Offensive of 1916 saw the use of a coordinated effort to destroy strongpoints in the line. Seven British tunnelling companies (174th, 178th, 179th, 181st, 185th and 252nd) were given orders to assist the offensive action by digging and laying offensive mines to destroy German strongpoints at Beaumont Hamel (Hawthorn Ridge), La Boisselle (Y Sap, Glory Hole, Lochnagar), Fricourt (Triple Tambour), Mametz (East and West) and Carnoy (Kasino Point). In addition, the companies were also instructed to dig shallow 'Russian Saps' intended to provide cover for the attacking infantry, who would emerge from them into No Man's Land. Innovative approaches to softening the chalk was used here, with shallow augers dug through filled with water or even vinegar; this assisted the drive. But the tunnels, so carefully planned, were never used.[371] The offensive mine galleries were cut through the chalk at a relatively high rate – even though cutting through the mid levels of the chalk they met much harder flint levels.[372] For example, one gallery 4ft 6 in high, 3 ft wide and 900 ft long was driven in 28 days again with mixed or limited results.[373] Again, attempts at softening the chalk were made with water, and to attempt silent working chalk blocks were carved out using bayonets – rather than picks. It was intended that each of the Somme mines would not only

The Lochnagar Crater, La Boisselle, Somme. The crater is dry; the debris were thrown clear during the explosion. This contrasts with the crater at Hawthorn Ridge. (Richard Dunning/ Lochnagar Crater)

Hawthorn ridge mine crater

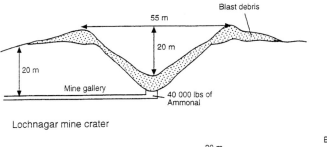

Lochnagar mine crater

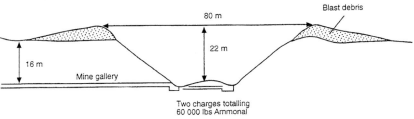

Mine craters on the Somme: comparison of Lochnagar and Hawthorn Ridge.

destroy the German strongpoints – but would be 'overcharged' with explosives so as to create a crater with a pronounced lip that was huge compared with others, providing a 'temporary breastwork' for the attacking troops – if they could reach the crater first.[374] More often than not this was not achieved. Hawthorn Ridge was blown a full ten minutes before zero hour; its crater was captured by the Germans. The others for the most part were exploded at 7.28 am. Lt Cecil Lewis of the Royal Flying Corps experienced the explosion of the Lochnagar mine while in the air:

> At Boisselle the earth heaved and flashed, a tremendous and magnificent column rose up into the sky. There was an ear-splitting roar, drowning out all the guns…The earthy column rose, higher and higher to almost four thousand feet.[375]

The mine crater itself was observed by war artist Sir William Orpen, in 1917:

> The great mine at La Boisselle was a wonderful sight… I walked up to it and suddenly found myself on the lip of the crater. I felt myself in another world. This enormous hole, 320 yards round at the top, with sides so steep one could not climb down them, was the vast, terrific work of man.[376]

Though the mines achieved their aim of the destruction of the German strongpoints above them – they had limited impact on the outcome of the offensive. That would be left to the bravery of the infantrymen who rose from their trenches to meet the German front line on 1 July 1916.

In the Ypres Salient, from the end of 1914 the British occupied positions on the clay plain and the lower slopes of the Passchendaele Ridge, with the Germans generally occupying the upper slopes and ridge tops. While this presented a topographical advantage to the Germans, in offensive mining terms, it was a disadvantage. For the British, for the most part undermining their enemies required little more than driving shallow inclines down sufficiently to intercept the clay; but for the topographically higher Germans undermining their enemies was so much more complex. To get below the British lines, for instance, the German tunnellers would be required to through the clay and sand layers of the Paniselian, layers that more often than not harboured levels and pockets of water-saturated sands.[377]

Directly overlying the Ypres Clay, the Paniselian Clay (nicknamed 'bastard blue clay' by the miners) is sandier in texture, and lies above immediately below the typical complex of sand and sandy clay layers of the ridges. At the base of the high ground, this became the favoured medium for mining by the British,[378] as

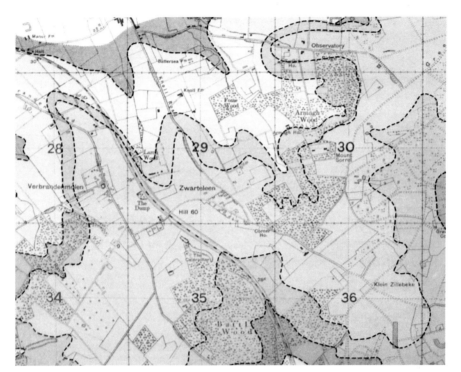

Extract from British 1;10,000 map geological Zillebeke, showing the environs of Hill 60. The colours indicate wet and dry strata, with blue representing the most wet. Capping the ridge top is a drier layer here coloured pink; immediately below that is a much bluer, water-logged level, referred to by the British as the 'Kemmel Sands'. (The National Archives)

the mixture of sand lessened the plasticity, and therefore lowered the pressures exerted by easily-expanded purer clay on timbered galleries. Above this was the 'Kemmel Sands', an influential unit that separated the British from the Germans both physically and tactically, and which entirely controlled military activities in both defensive fieldworks and offensive mining.

Found at around 50 m above sea level, the Kemmel Sands is a layer of fine sands with high porosity capable of soaking up all the water that fell on the ridge tops, its downwards movement inhibited by clay.[379] An aquifer, it was situated between the layer of moist or dry clays beneath, and a unit of moist sandy clays above, part of the Paniselian. The origin of the term 'Kemmel Sands' is unclear, but it is localised and may well have been applied by the British military geologists themselves, in the field. The permanent saturation level effectively meant that the Kemmel Sands were nothing less than a layer of quicksand, the German *Schwimmsande*.[380]

For the topographically higher Germans, every attempt at constructing deep tunnels intercepted the Kemmel Sands, the saturated layer presenting a significant problem. As soon as a shaft broke into them in some places the pressure was so great that sands 'fountained' in the shaft. Coping with a metre or so of this kind of ground was manageable, but at several points on the ridges the Kemmel Sands showed thicknesses of up to ten metres – a significant engineering trial, as described by Oberstleutnant Otto Füsslein, *Kommandeur des Mineure,* 4th German Army.

When we went deeper in Flanders, we soon hit water. Was there not, you might ask, anywhere that the ground was firm and dry? Yes indeed, but only below the water. But at that time we were not in the clay, but in the water. For all the water that percolates down through the ground is trapped on top of the clay and the bands of impermeable material within the Ypres [Kemmel] sand. The ground is almost always waterlogged to just

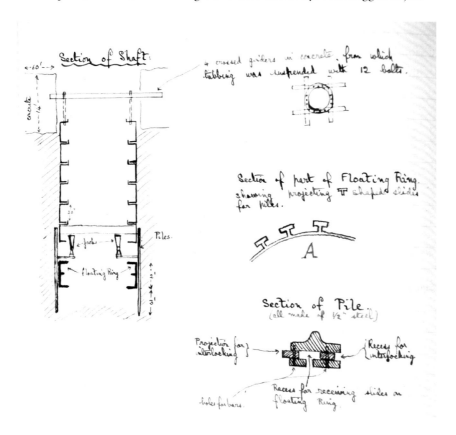

Extract from Major Buckingham's diary showing 'tubbing', here as used in running sands. Buckingham was Assistant Inspector of Mines in the BEF. (The National Archives)

below the topsoil, and in winter to the surface itself. Even the high, broad ridges on which stood the once-proud villages of Passchendaele, Bezalaere, Wytschaete and Messines are sodden with water, as we found when we dug there. Only in deep valleys, such as the terrain in front of Ypres, held by the British, and to the south in the valley of the Douve, is this layer of wet quicksand absent.[381]

For the British, situated on the lower slopes and in the valleys of the Passchendaele ridge, the Kemmel Sands were mainly either thin and manageable, on the contour of the British trench lines, or topographically above where their tunnellers were working, and therefore effectively non-existent. Even in places where they were problematic the British were often able to drop their shaft site back on to a slightly lower contour to find better geological conditions, an option not available to the topographically higher Germans.

To penetrate the surface in order to commence mining at depth, either a horizontal adit or a vertical shaft was required, the latter option being the most common.[382] Some of the earliest British mines were driven directly into hill slopes (as at Hill 60) but no significant depth could be gained unless the target was well above the adit entrance, i.e. unless the hill was of substantial height. Shafts and inclines were a better proposition. Shafts were vertical, using ladders or hoists for access, with inclines gently sloping with a flat floor, forming a sort of thirty degree chute, or built as a stairway on a steeper gradient, usually forty-five degrees.

Fig. 11.—Crater at Ontario Farm.

Ontario Farm; here the alluvial soils are so deep that the crater formed left no vertical expression. (Institute of Royal Engineers, 1922a)

Wooden shafts were attempted, but the high pore pressures of the Kemmel Sands meant that a new system, employing cast steel sections, was required.

The circular steel shaft approach was known as 'tubbing' – 'a material used for the lining of a shaft or tunnel for the purpose of keeping back water. It usually consisted of cast iron segments, made as to bolt together'[383] and the prefabrication of both metal, and later concrete, rings became a necessity in dealing with sands that were liable to run or flow. Tubbing was first used on 6 May 1915 in French Flanders, at Cuinchy, near La Bassée. Here, a section of 170 Tunnelling Company (commanded by Lieutenant J. A. Leeming) successfully sank a 1.8-metre diameter timber shaft, through 2 metres of running sand to reach the dry clay bed beneath. On the strength of this success, steel tubbing was routinely bought and manufactured in France for immediate application, and also put into production in Britain for the use of his tunnellers the full length of the front. The Germans, for their part, also attempted a similar system, though employing cast concrete rings.

Tubbed sections made the sinking process very simple, very fast, very dry and very safe, with, in some places, twin shafts being used, with a 1.6-metre diameter shaft fitted inside a 1.8-metre diameter one. Joints were sealed with strips of rubber cut from car tyre inner tubes, and the gap between the two sleeves filled with concrete, making the structure both strong and watertight. Metal shafts were necessary only where the groundwater determined it to be so; as soon as the steel tubbing reached dry and stable strata at depth, the shaft was continued in timber, and built to traditional designs. If steel was available the running Kemmel Sands and similar water-saturated strata were no obstacle to the British, and the clay could be reached through any depth of what was termed 'bad ground'.[384]

In addition to the Kemmel Sands, were considerable thicknesses of wet sand and silt in the Ypres Salient, Ice Age soils and the products of rivers, and their floods (known as 'alluvials') over millennia that had covered the Flanders Plain to a greater or lesser degree. In 1917, the British 171 Tunnelling Company had to tackle this medium where they were sinking two shafts for the mine scheme known as Ontario Farm, situated to the south of the Messines Ridge, on the dip slope of the ridge, and in the valley of the east-west flowing River Douve. The ground here was waterlogged to a depth of 20 metres, with the sediments of the Douve lying directly upon the impervious Ypres Clay.[385] By tubbing entirely in steel to 30 metres the clay was pierced and the driving of offensive galleries begun. After 100 metres of gallery had been installed a further shaft was sunk another 10 metres, to avoid the valley floor. At 40 metres below ground level, the tunnel was successfully driven, until around 180 metres from the shaft the face of the tunnel failed. This led and a rush of yellowish water-saturated 'quicksand' filled over 30 m of gallery before it was finally stopped with a timber dam.[386]

Following the advice of Major Edgeworth David – the sole British military geologist with responsibility for tunnelling – based on borehole data published on the Belgian Geological Survey maps,[387] the tunnellers diverted their gallery, pushing forward with an incline from the dam, and eventually reaching the target and charging the mine.[388] In this way the galleries were effectively stepped down to avoid breaking through the dry clays, to penetrate the wet sediments of the valley of the Douve. David had almost certainly averted disaster; if a breakthrough had of

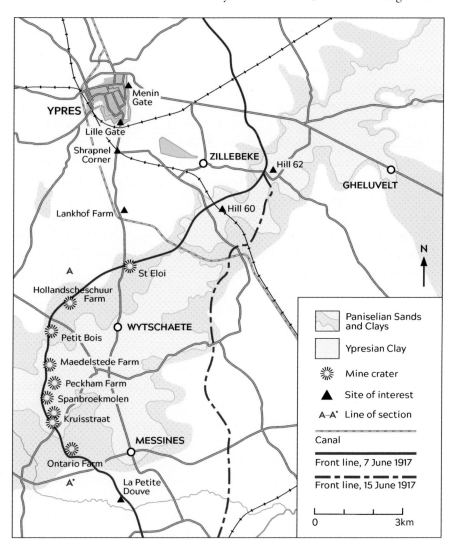

The Messines Ridge and the location of the mine craters. Cross section of the ridge at A-A is illustrated on page 198.

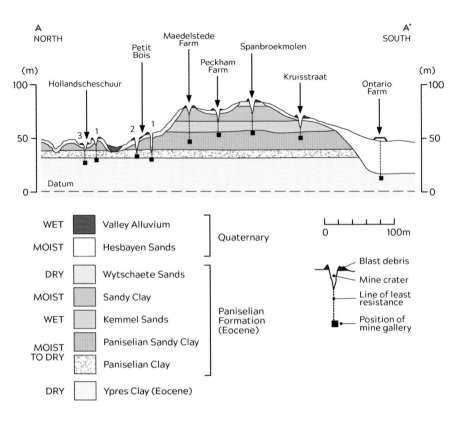

Cross section showing the location of British mine galleries at Messines. Location of section A-A is given on page 197. The British were able to dig adits, shallow inclines or shafts to access the clay levels.

occurred, then the gallery would have been filled with wet, running sands. David's timely intervention was 'a sufficiently severe lesson to impress on all military miners the grave risks attached to mining without geological advice.'[389]

From the summer of 1915 many permutations for concentrated mine attacks under the Messines–Wytschaete Ridge of the Ypres Salient had been discussed British GHQ; with time they would develop into a scheme that would lead to the complete capture of the ridge – but which would require two years of work to do so. Field-Marshal Sir Douglas Haig had long sought to clear the Germans from the clay plain and maritime region of West Flanders, opening up a route to the Channel ports of Ostend and Zeebrugge, and unlocking the way to the rail hub of Roulers, the key arrival and distribution point of the German army's materiel and troops. All this would be achieved by punching through the German positions on the ridges in front of Ypres before advancing along the Belgian coast at Nieuport. Originally planned for the summer of 1916, the offensive would be delayed, as

British attention was turned towards co-operation with the French in the great Somme Offensive in Picardy. In November 1916, with the Somme battles out of the way, Haig was free to concentrate on a Flanders offensive. It would be left to 2nd Army Commander Sir Herbert Plumer to develop plans for a series of attacks to begin in the spring of the following year.

Plumer's proposal was delivered to Haig on 12 December 1916, his concept a deliberately limited offensive at Messines, employing the explosion of many carefully laid mines, to destroy the coordinated defences of the German frontline. Though Plumer's limited objectives did not initially impress Haig (who wanted a breakout from the Salient), other pressing matters meant that the offensive *would* now stand alone, with a greater 'push' to take the Passchendaele Ridge later. Plumer's approach was to destroy all of the strongpoints that had, in obedience to *Stellungsbau*, been built into the German line. There were farms as strongpoints; there were spurs and opportune ridges. All of them would have been hellish to attack in a frontal assault – but their complete destruction, punching holes through

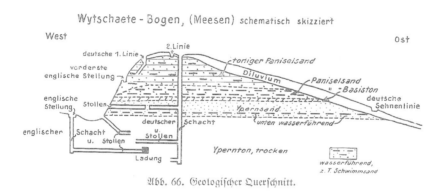

The relationship of British to German tunnels and shafts at the Messines Ridge. In order to probe and search out the British workings, or to undermine them, the Germans had to sink deep shafts through a variety of strata, some of them waterlogged. This placed the advantage with the British. (v.Bülow *et al.* 1938, *Wehrgeologie*)

the German lines, would be accompanied by an artillery bombardment that, on such a limited front, would render complete success. The limited destruction of strongpoints attempted on the Somme in 1916 – with widely spaced gaps between them, would not be repeated. Here the intention was to neutralise as many of the myriad German strongpoints as possible along the full length of the ridge.

While it is widely thought that twenty-five big charges were laid in preparation for Messines; there is evidence that as many as least forty-nine separate mines had been proposed; and a substantial number were either completed or well underway by zero day.[390] The gaps seen between the surviving craters varies; closer in the middle part, they are more widely spaced towards the northern limb between Hill 60 and St Eloi. Here, technical challenges of 'bad ground' had been too much. In all seventeen mines had been laid, charged and tamped by the close of 1916. Four had been completed during April and May of that year at Trench 127 and Trench 122 at the southern end of the ridge, in front of Ploegsteert Wood. Just a single British charge at La Petite Douve Farm was lost to enemy countermining – an incredible feat after eighteen solid months of work on so many schemes. It was the tell-tale presence of blue clay that gave away the British activities, and led the success as La Petit Douve – known as *Weihnachtshof* – as the Germans looked for evidence of enemy miners toiling below ground.[391]

> At the *Weihnachtshof* we had laboriously sunk two timber-lined shafts, *Heinrich I* and *II*, into the clay and were already quite well advanced with the galleries. We heard no sound from the enemy, but the grey-green sandbags around his trenches told us that he was there.[392]

Apart from four other mines at 'The Birdcage' south of Ploegsteert Wood, just outside the southern edge of the theatre of battle, the nineteen mines which were detonated on 7 June 1917 were the only ones ready to fire on that date. The problems of wet ground would claim some galleries: Peckham No. 2 was a large mine lost, with the gallery engulfed and flooded, and there were others threatened though within a few short weeks of completion. In the weeks before zero the German Army were fully aware that something significant was about to happen, but still had no inkling of the full scale of the scheme. When the mines were blown, the effect was devastating; the force of the explosions and the coordination of the artillery meant that the tunnellers – guided by their geological advisors – had triumphed. One soldier, Private Benn of the Loyal North Lancashire Regiment, found himself in the maelstrom on 7 June 1917:

> Someone in our platoon said 'two minutes to go'. Exactly at 3.10 A.M., there was a terrible explosion on our left. It was the blowing up of a mine, which was the signal for everything to start. The next second their was such a roar, the like of which I had never heard before or since – and I hope I never hear such a one again. It was caused by the explosion of a further 18 mines. Every gun on the front had been standing with a shell in the breach,

and all were discharged on that second. It is an impossibility for me to describe all that happened… The concussion from the mines and guns was terrible, and the earth trembled under us.[393]

Messines was undoubtedly a success; but there would be no more grand mining schemes like it for the rest of the war. There would be no time for such patient preparation in the mobile phase that was coming – other means of 'breaking the siege' would take the place of mines.

GAS WARFARE

If the purpose of mine warfare was to punch holes in the line, thereby 'breaching' the 'walls' of the linear fortress, the lesson of the Battle of Messines was that a coordinated effort of tunnellers, artillerymen and infantry – and a skilful use of specialist engineers, advised by geologists – was required to gain success. But there was another possibility of breaking the siege, through the use of chemical weapons.

Cloud gas attacks in 1915–16 were delivered from cylinders like these; movement of the gas was heavily dependent on both wind and topography. (Foulkes, 1934, *Gas!*)

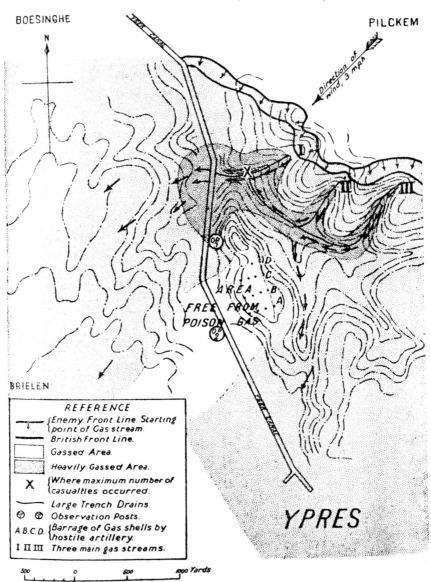

GERMAN GAS ATTACK, 19TH DECEMBER 1915.

MAP SHOWING THE DISTRIBUTION AND FLOW OF POISON GAS.

Compiled from ⎰ 1. *Observed facts.*
⎱ 2. *Reported facts.*
⎱ 3. *Distribution of casualties due to gas.*

BOESINGHE

PILCKEM

N

Direction of wind, 3 m.p.h.

X

OP

D
C
B
A

AREA FREE FROM POISON GAS

OP

II III

BRIELEN

REFERENCE

⎰	*Enemy Front Line. Starting point of Gas stream.*
	British Front Line.
☐	*Gassed Area.*
▨	*Heavily Gassed Area.*
X	*Where maximum number of casualties occurred.*
	Large Trench Drains.
⊕ ⊕	*Observation Posts.*
A.B.C.D.	*Barrage of Gas shells by hostile artillery.*
I II III	*Three main gas streams.*

500   0   500   1000 Yards

YPRES

Analysis of the flow of gas relative to topography during an attack at Ypres in 1915. The flow of the heavier than air gas was heavily dependent on the position of slopes and valleys.

The release or delivery of chemical agents had the potential to kill or disable the occupants of the opposing trenches – thereby leaving them intact, and available for occupation. This was first attempted, at Ypres, in April 1915. But the release of gas would be wholly dependent upon the following factors: that sufficient reagents could be obtained; that the gas could be released without harm to the attacker; and that both the atmospheric conditions – and the nature of the terrain – were sufficient to drive the gas towards the enemy. This was a big ask.

Though the use of poisonous gases had been outlawed by the Hague Conventions of 1899 and 1907, under Article 23(a) '… it is especially forbidden to employ poison or poisoned weapons',[394] the European nations had been experimenting with tear-gases that, in their view, did not constitute a 'poisonous' substance. The Germans for their part would later argue that chemical warfare as waged during the war 'was the result of recent scientific and technological achievements' that were not bound by the convention,[395] and it was the Germans who were the first to deploy shells filled with an irritant, against the Russians in January, and the French on the Belgian Coast in March 1915.[396] These early deployments were unsuccessful, but

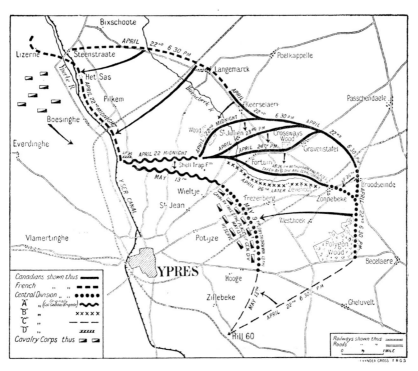

At Ypres in April 1915, the Germans unleashed a gas attack under favourable conditions that drove in the northern limb of the Ypres Salient; the scale of the success was unexpected.

they paved the way to greater use of such gases in warfare, especially when Dr Fritz Haber, director of the Kaiser Wilhelm Institut in Berlin-Dahlem, a future Nobel Laureate and expert in compressed gases, made the suggestion that chlorine gas could be released from cylinders to form a toxic cloud, rather than used in a shells as part of a bombardment.

Chlorine gas was always the reagent most likely to be used in the early part of the war. The gas was an easily produced and readily available chemical, commonly used in the German dye industry, and was well known as a powerful irritant that attacks the pulmonary tract, with prolonged exposure creating fluids that would quickly fill the lungs and cause the victim to effectively drown.[397] Released as a liquid, chlorine soon adopts a gaseous state in temperatures greater than 3°C, forming a light green cloud. Significantly, chlorine is much denser than air, almost three times greater in fact.[398] This density means that chlorine is likely to form clouds that have a propensity to 'settle in low-lying areas',[399] and clouds that would require a force to drive them across a landscape if released. That force would either be by the *pushing* of a prevailing wind, or the *pulling* of gravity – best developed as slopes with a sufficient gradient to persuade gas to flow. As General Foulkes, commanding the RE gas companies, wrote in 1934:

> If the velocity of the gas cloud was low it would be deflected by ground obstacles, would linger in hollows, flow into trenches and dug-outs and follow valleys, leaving hill tops as islands, just as water in a slow-moving stream swirls round the pebbles and boulders in its bed: when moving at a higher velocity it would surmount these obstacles more or less.[400]

Despite those factors, for the most part, it was upon wind that the military relied to drive the gas clouds – with little reference to topography. Without it, as Foulkes suggested, the gas would refuse to budge.

The first German cloud gas attack took place in the Ypres Salient on 22 April 1915. Some 5,730 gas cylinders – 340 tonnes of chlorine – had been put in place by 11 April.[401] After some debate over prevailing winds, the attack was to be targeted at the French 87th Territorial and 45th Algerian divisions on the northern flank of the Ypres Salient, between Steenstraat and Langemarck–Poelcappelle. To the east of the Algerians was the 1st Canadian Division. Here the gradient was low. The Hannesbeek stream,[402] draining off the Passchendaele Ridge, crossed the line of the front and formed a valley between the lines, such that while the Allied and German lines ran along 10 metre height contours, the ground between them sank to the valley bottom at around 5 metres. The attack was planned for the 15 April, but had to be postponed – there were no favourable winds. And without winds capable of driving the gas there was every possibility that the released chlorine would sit in the valley of the Hannesbeek, and remain there. With 'favourable winds' capable of pushing the gas, it was decided to release the chlorine at 17.00 on 22 April. The attack was a success – so successful in fact that the Germans were ill prepared to follow up what had been achieved.[403] But the cost was severe:

> The effect of the poisonous gas was so virulent that it completely annihilated the action capacities of the troops who occupied this part of the front. The smoke and steam covered the theatre of operations and plunged hundreds of men into a comatose state, and subsequently death.[404]

Though the Germans did not exploit the gap made in the line, all nations were now aware of the possibilities of gas as a means of 'breaking the siege'. The element of surprise in releasing gas would now be so much more difficult to achieve. If an attacking force could advance behind a cloud of toxic chemicals, then they could exploit the gaps in the line left as men retired or where asphyxiated. For the British, suffering a shortage in shells and manufacturing capabilities in 1915, the chance to use gas in a retaliatory measure was an attractive proposition. With the French pressing for more British involvement in offensive actions, and with an insistence that this action be fought in Artois, close to the village of Loos. The stage was set for the first British use of the chemical weapon.

The Loos battlefield (see map on page 206) lies between the canal at La Bassée and the Lens–Noeux les Mines railway. Topographically, conditions were variable across the front assigned to the British in the coming offensive. Here, in Artois, the chalk ground was relatively dry, with surface water draining away to join both the La Bassée canal to the north, and the Canal de Lens to the south. In the sector closest to Lens, and to the Artois plateau itself, the ground has a rolling aspect, the village of Loos nesting in a low valley between two spurs – one at Grenay, the other from Lens itself. To the north, the ground flattens out and becomes open, windswept and desolate, much flatter. It was a challenging place to stage a battle – if only due to the strength of their enemy's positions.

The German lines trending across the region were once more deliberately sited to give maximum natural support to the trench fortifications that had been dug there. The Germans had greatly strengthened their defences *in situ*, with a chain of mutually supporting strongpoints (*Stutzpunkts*), some of which would be significant redoubts or forts. Two of the most infamous were the Hohenzollern Redoubt, between Haisnes and Hulluch, and Hill 70, a natural feature forming

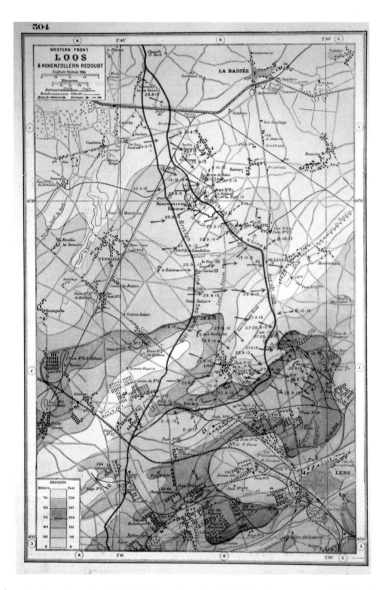

Topography of the Loos battlefield. When released, with little wind, the gas stalled in the north and centre; gas flow was much more successful in the south.

the backdrop to the village of Loos, itself defended by linked strongpoints. As usual, they had constructed strongpoints at regular intervals, sweeping around on contours to skillfully enfilade attackers, supported by deep trenches and thickly-spread barbed wire thickets.

For Sir Douglas Haig, commanding the First Army, the terrain represented a distinctly tough nut to crack. In June 1915, Sir John French had dispatched Haig to make an appreciation of the ground, and on making his assessment, the Commander of the First Army was not confident, 'the ground, for the most part bare and open, would be so swept by machine-gun and rifle fire... that a rapid advance would be impossible.'[405] Not only were the German lines strong, but miners' cottages and slag heaps provided the Germans with numerous opportunities for active observation and spirited defence, and between the industrial paraphernalia was an agricultural landscape largely barren of trees and open in aspect.[406] Despite Haig's reservations, the French were adamant; the British would support their actions in Artois, and fight on the ground allotted to them.[407]

Sir John French issued his orders for the 'Big Push' on 18 September 1915. The battle was to be fought between Lens and La Bassée, and was to be conducted by Haig, his First Army carrying out the main assault. To I Corps was allotted the task of taking the position from just North of the La Bassée canal to the Hulluch–Vermelles Road, facing the considerable fortifications of the German first line, including the Hohenzollern Redoubt, and behind it the fortified slagheap of *Fosse 8*. South of the Hulluch–Vermelles road, the frontage was allotted to IV Corps. Here the line swung round the disputed 'unfavourable' ground before approaching the outskirts of the village of Loos, and the long, dark mass of the Double Crassier, a double-lined, linear slagheap of colliery waste.

The battle was to open with a preliminary bombardment at 7.00 am on 21 September 1915. With the numbers of guns, howitzers and ammunition in short supply to the British maintaining a significant, pre-battle bombardment of the heavily entrenched enemy positions was a major issue. Mustering all the artillery pieces that could be spared, shells had also been husbanded to provide a fighting chance of destroying the enemy positions. Not only that, at this stage of the war the science of counter-battery fire was limited and less than ten percent of the artillery effort would be focused against the enemy guns. Though parts of the battlefront were pretty open, in others, the rolling contours derived from the slopes of the Artois plateau meant that the howitzer batteries of the Royal Field Artillery were placed on reverse slopes, situated some 3000–4000 yards away from their targets. None of this was helped by the fact that during the bombardment observation of fire accuracy was difficult, clouded by chalk dust and mists that spread across the battlefront.

The inadequacies of the artillery bombardment were well appreciated by General Haig in advance of the attack. The weight of fire mustered by the artillery at this stage in the war would still be inadequate. In Haig's view gas would effectively make up for the deficiencies, with the estimate that the planned gas attack could double the effectiveness of the guns. Sir Douglas Haig was quick to grasp the

Release of the cloud gas at Loos, 22 September 1915.

opportunity of this weapon following its deployment by the Germans farther to the north at Ypres. The British Secretary of State for War, Lord Kitchener, had given instructions that retaliatory measures be prepared to use gas against the Germans themselves. Haig was convinced. Some 5000 gas cylinders would be concentrated in the frontline trenches, and to ensure that the cloud was thick, there would be 'smoke candles' to plug any gaps and cover any deficiencies.

As with the German attack in April, Haig's plan to use poison gas was necessarily predicated on satisfactory wind conditions, and elaborate precautions were put in place in order to make sure that the gas cloud would form and would then roll over the ground towards the German trenches. Given the frontage, it would be essential for the gas to be released over a significant time frame – sufficient time, in fact, to overcome the usefulness of the German respirators, which were thought to be proof only to 30 minutes exposure. If the gas could overcome this, then the German troops themselves would be overcome in turn; the British would be able to walk through the line, their defenders dead or dying – if they had not already run away. With gas replacing the effect of heavy artillery, then it was essential that a sufficiently deadly cloud would be produced to silence the enemy. The wind would have to be favourable, blowing from the west, if the heavier-than-air gas was not to hang around at its point of release.

The conditions on 15 September 1915, the original date for the attack, were 'near perfect', with a breeze of four miles per hour blowing eastwards. But as the attacks would necessarily be in concert with those of the French (and as the French attacks were not predicated on the use of gas), it was agreed with the French commanders that the attacks would proceed together on the 25 September. With General Haig unequivocal in his plans for the use of gas, he nevertheless built in options that allowed for three separate circumstances based on wind conditions. The first assumed optimum conditions, under which the attack would proceed. The second, with limited wind, allowed for a partial assault against the Hohenzollern Redoubt and the north of Loos, to be followed up with a complete attack a day later; the third option was similar to the second, but allowed for a further delay.

The question of whether gas would be able to achieve what was expected of it literally hung very much in the air. If the gas cloud was to form, and was to roll across No Man's Land, then wind would be needed, with a steady breeze of 6–8 miles an hour at very least. Sir Douglas Haig deployed a team of experts who would be in a position to advise, from noted meteorologist Captain E. Gold of the Royal Flying Corps, to a team of forty gas officers, who were specially trained in wind speed and direction estimation. On their shoulders was the responsibility of advising the GOC First Army; if all was not well, then the attack would stutter. The wind had to be right.

On 24 September, Haig and his Corps commanders met with Gold. There was no chance of a favourable wind that day; but there was the possibility that there would be a breath of wind blowing from the west the following day.[408] Nevertheless, there was the possibility that the forecast could be wrong. With the assault timed to start at 6.30 am, and the gas release at 5.50, Haig and his staff were understandably nervous when, at 5.00 am, there was hardly a breath of wind. And when his senior Aide de camp, Major Fletcher, lit a cigarette the puffs of smoke were see to drift in exactly the opposite direction.[409] But it was too late to hold the attack, and with the breeze picking up from the southwest, Haig committed his troops to action. At zero hour, the artillery bombardment lifted, and the gas was released.

At forty minutes past zero, or 6.30 a.m., every battery lifts its fire from the front line to the second line, and still the furious fire continues. And then suddenly came time zero, bringing with it a scene that could never be forgotten. From the whole length of our front trench, as far as the eye could reach, rose, vertically at first, a grey could of smoke and gas, that, impelled by a gentle wind, spread slowly towards the enemy's trenches.[410]

The gas release had variable effects. With the wind conditions poor, the heavier than air gas had to rely on the ground – the natural slopes that would help propel the gas forwards by gravity, rolling downslope so that it could settle in low areas. This meant of course that any low points in the line would cause difficulties. To the north of the battlefield, close to the low-lying La Bassée canal, the gas refused to budge. In this sector, the influence of the rolling spur terrain descending from the

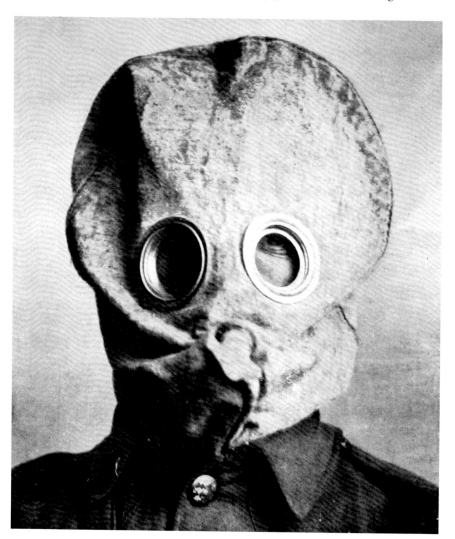

The Phenate gas hood, as issued to British troops at Loos. Though effective, it was clammy and suffocating; men were gassed when they removed them in battle.

Artois plateau was much reduced, less than 30 metres above sea level. On release, the gas and smoke was actively carried back towards the attackers, who had to rely on their stuffy and suffocating smoke helmets. Here, in this low lying place, it was not possible to rely on topography to drive the gas forwards, and a breeze offered resistance to their aims, blowing the gas backwards. This was the flat, open, plain so disparaged by Haig in his damning report submitted to Sir John French earlier in the summer. Haig's expectation was that this would be a particularly shell-blasted and machine-gun swept piece of ground; this view would not be challenged by events. Without wind there was nothing here to persuade the gas to flow. Here, the attack of the northerly divisions of I Corps was held up.

Moving southwards, the British line rose slightly to a flat, plateaued area, between 30 to 40 contours close to the Vermelles–Hulluch road. Close by was the toughest nut to crack – the Hohenzollern Redoubt. Here, conditions were variable for the dispersion of the gas, but in the main the release was effective. They were too effective in some situations, and the unpleasant, dank, suffocating gas hoods played their part in tempting the British soldiers to remove them, and risk being gassed. In parts, the gas stuttered, hanging around on the saddle of the plateau before dispersing. Together topography and wind had created a problem mix. But the greatest success came in IV Corps area. With the British line running the length of a spur, the Grenay Spur, the flow of the gas was down slope. At its highest, the British line was above the 70 metre contour line; Loos lay within a valley to the east, 30–20 metres lower. With the gas released, it flowed successfully down the chalk slopes to engulf the village; the British were able to exploit this, carrying Loos and moving on to the spur beyond, and Hill 70. Eventually, after days of battle, Loos ground to a halt, the expectations of the value of gas in replacing the offensive power of artillery much reduced.

After Loos, gas warfare would move on, with new and more deadly gas mixtures – and with much more efficient ways of delivering gas by shell or mortar, or even by grenade – so that it was neither dependent on wind, nor ground. Gas was no longer seen as a breakthrough weapon.[411]

TANK WARFARE

Tanks were a true innovation of the Great War. The germination of the idea owed much to naval principles of creating a 'landship', a 'machine gun destroyer', a mobile fortress capable of crossing the devastated terrain of the battlezone to take the fight to the enemy. As such, a Landships Committee was set up in early 1915 to examine the capability of the construction of such mechanical devices, and through this committee 'at a moment when the military authorities were inclined to regard

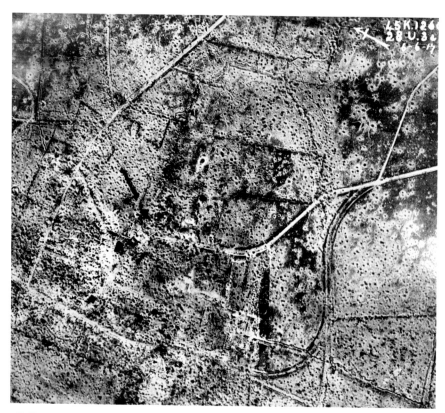

Shell cratered ground at Messines. Tanks could negotiate craters if dry; when wet they were a serious hazard. (P. Reed)

the difficulties connected with the problem as likely to prove insuperable.'[412] From this committee grew the requirements for their landships, that these caterpillar-tracked vehicles should be used in numbers, that it should be proof against rifle and machine gun fire, that it should be armed, and that it should be 'capable of crossing craters produced by the explosion of high-explosive shell, such craters being of 12ft diameter, 6ft deep with sloping sides' that it should cross 'an extended width of barbed wire entanglements' and significantly it should be able to span 'hostile trenches with perpendicular sides and of 4 ft breadth.'[413] It was much to ask of the new weapon.

Tanks were first used on 15 September 1916 at Flers–Courcellete, part of the ongoing battle at the Somme. Here tanks were used against strongpoints, acting to despatch them, punching a way through the line to allow the infantry through. The attack was grounded on the Thiepval plateau, the chalk crest capped with a heavy ground of *Limons* underlain with *Argiles à silex* – the impermeable clay with flints.[414] At their first use, these lumbering armoured vehicles suffered mechanical breakdown and numerous difficulties; of 49 that started, only 18 would be involved in the battle directly.[415] Fortunately, the weather was dry, cool at 15°C,[416] and the ground was dry underfoot. This permitted those tanks capable of moving to do their job, and cross the difficult terrain. A tank commander, Lt. A.E. Arnold, recorded his thoughts as the time for battle dawned:

> As dawn began to show the ground up we were still far behind the front line and it seemed certain we could not get there by zero hour for the going was now simply one succession of shell craters. But the ground was dry and it was thrilling the way the tank would go down into a crater, stick her tracks into the opposite wall and then steadily climb out.[417]

If the 'going' had been wet, then the unrelenting conditions of fluidised loam and loess that capped the ridge top would have undoubtedly have proven too much for the mechanical beast. Shades of things to come were evident when tanks were used again in the Battle of Arras, on 9 April 1917. The weather was not so kind, and the soils above the chalk ground were now too soft for good tank 'going':

> On April 7 and 8 the weather was fine, but, as ill-luck would have it, heavy rain fell during the early morning of the 9th. At zero hour (dawn) the tanks moved off behind the infantry, but the heavily crumped area on the Vimy Ridge, soaked by rain as it now was, proved too much for the tanks of the First army, and all became ditched at a point 500 yards east of the German front line…[418]

The real test was to be at the Third Battle of Ypres. Here there was no suggestion of firm ground, and no conception of solid chalk, on the clay plain and saturated sand ridges of the Salient. If tanks were to be deployed, they would have to face the challenges of the Ypres Clay, and the difficulties of the Paniselian. From the perspective of tank pioneer J.F.C. Fuller: 'From the tank point of view the Third Battle of Ypres is a complete study of how to move thirty tons of metal through a morass of mud and water'.[419] Yet a survey of the whole battle, and its constituent parts, shows that while some tanks became bogged, others were more successful. Thus, on 31st July, the first day of the battle, between the Menin Road and Glencorse Road 'five tanks came up but were bogged in the mud; four were finally knocked out by shellfire' whilst on the same day, on the Pilckem Ridge, and attack on Macdonalds' Farm 'Tank G50 fired six rounds into the farm, helping to weaken the enemy's resolve, and the position fell.'[420] Clearly the situation is more complex than just tanks stuck in mud or floundering in a morass of mud and water.

It was for this battle, and knowing this ground, that tank 'going maps' first appeared. Here tank officers annotated and prepared a range of maps, at a scale of 1:10,000, both retrospectively and also to aid in operations. While these tank officers consulted the materials that the British military geologists had at their disposal,[421] the maps were based mostly on the local knowledge, and interpretation of maps and photographs.[422] One such map, prepared by an officer of the 2nd Brigade Tank Corps displays the ground over which the Menin Road tanks traversed; it shows 'ground impassable for tanks' as well as 'good going', with the former, situated on the lower slopes of the ridge and part of the Paniselian, compared with the higher, drier and less shell pocked ground.[423] An assessment of the work done by the Regimental Officer of A Battalion, Tank Corps, showed it was accurate, with 'marshy ground' proving to be the chief obstacle to the tanks, while 'dry shell holes' were 'easily negotiated, and 'no trench was encountered that was wide enough to form an obstacle to Tanks.'[424]

Tank hopelessly bogged in the wet ground near the Menin Road. Here the water-bearing Paniselian layers, overlying the clay, have proven too much for the mechanical monster when deployed at the Third Battle of Ypres.

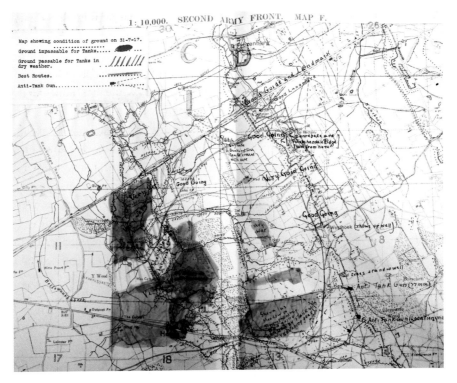

Tank 'going map' produced by a tank officer with the 2nd Brigade Tank Corps. Going is shown through a series of annotations, with waterlogged areas picked out, and passable routes noted. These were heavily dependent on the local geological conditions. (Colin Hardy/The National Archives)

These maps were a sign of things to come: considerations of the 'trafficability', the capability of vehicles to negotiate different terrain types, would become a serious preoccupation in the war that would follow.[425]

If Third Ypres was the most challenging terrain, then Cambrai (November 1917) and Amiens (August 1918), both of which were situated on chalk, showed what could be done. The attack at Cambrai commenced at dawn on the 20 November 1917; some 350 tanks attacked the German Hindenburg Line with five infantry divisions following behind. 'On the principal front of the attack, the tanks moved forward in advance of the infantry, crushing down the enemy's wire and forming great lanes through which our infantry could pass.'[426] Aided by smoke – and morning mist – the main position was soon overrun, the attack 'by Western Front standards, one of exceptional success'.[427] There had been no preliminary bombardment. Those terrible ingredients – rain (and heavy rain at that), and an artillery-churned, loess-soil battlefront – were not present here:

The area was ideal for tanks. It was mostly open rolling chalk plateau which, as it had lain uncultivated for the past two years, was covered with long grey withered grass matted into a surface idea for tank tracks. Save for Bourlon's wooded hill to the north-east of the area, there were no prominent features, low ridges ran across the front from north-west to south-east.[428]

The plan ensured that the tanks would start along a line from Gonnelieu to beyond Trescault, moving northeastwards along the spurs of a chalk plateau, capped with thick *Limons de Plateaux*.[429] Undisturbed, vegetated, this was a perfect terrain to operate upon; and the tanks assaulted the German trenches –'hidden from the eyes of the British observers'[430] and formidably deep and wide, – as they had been designed to do.

A similar terrain was to be seen at Amiens, the start of the great '100 Days' offensive that commenced on 8 August 1918. Here, on the battlefield south of the Somme River massed tanks and infantry would once more cross the chalk ground. Again comprising a chalk plateau capped with a substantial thickness of *Limons* (overlying the clay-rich *Argiles à Silex*), it was fortunate the soils were dry in the August weather. Once again the heavy tanks and infantry surged forward into the morning mist, followed by a combined assault of infantry, cavalry and light 'Whippet' tanks.[431] It was a tremendous success, sweeping through the forward defences. At both Cambrai and Amiens, tanks, used in great numbers, and with new tactics, sped across 'good going' and changed the history of warfare forever – the horrors of the clay ground of the Ypres Salient left far behind: 'through mud and blood to the green fields beyond'.[432]

One of the victors; a tank preserved at Ashford in Kent – given to the town in honour of their wartime fund raising. This is the only such trophy tank in existence. (P. Doyle)

6 MILITARY RESOURCES: WATER SUPPLY AND AGGREGATES

The supplying of a huge modern army with water is one of the largest tasks that falls to the military engineer. It is difficult enough to develop the water supply needed in rear areas and under stationary conditions of trench warfare, but the task becomes far more complex and serious in time of advance and mobile warfare.[433]

For its originator, Walter Kranz, *Kriegsgeologie* was more than just the use of geological information in building trenches, or the consideration of ground. There was the survey of resources to be carried out, too. While these resources might reflect the traditional occupations of peace-time geologists – namely the exploration and evaluation of minerals for the use of nations – one step removed from the battlefront, there were others that had a direct bearing on the prosecution of battle.[434]

Water supply has been a major preoccupation of military nations in state of war – and peace – for centuries.[435] With armies numbering millions, and with horses and pack animals upon which other branches depended, finding and supplying water was no mean feat; and this was particularly challenging in arid conditions. At Gallipoli, in 1915, the Ottoman Turks controlled most of the water supplies, particularly in the Anzac Sector, where the depth to groundwater was extreme. Here the ill-fated campaign was significantly hampered by the absence of adequate water supplies, and there the military spent its time seeking new groundwater sources – and wasting valuable resources shipping water from Egypt.[436] As far as A. Beeby Thompson was concerned, exploration for water was a demanding task: 'the execution of emergency water supplies, such as are usually needed during a military expedition, call for quick, confident, and perhaps, courageous decisions, and these cannot be made without a fair knowledge of the principles of geology and hydrography.'[437]

Hard lessons were certainly learned from this experience, as expressed by American military geologist H.E. Gregory in 1918:

For military purposes near the front both quantity and quality of water are important. A minimum supply necessary to support life and essential mechanical operations must be provided, regardless of difficulties, or operations must be abandoned.[438]

It was for this very reason that the nations at war drew up 'water supply maps', or *Wasserversorgungs-Karten*, that sourced their information from local knowledge, official documents, and archived borehole information.[439] These maps served to advise the armies as they manoeuvred across Europe, and gave some inkling of the resources available. These maps gave indications from 'good but scarce' to 'abundant but bad'.[440]

But finding resources to maintain the health of the fighting troops was not the only way that geologists could contribute; there was also the question of aggregates that could be used in both the construction of fortifications, and in the development of roads. Both would assume large significance in the war of the trenches; both would require expert geological knowledge to exploit them.

WATER SUPPLY

With the mass armies of the Allies and their enemies encamped and entrenched across the continent of Europe, it was not surprising that the demand for suitable drinking water (known as potable water) would increase. What would be surprising, however, is the inadequacy of water in a region of Europe, France and Flanders, where there was a high degree of rainfall. Providing an adequate supply of potable water would therefore be a significant problem on the Western Front, with an estimate of the minimum requirement for massed troops being '150,000 gallons a day for every square mile of territory occupied.'[441] There were horses to be supplied, not to mention static hospitals and bases behind the lines. Water needs were universal. With the British Expeditionary Force comprising five armies by 1917, this amounted to some one and a half million men in the field and a further half million animals.[442] Supplying water for this number meant a significant degree of sophisticated knowledge on the location and exploitation of underground resources.

The German Army identified three basic sources for water supply in 1916: surface water; groundwater abstracted from dug wells, boreholes and other means; and the purification of local water, or abstraction of water from a remote source.[443] As surface water – where available – was almost certainly polluted by the detritus of war, to the geologists fell the task of finding and exploiting suitable groundwater sources. This level of sophistication required professional geologists in uniform. As already discussed, the Imperial German army employed at least 250 geologists,

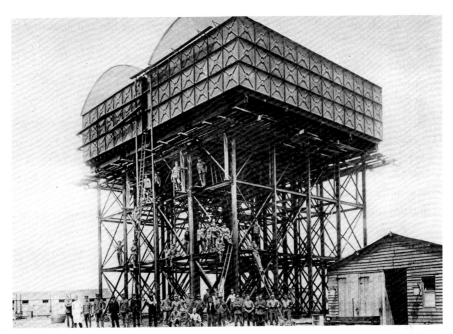

British water tower constructed to supply a base; water supply was a serious issue for all.

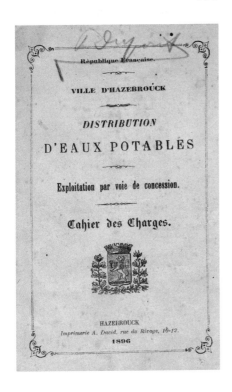

probably more – and in line with the expected roles for *Kriegsgeologen*, and as many as half of these men would be engaged on water supply issues.[444] For the British, the first military geologist employed in this role was Lt W.B.R. King, who contributed materially to the understanding of the armies in the dry, chalk zone of Artois and Picardy, where surface water is scarce.[445]

Nevertheless, early war, advice was sought from civilian geologists in Britain and the other Allied nations in order to frame some form of understanding of the presence of water. As an example, the Royal Army Medical Corps of the '1st London

Use of civilian resources and sources of information was essential in locating and exploiting water supplies. (Myer Coplans Papers)

Division, TF' (actually the 56th (London) Division), charged with supplying adequate water for hospitals and other facilities, made use of a report prepared by the Director of the Geological Survey of Great Britain, Dr Aubrey Strahan, 'General Notes on the obtaining of drinking water in the chalk and Tertiary deposits on the Continent'.[446] Not surprisingly, this document made the recommendation that 'the best source of water would probably be found in the chalk' and that, as confirmed and mapped later by Lt King, that 'the level of saturation in the chalk is determined by the depth of the neighbouring valleys which contain running water.' Strahan was less confident about the quality of water from Flanders, particularly close to the Polder plain. While acknowledging that the surface sediments were likely to be saturated, and that waters could be obtained by 'driving tubes to a depth of a few feet' it would be advisable that 'the water thus obtained be most carefully tested for organic impurities before being used for drinking.' His advice was sound.

FIG. 1.—HOW WATER-BEARING STRATA IN HILLY COUNTRY MAY BE TAPPED TO SUPPLY AN ARMY : A TUBE-WELL DRIVEN THROUGH ROCK IMPERVIOUS TO WATER.

Diagram from the *Illustrated War News* explaining the principle of military groundwater extraction for the general reader.

By 1915, Water Boring Sections had been organised by the Royal Engineers, and plans were put in place to supply water to the British Expeditionary Force.[447] There would be a need for water storage, divided between several active water points, and to supply them there would be pumping stations. This set the scene for the way in which water supply within the British Expeditionary Force was developed in advance of battle on the Somme and in subsequent operations,[448] and that this would rely upon the improvement of those wells already existing, and on the provision of both deep and shallow bores – the deep bores demanded the provision of specialist boring rigs.[449] The location of such bores required geological knowledge – which until the appointment of Lt King, was not altogether forthcoming from local knowledge: 'It was clear from the outset, that future requirements of the army for… water supply could not be gauged accurately until a considerable amount of information regarding engineering and physical conditions in the area of operations had been collected. This intelligence was practically non-existent both in the French Army and in the departments of the French civil administration.[450] With King's appointment, water supply maps were prepared for the whole of Belgium and northern France, based on a range of geological sources, including boreholes and geological maps.[451] King also supervised some 414 boreholes in the chalk area, designed to identify the geological conditions controlling water supply here, and in particular the presence of the clay layers at depth; data that were extremely valuable in ensuring that water requirements were met, and that boring for water was not random or ill founded.

The British were not alone in their reliance on geologists and geological advice for water supply purposes; after all Walter Kranz had helped define the relevance of military water supply issues in his definition of *Militärgeologie* in 1913. The supply of water was based on a German military order – *Kriegssanitätordnung* – of 1907, that set the standards for drinking water, its filtration using sand bodies, the protection and digging of wells, and water purification.[452] With the adoption of military geology as a serious component of each army in the field, German geologists were at work compiling data and constructing maps that would give the occupying forces sufficient information of where to find appropriate resources – and in particular water.[453] Walter Kranz himself would be employed on wartime water supply issues, taking time to submit a doctoral thesis on the topic in 1917.[454] In the Ypres area, peace-time water supply was largely derived from surface water in lakes, together with shallow wells tapping water perched on the Ypres Clay and other clays in the sands, surface loams and other layers. For most of the soldiers serving in the Flanders, such surface water was all too evident, filling shell holes, flooding trenches and standing wherever there was a depression. But for the thirsty soldiers in the frontline, use of such dubious water sources was only taken in extreme circumstances – as all too often, that water was contaminated with the destruction of war. Dysentery, diarrhoea and other diseases were a constant companion in the trenches, a consequence of contaminated water supplies – something to be combatted by engineers and medical corpsmen in finding and purifying water supplies. It was a huge undertaking.

In the chalk region, surface water is relatively rare. This was all down to the geological make up of the Artois and Picardy, for although an abundance of water falls as rain on the countryside, its geology ensures that the water is quickly moved

Diagram from *Memorandum on Advance Water Supplies*, Third Army, (March 1917) showing the water supply system in place for the Battle of Arras. (Myer Coplans Papers)

from the surface, to be stored underground. A secret memorandum for the British Third Army, produced in March 1917 in advance of the Battle of Arras, made plain the geological difficulties of chalk ground:

> In the area defined by the line Arras–Cambrai–St. Quentin–Peronne–Suzanne, an area of about 400 square miles, the difficulties of supply are most accentuated. A large part of this area consists of elevated chalk plateaux, on which supplies of drinking water are obtainable from wells between 150 ft and 250 ft in depth…Generally speaking, the domestic wells on the plateaux are few in number and are probably scattered throughout the village communes. They could be easily damaged by the enemy, polluted or poisoned.[455]

The level of saturation was variable, however. The position and shape of this water table was known to be variable, rising under the hills, and sinking towards the main river valleys, and constrained by underlying marls. The height of the water table was found to be in direct relationship with the amount of rainfall and evaporation, particularly in the winter, when rainfall was at its maximum, and evaporation at its minimum. This complex mix meant that specialist knowledge was required – and for the British, Lt King supplied it, essential when the Third Army advanced across the chalk country in 1918:

> We had to cross practically a desert area… in which there was practically no surface water. We got across this desert largely owing to our accurate geological knowledge of the ground…To take 300,000 men and 100,000 horses across an area like this is a feat that I think has seldom been equalled. Of course we depended largely upon borings. During the advance and in the face of the enemy we made 13 bores 250 to 300 feet in depth; in some cases the boring plants were in line with field guns…The bores were most successful, and as a result, the Army was well supplied with water.[456]

There was an irony that though the winter rains brought mud, here the soldier would find it difficult to find water. And if finding water was difficult for people on the Somme in peacetime, when there was ample opportunity to dig wells, and seek water supplies – it was much more difficult while under shellfire. In the dusty, dry conditions of the summer months, conditions were tough for the soldiers. Joseph Förster of Jäger-Btl 12 recalled a typical example in a letter home in 1916:

Even worse than the incessant artillery fire is the thirst. We now haven't received any supplies for more than a week. The field in front of us is full of decaying bodies which are emitting a horrendous stench. My mouth and nose are constantly clogged with dust and I would kill my neighbour for a glass of fresh water. Even though we are under constant fire the only thing I can think about is the regulars table in the pub at home and ice cold glasses of beer. A couple of days ago I was on an armed patrol and we came across the remains of a well in the ruins of a farmhouse. I can't describe our disappointment when we found out that the water was undrinkable as it had been spiced with the remains of a dead Frenchman.[457]

AGGREGATE SUPPLY

Another of the many tasks given to military geologists was to seek out and identify sources of aggregates – 'particles of rock, which when brought together in a bound or unbound condition, form part or whole of an engineering or building structure',[458] that could be used by military engineers. Hardly glamorous, the sourcing and working of such raw geological materials nevertheless had great military significance – so much so that in his *Despatch* for 1917, the British Commander-in-Chief singled out the men of the Royal Engineer Quarry Companies who worked stone in the hinterland of the British Army in France:

Soldiers breaking stones for use in breakwaters and other constructions at Gallipoli, 1915. Supply of aggregates in this way was essential to military operations.

Some idea of the magnitude of the work involved can be gained from the fact that from quarries in a single locality [Marquise] over 600,000 tons of material were produced in the nine months ending 31 August 1917. Between March and October of this year the total weekly output of road metal received in the Army areas has nearly doubled. The average area of new and re-made roads completed weekly during October was seven and a half times greater than the weekly average for March.[459]

Roadstone Resources for the British Army in France

Rock type	Location	Notes
Limestone	Marquise (between Calais & Boulogne)	Hard limestone (of Carboniferous age) suitable for roadstone
Quartzite	Dennebroeucq, Matringham, Bergin, Rebreuve, Marquefles	Hard, quartz-rich crystalline rock (of Devonian age); found at the surface in certain areas in otherwise chalk country
Porphyrite	Brittany	Very hard green crystalline rock of 'volcanic' origin.
Burnt shale 'Perre de fosse'	Lens Coalfield	Colliery waste 'burnt to consistency of brick' through 'spontaneous combustion'.
Flint gravels	Pas-de-Calais	Flints weathered out of chalk layers, forming a hard residue and sediment load in rivers and beaches.
'Sarsen' quartzite	Pas de Calais-Nord	Remnants of sandstone layers, made extremely hard with silica in pore spaces.

Source: Institution of Royal Engineers (1922) *The Work of the Royal Engineers in the European War, 1914-19*, W& J Mackay, Chatham, p. 58.

Haig was referring to the need for roadstone in advance of the Third Battle of Ypres; constructing and upgrading roads so that they were capable of carrying the mass of men, machines and materiel required by modern warfare. While roads in the forward areas were more often than not created from timber planking, in the rear areas, closer to the channel ports, more hardy roads were needed.[460] The effort required was prodigious:

> During 1917, the new roads built and depot areas metalled were equivalent to 85 miles of 18-ft roadway, while 190 miles were reconstructed. At the end of 1917, D.Rds [Director of Roads] was maintaining 1,900 miles of roads in army areas, and 1,200 miles elsewhere.[461]

The survey and exploitation of locally-derived aggregates was therefore of great importance, as the static condition of the lines meant that enough resources had to be available for the construction not only of new roads but also for concrete emplacements. Aggregates for road construction were mostly obtained from northern France and Brittany, outside the immediate area of operations on the Western Front. With this part of France free from occupation, collaboration with local French experts was most fruitful.[462] Transporting aggregate was a major issue, as 'rock is bulky and expensive to transport, and in war, only transportation that is absolutely necessary is possible' – and local resources were favoured.[463] Not only was it possible to extract and crush aggregates by quarrying; there was also the possibility of examining the flint gravels left behind after the Ice Age. Such valley gravels were examined for road stone, and it was estimated that they had a yield of approximately 500,000 tons.[464]

Road construction was just one issue for the military engineers; with the evolution of trench warfare came the creation of more and more concrete fortifications. Aggregates for concrete emplacements were also mostly derived from outside the immediate area of operations, quite simply because there were few suitable materials. Military geologist H.E. Gregory made an assessment of the situation in 1918:

> The Germans made extensive use of concrete emplacements in the Ypres region, and aggregate resourcing for this was a considerable problem. The British were able to demonstrate during the war that aggregates used by the Germans in concrete emplacements on the Passchendaele Ridge, which were captured in 1917, had been transported considerable distances through Holland from the Rhine, an infringement of Dutch neutrality.[465]

An alternative to deep dug-outs was to construct strengthened surface shelters. In the Ypres Salient, on the *Flandernstellung* the Germans had long held the upperhand. Taking the ridge tops had meant that the British and their allies were under continuous observation, shelled on three sides. Removing the Germans from

German monolithic MEBU or 'pill box' preserved on the Passchendaele Ridge, within Tyne Cot Cemetery. Use of 'pill boxes' on the ridge tops was determined by ground water.
(P. Doyle)

their vantage points was always a dream of the Allies, so ensuring that they would have to advance over long forward slopes, under direct observation was essential. But the ground here was very different from that held down in Artois and Picardy. There the Germans held free-draining chalk soils, capable of supporting deep dug-outs and comfortable trenches. For the Germans on top of the ridges in Flanders the topographical advantage was compromised by the fact that the soils beneath their feet were water-saturated – even more so, if that could be possible, than those experienced by the British on the clay plain below. It was all to do with the way the rain soaked away into the ridge tops – it had nowhere else to go.

The Pill Box system of holding the front line in Flanders had been introduced by the German 4th Army Commander – General von Armin – in June 1917. Our troops first came into contact with them in the Messines Ridge attack at this date, and later with often disastrous results in the 3rd

Battle of Ypres. The water-logged soil in the Ypres sector made the defence of deep trenches impossible, so the problem of holding their ground was solved by erecting the Pill Boxes.[466]

The German approach had therefore been to construct huge numbers of ferro-concrete surface shelters with comparatively few dug-outs. This was a tactical move: serving as both troop accommodation and defensive machine gun positions pillboxes fulfilled a dual purpose.

> The Germans relied on defence by a deep belt of concrete machine-gun posts manned by little garrisons who, so long as their shelters were not directly hit, seemed able to hold out until the assaulting troops literally reached their loopholes and dropped hand-grenades inside…A direct hit on the roof would often kill all the occupants by concussion, but the enormous expenditure of ammunition required for the systematic destruction of so many of these strong-points resulted in still further increasing the sea of mud.[467]

And a British propaganda book from 1918 makes reference to the challenges of trenches and dug-outs, the basis for the adoption of concrete fortifications.

> A German order of this time [1917] confesses to the conclusion that a line of trench, no matter how strongly fortified, cannot be relied upon 'The continuous lines constituting a front position are regularly and methodologically destroyed by artillery before an attack begins. Subterranean shelters, especially in the first and second lines, have proven to be traps.'[468]

Concrete shelters were intended to provide troops with maximum protection from regular and prolonged artillery fire. These concrete defensible posts *Mannschafts Eisenbeton Unterstande* (MEBU) commonly called 'pillboxes' by the British, demanded walls and roof with a minimum thickness of 1.0–1.5 metres of steel reinforced concrete to withstand heavy howitzer fire. V.C. Eberle was a officer with a Royal Engineer Field Company in the 48th (South Midland) Division. He moved to the Ypres Salient in July 1917, and saw for himself that the German defences were reliant on MEBU:

> A year earlier, on the Somme the German defence had comprised several lines of connected trenches. In this sector the defence depended on shorter

Block-work MEBU in German frontline positions in Bayernwald, at Wytschaete. Pouring concrete in this location was hazardous, so the blocks were cast and brought up to the line using tramways. (P. Doyle)

lengths of trench, and a series of 'strong-points' mutually supporting one another, and even greater depth. The keynote of these were numerous concrete blockhouses. They were always known to the troops as 'pill-boxes'. Fully protected all round, they were sufficiently strong to resist direct hits from all but the heavier-weight shells. With only narrow slits for two or three machine guns, and with protected or tunnelled entrances at the back, they were very difficult to capture, and were held by the German troops with great gallantry.[469]

Commenced in 1915, MEBU were built up until the beginning of the Third Battle of Ypres in 1917.[470] It is estimated that, from Pilckem Ridge to Hill 60, some two thousand concrete constructions were built by the Germans, most of them in groups, and created to provide supporting fire for each other.[471] The idea behind the shelters was the same as that for dug-outs, namely to provide protection against 'continuous fire of field guns and against individual shells from 15 cm field howitzers'[472] Construction varied, though all relied on ferro-concrete – concrete reinforced with iron bars, or whatever was available:

> Ferro-concrete was used from the very first in preference to plain concrete, but to begin with the reinforcement was not entirely satisfactory, as steel joists, screw pickets and any kind of scrap iron were thrown in and buried in the concrete. Later this form of construction gave place to ⁵/₈-inch round iron rods uniformly distributed…[473]

Pouring and casting concrete in the frontline required much labour. Materials would have to be brought up at night, using trench railways, and not only were military engineers involved, but also civilians.[474] But constructing monolithic pill-boxes in the front line was a task that would be easily observed by the enemy, so in exposed areas pre-cast concrete blocks were used; these were manufactured in a factory behind the lines and then put into position, using iron bars to form the structure, the blocks built around it.[475] Whereas the 'monolithic' concrete was capable of withstanding direct artillery fire,[476] the concussive force was such that men inside would be killed; the blockwork 'pill boxes' were able to absorb more of the shock.[477] Supply of aggregates for the concrete was a challenge. Needless to say, with an insatiable requirement to build more structures, came a requirement to find more sources of material.

Sand and road material for the manufacture of the concrete was requisitioned locally, but later the gravel for the best quality concrete was brought from the Rhine through Holland via the Meuse and Scheldt in barges and by rail. It consisted of water worn gravel, of flintstone and quartz broken to about ½-inch gauge. The sand was mostly coarse, sharp and clean.[478]

Although the Germans were almost entirely reliant upon MEBU in the Ypres Salient given the nature of the ground at ridge top, the British attitude to pillboxes was more reserved, most probably a function of the greater opportunity for deep dug-outs afforded by their position at lower levels. In addition, a contemporary *Engineer-in-Chief's Fieldwork Note* states that 'The work involved in the construction of concrete dug-outs is so great in proportion to the accommodation provided that, as a general rule, they should not be attempted.'[479]

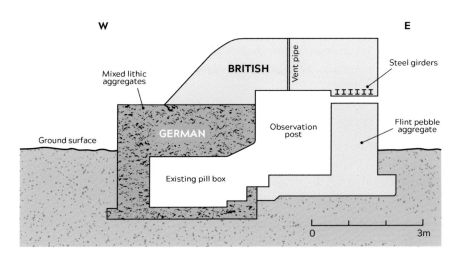

Plan of the observation post at Hill 60, showing the different aggregates used; the German aggregates were brought through neutral Holland.

That attitude was finally to change in 1917, when the British realised that concrete was an answer to the protection of the infantry from artillery, and the Royal Engineers were in a position to assist.[480] At Hill 60, near Zillebeke in the Ypres Salient, German and British shelters are found together. Hill 60 was so named as it was 60 metres above sea level, a spot height only just above the 60 metre contour line. Hill 60 was the scene of much offensive mining activity, and an additional crater, that of the Caterpillar, can be seen on the other side of the railway cutting. Hill 60 and the Caterpillar are not favourably placed with regard to groundwater, as the water-bearing 'Kemmel Sands' are seen here.[481] The area was subject to a large amount of mining activity from 1915–1917, with the Allies and Germans each attempting to dislodge each other from this landmark. Evident here are a number of monolithic concrete MEBU (at Hill 60 and the Caterpillar), the vast majority of which are broken – a result of the fighting here in 1917, and more particularly the explosion of the mines on 7 June 1917 as part of the Battle of Messines.

Cast in situ, the MEBU had their entrances pointing eastwards to protect against Allied shell fire – though most consist of fragments of concrete rather thank actual structures in situ. Examination of the aggregate mix of the structrures demonstrates a wide variety of rock types, with rounded quartz pebbles, and particularly flatter, dark stones that are volcanic in origin. These are examples of the aggregates that were identified by geologists at the Geological Survey as Rhine gravels.[482] However, the most prominent structure here is a British observation post (with its observation slit facing east). This was constructed by the 4th Field Company Australian Engineers in early 1918, built upon an existing German structure that was left more-or-less intact.[483] The aggregate mix of the British structure contrasts very strongly with the German one, comprising as it does mostly flint pebbles

Concrete observation post built by 4th Field Company Australian Engineers in 1918 at Hill 60. It sits on an earlier, German pill box. (P. Doyle)

derived from the French River valleys outside of the immediate battle zone, and most likely from Artois/Picardy.

There are other survivors in the Ypres Salient, monolithic block houses preserved in cemeteries at Langemarck, Tyne Cot and Messines, all of which give testimony to the strength of the design, and the resistance of their defenders. They are also physical records of the importance of geology and engineering to the war, 'reminders of the scenes of heroic deeds, of comradeship, and of the prowess of those who fought in the Salient…' relics of 'possibly the fiercest fighting and certainly the worst conditions of warfare the world [had] ever know.'[484]

Aggregate sources in the observation post at Hill 60. Above, locally-sourced flint pebble aggregate in the Australian concrete. Left, Rhine-sourced pebbles in the German concrete. (P. Doyle)

ENDWORD

After the Great War, the lessons of *Kriegsgeologie* originally taught by Walter Kranz were variously received. It was right that the German Imperial Armies had constructed the stongest postitions. They had used the ground carefully, and ensured that the strategic doctrine of holding the western Allies while the Russians were beaten had worked. For four years the Germans held the line while the increasing weight and numbers of the western Allies was lined up against them. In this time, new armies were fielded, new allies joined, new technologies created. But still the Germans held them, and did so from the security of their deepest dug-outs, their strongest MEBU, their most open fields of fire. For the Germans, Kranz's principles that geologists should be involved in all stages of the development of warfare – particularly siege warfare – was vindicated.

For the Allies themselves, an indifferent attitude to the employment of geologists had been overcome. Though geological staffs were small, they had contributed materially to the outcome of battle. There was innovation and application, in the survey of ground and of water, and in the application of mine warfare. With the arrival of the United States into the arena of the war in the west came trained geologists and geographers who learned from the lessons thrown up by the war, and who applied themselves to their application. At the end of war, both British and American geologists recommended the establishment of military geologists who would take on the mantle of advising the army of how to win a war. But with peace came ambivalence, and with ambivalence came neglect. Those recommendations were not acted upon, and once more geologists in military roles faded from sight.

When a new war erupted on the scene in 1939, the German army was well equipped. It was a war-winning machine, and at the heart of that were military geologists and geographers. All the lessons had been learnt; all the literature assimilated and pulled apart; handbooks and maps had been created on the lands that would shortly be conquered.[485] With *Blitzkrieg* there would be *Wehrgeologen*, men capable of advising the advancing panzers and considering the mineral capacity of the captured territory. Once again it would take a war emergency to propel military geologists onto the stage in Britain and America. In 1941–2 specialist Allied military geology units were created, and once more these men of science would work on seemingly arcane topics that would have the greatest significance to the free world. Without the efforts of these geologists, there would be no water supply for the armies in the Western Desert, no appreciation of terrain of the D-Day landing beaches, no chance of the consideration of the 'going surfaces' for armour across the plains of Europe. Military geology came of age at this moment. And it all went back to the principles laid down by one German engineer officer, who fought against ingnorance and disinterest to put this relatively new science on a war footing.

NOTES

1 C.E. Erdmann (1943) Application of geology to the principles of war. *Bulletin of the Geological Society of America*, v.54, p. 1174.
2 Hilaire Belloc (1914) *Warfare in England*. Williams and Norgate, London, p. 9.
3 Herbert E. Gregory (ed., 1918) *Military Geology and Topography*. Yale University Press, New Haven, p. 1.

Chapter 1: The Great War
4 Belgium. From Mary Borden (1929) *The Forbidden Zone*, William Heinemann, London, p. 1.
5 'Intrenched', the position whereby an army is 'dug-in' to face an enemy; this spelling, used in most British army manuals of the period, is also encountered as 'entrenched'. Both spellings are used, as they appear in original quotations.
6 General Staff, War Office. *Military Engineering (Part 1) Field Defences*, 1908, p.4
7 Professor John Horne, Public Lecture, King's College London, 1 November 2016.
8 Sun Tzu, *The Art of War*
9 See Doyle, P. & Bennett, M.R. (eds) 2002. *Fields of Battle, Terrain in Military History*. Kluwer, Dordrecht
10 See C.E. Erdmann (1944) Military geology: applications of geology to terrain analysis. *Bulletin of the Geological Society of America*, v. 55, p. 785.
11 Brown, A. 1962. *Geology and the Gettysburg Campaign*. Pennsylvania Topographic & Geologic Survey Educational Series n.5, pp.1–15.
12 Cuffey, R.J., Smith, R., II, Neubaum, J.C., Keen, R.C., Inners, J.D. & Neubaum, V.A. 2004, Lee vs. Meade at Gettysburg (July 1–3, 1863): The influence of topography and geology on command decisions and battlefield tactics. Geological Society of America Abstracts with Programs, v.36, n.2, p.48; Inners, J.D., Cuffey, R.J., Smith, R.C. II, Neubaum, J.C., Keen, R.C., Fleeger, G.M., Butts, L., Delano, H.L., Neubaum, V.A. & Howe, R.H. 2004. Rifts, Diabase, and the Topographic 'Fishhook': Terrain and Military Geology of the Battle of Gettysburg – July 1– 3, 1863. Pre-Meeting Field Trip 4, Guidebook. Geological Society of America Northeast/ Southeast Sections, 105pp; Doyle, P. (2006) Military geology and the Battle of Gettysburg, July 1863. *Geology Today*, v.22, 142–149.
13 Johnson (1917) *Topography and Strategy in the War*, Henry Holt, New York, pp. iii–iv.
14 Johnson (1921), *Battlefields of the World War*, Oxford University Press, New York, p. xvi.
15 See in particular Doyle, P. & Bennett, M.R. 1999. Military geography: the influence of terrain on the outcome of the Gallipoli Campaign, 1915. *Geographical Journal*, 165, 12-36; Ekins, A. 2001. A ridge too far: military objectives and the dominance of terrain in the Gallipoli Campaign, p. 7. *In:* Celik, K. and Koc, C. (eds) *The Gallipoli Campaign, International Perspectives 85 years on.* Cannakale Onsekiz Mart University, Cannakale, 5-34; Doyle, P. and Bennett, M.R. 2002. Terrain and the Gallipoli Campaign, 1915. *In:* Doyle, P. & Bennett, M.R. (eds) *Fields of Battle, Terrain in Military History.* Kluwer, Dordrecht, 149-169; Chasseaud, P. and Doyle, P. 2005. *Grasping Gallipoli. Terrain Intelligence, Maps and Failure at the Dardanelles, 1915.* Spellmount, Staplehurst, pp. 26–28; Doyle, P. 2008. 'Six VCs before breakfast', terrain and the Gallipoli landings, 1915. In: Nathanail, C.P., Abrahart, R.J. & Bradshaw, R.P. (eds) *Military Geography and Geology,*

History and Technology, Land Quality Press, Nottingham; Doyle, P. 2016. An unfortunate accident of geography: badlands and the ANZAC Sector, Gallipoli, April–September 1915 *In* MacDonald, E.V. & Bullard, T. (eds) *Military Geosciences and Desert Warfare, Past Lessons and Modern Challenges*, Springer, Dordrecht, 3–18.

[16] Carl von Clausewitz (1832), *On War*, Chapter 7.

[17] Vaughan Cornish (1915) Notes on the historical and physical geography of the theatres of war. *Geographical Journal*, v. 45, pp373–374

[18] *Ibid*, p. 379

[19] Johnson (1921), *Battlefields of the World War*, Oxford University Press, New York, p. 7

[20] *Ibid*, p.216; see also Anon (1916), The Geography of the Battle of the Marne. *Scottish Geographical Magazine*, v. 32, pp.31–35.

[21] D.W. Johnson (1918), *Topography and Strategy in the War*, Constable, London, p. 5

[22] Lt-Gen Sir William Pulteney and Beatrix Brice (1925) *The Immortal Salient*. John Murray, London, p. 4.

[23] General Staff War Office, March 1916, *Notes for infantry Officers on Trench Warfare*, p. 5: 'The importance assumed by trench warfare and the progress made in the application of field fortifications and in the science of the attack and defence of elaborate systems of trenches, have rendered necessary special instruction in the details of trench construction and trench fighting. It must, nevertheless, be clearly understood that trench fighting is only a phase of operations…'.

Chapter 2: Geology, geologists and warfare

[24] L.A. Cotton & W.R. Browne (1934) Notes on the life of a great Australian Scientist, *Environment*, v.2,p. 13.

[25] J.T. Parry, Terrain evaluation, military purposes, p. 570, in C.W. Finkl Jr (ed) 1984, *The Encyclopedia of Applied Geology. Encyclopedia of Earth Sciences, v.13*. Van Nostrand Rheinhold Co, NY.

[26] Erdmann (1943) *op cit.* p. 775; F. Betz, Military Geology, in C.W. Finkl Jr (ed) 1984, *The Encyclopedia of Applied Geology. Encyclopedia of Earth Sciences, v.13*. Van Nostrand Rheinhold Co, NY

[27] See C.E. Erdmann (1944) Military geology: applications of geology to terrain analysis. *Bulletin of the Geological Society of America*, v. 55, pp. 783–788; F.C. Whitmore Jr (1960) Terrain intelligence and current military concepts. *American Journal of Science*, v. 258-A, pp 375–387; Parry, *op cit*; Colin Mitchell (1991) *Terrain Evaluation*, 2nd Edition. Longman, London.

[28] Erdmann (1943) *op cit,* p. 1184.

[29] Erdmann (1943) *op cit.*

[30] Marshal Foch (1903) *The Principles of War*. Translation, 1920, Henry Holt & Co, New York, pp. 15–16.

[31] George A. Kiersch (1998) Engineering geoscience and military operations. *Engineering Geology,* v. 49, p. 124; E.P.F. Rose (2004), Napoleon Bonaparte's Egyptian campaign of 1798: The first military operation to be assisted by geologists? *Geology Today*, v. 20, p. 24–29.

[32] F. Betz (1984), *op cit*, p. 356; Kiersch (1998) *op cit.*, p. 126

[33] Discussed in A.H. Brooks (1920) The use of geology on the Western Front. *US Geological Survey Professional Paper* 128–D, pp. 88–91 and E.P.F. Rose (2014) Military geosciences before the twenty-first century. *Reviews in Engineering Geology*, v.22, pp.19–26.

[34] 'I hope, however, this partial neglect of our science will pass away, and that ere long, at all

our stations, there will be found observers amongst ourselves ready to elucidate the natural history, and discover the economic value, as well as describe the military capabilities, of the countries in which they serve'. Major E.F. Portlock (1868) Geology and Geognosy, in *Aide-Mémoire to the Military Sciences, v. II.*

35 Maj-Gen J.E. Portlock, (1868), *A Rudimentary Treatise on Geology*, 5th Edn, London; quoted in Brooks *op cit.*, pp.88–89

36 Brooks (1920) *op cit.*, p. 90

37 Brooks (1920) *op cit.*, p. 91.

38 From King's obituary in the Quarterly Journal of the Geological Society of London (1898) v. 54, p. lxxiv-vi.

39 Kiersch *op cit.*, p. 126–130.

40 See Häusler, H. (2003), Dr. Walter Kranz (1873–1953): Der erste Militärgeologedes 20. Jahrhunderts: *MILGEO: Organ des Militärischen Geowesens des Österreichischen Bundesheeres*, v. 12, p. 1–80.

41 W. Kranz (1913) Militargeologie. *Kriegstechnische Zeitschrift* v. 16, pp.464-471; see also Anon [Steinmann] (1915) Geologie im Kriege. *Geologische Rundschau*, v. 6, pp.94–95. For a discussion of the various technical definitions of the subject, see H. Häusler (2015) Military geology and comprehensive security geology – applied geologic contributions to new Austrian security strategy. *Austrian Journal of Earth Sciences*, v. 108, pp302–316.

42 Brooks (1920) The use of geology, *op cit.* p. 91.

43 See review in E.P.F. Rose (2014) *op cit.*

44 'Geological knowledge can be turned into success in mine warfare, consideration of water supply, the removal of wastewater from field positions, and in the review of ground in advance of new fortifications. Anon (1915) *op cit.*, p. 94, translated by Robin Schäfer

45 *Ibid*

46 W. Salomon (1915) *Kriegsgeologie.* Carl Winters Universitätbuchhandlung, Heidelberg.

47 K. von Bulow, W. Kranz & E. Sonne (1938) *Wehrgeologie*, Quelle und Meyer, Leipzig.

48 Much has been written on the application of geology in the prosecution of the Second World War. A good review is given by Rose (2014) *op cit*, who provides access to the many sources.

49 See Department of the Army (1952) US Army Technical Manual TM 5-545 *Geology and its Military Applications*, Washington D.C.

50 A similar list was provided as early as 1920, by Lt-Col. Alfred H Brooks, in an address to the Washington Academy of Science (reported in the *Engineering and Mining Journal*, v.109, p. 709). Brooks adds estimation of an enemy's mineral resources; 'earth telegraphy' i.e. listening devices; site investigation for camps; and the possibility of 'artificial inundation'.

51 Price, P.H. & Woodward, H.P. (1942) Geology and war. *Bulletin of the American Association of Petroleum Geologists*, v. 26, pp.1833.

52 'In military operations, the geologist can translate geologic information into concepts which can be used readily and effectively in conjunction with combat and engineering needs. Combat units, for example, benefit from geologic information in the evaluation of the trafficability of soils, the estimation of the fordability of streams, and the availability of concealment and cover' Department of the Army (1952) *op cit.*, p. 2; The geologist is trained to predict conditions by means of a very wide range of observations, by understanding processes, and by integration of results' Ministry of Defence (1976) *Military Engineering vol. XV Applied Geology for Engineers*, HMSO, London.

53 E.P.F Rose, H. Häusler & D. Willig (2000). Comparison of British and German applications of geology in world war. In Rose, E.P.F. & Nathanail, C.P. (eds) *Geology and Warfare:*

Examples of the Influence of Terrain and Geologists on Military Operations. Geological Society, London, p. 115

[54] Brooks (1920) The use of geology, *op cit*. p. 91.

[55] Memorandum, 17 April 1914, quoted in W. Kranz (1927) *Die Geologie im Igenieur-Baufach* Enke-Verlag, Stuttgart; translation from Rose et al. (2000) *op cit*, p. 116.

[56] See review in Anon (1915) *op cit*., and discussion in W. Cross (1919) Geology in the world war and after. *Bulletin of the Geological Society of America*, v. 30, pp. 168–169.

[57] Brooks, *op cit*. p. 95; H. Häusler (2000) Die Österreichische und Deutsche *Kriegsgeologie* 1914– 1918. *Informationen des Militärischen Geo-Dienstes*, v. 75, pp. 1–161.

[58] Institute of Royal Engineers (1922a) *op cit*, pp. 64–67.

[59] Häusler (2000) *op cit*; W. Schiller (1923) Die Geologie im Weltkriege. *Heerstechnik*, v. 1, pp. 25-29; D. Willig. & H. Häusler provide a figure that is much greater, at ~366 geologists; Willig, D. & Häusler, H. (2012) Aspects of military hydrogeology and groundwater development by Germany and its allies in World War 1. In: Rose, E.P.F. & Mather, J.D. (eds) *Military Aspects of Hydrogeology*, Geological Society, London, p. 88

[60] Institute of Royal Engineers (1922a) *op cit*, pp. 65–66. In a breakdown by task, Rose *et al.* (2000) illustrate that German military geologists spent most of their time on water supply and drainage matters (57.4%), with lesser duties including work on 'infrastructure' (21.8%), provision of raw materials (17.8%) the remainder on 'general geological' duties.

[61] The Anniversary Address of the President of the Geological Society of London by G.W. Lamplugh in 1919 noted ' The war has deprived us this year of five Fellows; one killed in action in France; one missing–presumed killed–in Gallipoli; two, dead from sickness contracted during service; one drown at sea. Their lives were demanded, and given at the urgent call of National duty, and science is inestimably the poorer for the loss.' *Quarterly Journal of the Geological Society*, v. 75, p. li. This was a small sample of those who served; few indeed would be called to use their skills.

[62] E.P.F Rose & M.S. Rosenbaum, M.S. 1993. British military geologists: the formative years to the end of the First World War. *Proceedings of the Geologists' Association*, v.104, pp.41-50; Rose *et al.* (2000), *op cit*. pp. 112–115.

[63] See King (1919) *op cit*.; Insitution of Royal Engineers (1922a) *op cit*.

[64] See K. Wiggins (2003) *Siege Mines and Underground Warfare* Shire, Princes Risborough, and Barton *et al.* (2004) *op cit*. for examples

[65] Discussed by Rose & Rosenbaum (1993) and Rose *et al.* (2000).

[66] Discussion in Ball (1919)

[67] See D. Branagan (1987) The Australian Mining Corps in World War 1. *Bulletin and Proceedings of the Australasian Institute of Mining and Metallurgy*, v. 292, 40-44; Rose *et al* (2000), *op cit*. pp. 112–115

[68] See M. Edgeworth David (1937) *Professor David. The Life of Sir Edgeworth David KBE, DSO, FRS*. Edward Arnold, London

[69] WO158/135 AEMMBC Weekly Progress Report on Borings; Loftus Hills submitted detailed reports with carefully annotated logs of the borings, labeled and coloured appropriately.

[70] See E.P.F. Rose & M.S. Rosenbaum (2011) British geological maps that guided excavation of military dug-outs in Belgium during World War 1. *Quarterly Journal of Engineering Geology and Hydrogeology*, v.44, pp. 293–306.

[71] Rose & Rosenbaum (1993) *op cit*.

[72] *Ibid*

[73] See Ian Passingham (1998) *Pillars of Fire, The Battle of Messines*. Sutton, Stroud.

[74] Walter Kranz, (1935) Minierkampf und *Kriegsgeologie* im Wytschaetebogen. *Vieteljahreshefte für Pionere*, v. 2/3.

Chapter 3: Geology of Flanders and northern France

[75] D.W. Johnson (1917) *op cit.*, pp. 1-2.

[76] W. Cross (1919), *op cit.* p. 168.

[77] See discussion in D.W. Johnson (1921), *op cit.*, chapter 1.

[78] Aubrey Strahan (1917) Geology at the seat of war. *Geological Magazine*, v. 64, p. 69–70.

[79] John Masefield (1917) *The Old Front Line*, Heineman, London, p. 27

[80] *Ibid, p. 13.* The geology and geomorphology of this region have been discussed more recently by Robaszynski & Dupuis (1983), Doyle (1998), and Doyle *et al.* (2001a, b, 2002).

[81] Burwash, E.M.J. (1940) Bomb craters in different soils. *Bulletin of the Geological Society of America*, v.51, pp.1922–1923.

[82] L. Dudley Stamp (1922) The Geology of Belgium. *Proceedings of the Geologists' Association*, v. 32, p.2. Stamp led a trip to see the geology of Belgium in 1921, just under three years after the war had ended. The only mention made of the war that had devastated the west of the country was when the party visited St Symphorien and the 'military cemetery wherein lie the victims of the Battle of Mons, 23rd–24 August 1914'. L. Dudley Stamp (1922) Long Excursion to Belgium. *Proceedings of the Geologists' Association*, v. 32, p.51.

[83] Johnson (1921), *op cit.*, p. 5

[84] See Doyle (2012) Examples of the influence of groundwater on British military mining in Flanders, 1914-1917, in: Rose E.P.F. & Mather J.D. *Military Aspects of Hydrogeology,* Geological Society of London, pp. 73-83; and Heyse, (2015) geomorphology and geology of 'Flanders Fields' (the Ypres to Coastal Plain Region of West Flanders, Belgium) and their impact on military tunneling and defensive flooding in the 1914–1918 World War. *Geoinformationsdienst der Bundeswehr Schiftenreihe, Heft 4*, p. 51–70.

[85] D.W. Johnson (1918), *op cit.*, p. 48

[86] See Tatham (1919). The geology of the dune belt and the evolution of the Holocene sediments of the coastal strip have been discussed by De Ceuynck (1984) and Denys (1999).

[87] D.W. Johnson (1918), *op cit.*, p. 48

[88] Tatham *op cit*; Johnson (1918) *op cit.*

[89] Charles Douie (1929) *The Weary Road. The Recollections of a Subaltern of Infantry.* John Murray, London, p. 189.

[90] I. Heyse (2015) Geomorphology and geology of 'Flanders Fields' (the Ypres to Coastal Plain Region of West Flanders, Belgium) and their impact on military tunnelling and defensive flooding in the 1914-1918 world war, in D. Willig *et al.* Militärhistorisch-kriegsgeologiischer Reiseführer zum Wytschaete-Bogen (Messines Ridge) bei Ypren (Belgien). *Schriftenreihe Geoinformationsdienst der Bundeswehr*, v.4, p. 54.

[91] See Volker 1961

[92] D.W. Johnson (1921) *op cit.*, p. 42.

[93] De Moor & Heyse (1978)

[94] See Baeteman & Paepe (1991); Baeteman (1999) and Denys (1999)

[95] 'Notes on the cross country conditions considered from a Geological Point of View', TNA WO153/982

[96] Generalstab des Heeres Abteilung fur Kriegskarten und Vermessungswesen (1940) *Militärgeographische Beschreibung von Frankreich. Teil 1 Nordost-Frankreich.* Including

Wehrgeologische Übersichtskarte for the region. Berlin; quoted in Martin Marix Evans (2000), *The Fall of France, Act with Daring.* Osprey, Oxford, p. 95.

[97] Marix Evans (2000) *op cit.,* pp. 95–96.

[98] See Barton *et al.* (2004) *Beneath Flanders Fields. The Tunnellers' War 1914-1918.* Spellmount, Staplehurst.

[99] Charles Douie (1929) *The Weary Road. The Recollections of a Subaltern of Infantry.* John Murray, London, p. 191.

[100] Maurice Baring (1920) *Flying Corps Headquarters 1914–1918.* William Heinemann, London, p. 79.

[101] Leon Wolff (1959) *In Flanders Fields.* Longmans, London, p. 81.

[102] Hussey (*op cit.*) describes the plain thus 'Ypres is 22 miles from the sea and stands on the 20 metre contour…Eastward from Ypres the county stays at between 20 and 35 metres [above sea level] for several miles…The horizon to the east is bounded by a low and unimpressive ridge…', p. 141.

[103] Kortrik Formation = Ieper/Ypres Clay: see Steurbaut (1987); Nolf & Steurbaut (1990); King (1990); Laga *et al.* (2001); De Geyter *et al.* (2006).

[104] See Cornélius (2001)

[105] The variations and geotechnical characteristics of the clay have been discussed by Verret (1980) and Mercier-Castiaux & Dupuis (1990)

[106] Strahan (1917) *op cit.,* p. 71

[107] See Institution of Royal Engineers (1922a), *The Work of the Royal Engineers in the European War, 1914-19. Geological Work on the Western Front.* Mackay & Co, Chatham, and Barton *et al.* (2004) *op cit.*

[108] Thanetian (formerly ascribed to the Landenian; see De Geyter *et al.* 2006 for the equivalence of these units) fine sands that act as an aquifer (Mania 1972).

[109] Strahan (1917) *op cit.,* p. 71

[110] See Heyse (2015) *op cit.*

[111] C.E. Wood (2006) *Mud, a Military History,* Potomac Books, Dulles, p. 5.

[112] 'Water requirements in the field, per day: 1 man in trench, 4 litre; 1 man in readiness 10 litre; 1 horse ormule, 50 litre…' v. Bulow *et al.* (1938) *Wehrgeologie,* Duelle & Mener, Leipzig, p. 90.

[113] Johnson (1921) *op cit.,* p. 32.

[114] See Robin Prior & Trevor Wilson (1996) *Passchendaele the Untold Story,* Yale University Press, New Haven, p. 97; Hussey (1997) in Peter H. Liddle (ed.) *Passchendaele in Perspective. The Third Battle of Ypres,* Leo Cooper, London, p. 143

[115] Field Marshal Sir Douglas Haig, diary entry for 1 August 1917, quoted in Gary Sheffield and John Bourne (eds, 2005) *Douglas Haig. War Diaries and Letters 1914–1918,* Weidenfeld & Nicholson, London, p. 309.

[116] The Kortrijk Formation is considered to be the base of the groundwater reservoir, which is formed by the overlying 'Ledo-Paniselian' sands aquifer (Cornélius 2001; Walraevens *et al.* 2001). The influence of this aquifer is described below.

[117] Friedrich von Lossberg, (1939) *Meine Tätigkeit im Weltkriege,* E.S. Mittler & Sohn, Berlin, p. 294; (translated by Rob Schäfer)

[118] Reported in Royal Engineers (1922a), *op cit.,* pp. 35–37

[119] See Institute of Royal Engineers (1922a), *op cit.,* Fig. 9; and 1;10,000 Scale Map, Geological, 18NW4 & NE3, October 1917, TNA WO297/2468.

[120] Lyn Macdonald (1978), *They Called it Passchendaele*, chapter 2

[121] For example, see C.E. Wood (2006) *Mud, a Military History*, Potomac Books, Dulles: 'The fighting at Passchendaele was so difficult because the area was originally a swamp and the fighting had destroyed the elaborate ditching and drainage systems', p. 22.

[122] Sir J.E. Edmonds, *Official History of the War, Military Operations, 1917* volume II (1947), pp. vi-vii.

[123] Manuscript diary, Pte James H. Benn, 7th Loyal North Lancashire Regiment, 30 July 1917.

[124] Henry Williamson (1929) *The Wet Flanders Plain* [reissued in 1987], p. 96.

[125] J.H. Boraston (ed., 1919). *Sir Douglas Haig's Despatches*. J.M. Dent, London, p. 116.

[126] Captain Hugh Pollard, in *The Pilgrim's Guide to the Ypres Salient* (1920) Herbert Reiach, London p. 13.

[127] Johnson 1921, *op cit.*

[128] General Ludendorff (n.d.) *My War Memories 1914–1918. Vol II.* Hutchinson & Co, London, p. 488

[129] R.H. Mottram (1936) *Journey to the Western Front, Twenty Years After.* G. Bell, London, p. 52

[130] Pollard (1920) *op cit.*, p. 19.

[131] For example, see Laga *et al.* 2001; De Geyter *et al.* 2006

[132] See Steurbaut & Nolf (1986), Steurbaut (1987), King (1990), Nolf & Steurbaut (1990)

[133] See 1:10,000 Map, Geological Kemmel 28SW1, May 1918, TNA WO 297/2473

[134] Heyse (2015) *op cit*

[135] See Walraevens *et al.* (2001) and Cornelius (2001). The aquifer also has input from the sea, as it comes under maritime influence, though this is small indeed.

[136] Tertiary is a geological time period that encompasses most of the layers encountered in Flanders.

[137] Strahan (1917) *op cit.*, p. 72

[138] Depicted on a British Army 'Diagrammatic Section Across Passchendaele Ridge' produced in November 1917 TNA WO297/2462.

[139] *Ibid*

[140] Institution of Royal Engineers, 1922a *op cit*, p. 31

[141] Otto Füsslein (1921) Die Mineur in Flandern. In G. von Dickhuth-Harrach (ed) *Im Felde unbesiegt, der Weltkrieg in 28 Einzeldarstellungen.* F. Lehman, Munich

[142] See Barton *et al.* (2004) *op cit.* for discussion of the disadvantage of 'advantaged' terrain; see also Peter Oldham (1995) *Pillboxes on the Western Front,* Pen & Sword, Barnsley, for a discussion of the German approach to fortification.

[143] See C. Delattre et al. (1973) *Région du Nord, Flandre, Artois, Boulonnais, Picardie.* Guides Géologiques Régionaux, Masson, Paris. The ancient rocks are stacked up in what geologists call 'thrust slices', evidence of great pressures; the oldest rocks encountered are Silurian in age.

[144] See Romauld Salmon *et al.* (2001) Mine shafts in Nord Pas-de-Calais coalfield (France), Risk Assessment and treatment technique. In *Confronting Change: North East England and East European Coalfield,* Conference Proceedings, Newcastle.

[145] 'France and Belgium also suffer from the exposed position of their coal fields, and the worst misfortune of the war is that most of the chief coal-field of France…fell at once into the hands of the invaders'. Gregory, J.W. (1916-18) The geological factors affecting the strategy of the war and the geology of the potash salts. *Transactions of the Geological Society of Glasgow,*

v. 16, p. 6.

[146] Romauld Salmon *et al.* (2001), *op cit.* see Fig. 2

[147] Phillip Gibbs (1920) *Realities of War,* Heinemann, London, p. 133

[148] Captain W. Grant Grieve and Bernard Newman (1936) *Tunnellers*. Herbert Jenkins, London, p. 113.

[149] Capt. E.V. Tempest (1921) *History of the Sixth Battalion West Yorkshire Regiment. Vol. 1, 1/6ᵗʰ Battalion,* Percy Lund, Humphries & Co, Bradford, p. 76

[150] General Staff (1917) *The Construction of Field Positions (Stellungsbau).* (1916) Translated from German by the General Staff, May 1917, pp.3–4

[151] All part of the Upper Cretaceous period, the upper, flintless part is Santonian–Campanian in age, the middle, flint-bearing unit is Turonian–Coniacian in age, and the lower clay-rich unit is Cenomanian. See *Carte Géologique de la France a 1/50,000, Albert XXIV-8*; see also Delattre *et al.* (1973), *op cit.*, pp. 25-6.

[152] See W.B.R. King (1921a) Résultants des sondages exécutés par les armées britanniques dans la Nord de la France. *Annales de la Société géologique du Nord,* v.45, pp.9–26; W.B.R. King (1921b) The surface of the marls of the Middle Chalk in the Somme Valley and the neighbouring districts of northern France, and the effect on the hydrology. *Quarterly Journal of the Geological Society of London,* v. 77, pp. 135–143; see also E.P.F. Rose (2012) Groundwater as a military resource: pioneering British military well boring and hydrogeology in World War 1. In Rose, E.P.F. & Mather, J.D. (eds) *Military Aspects of Hydrogeology*, Geological Society, London, pp. 49–72.

[153] Lt C. Loftus Hills, 3 November 1916, memorandum to the Controller of Mines, 1ˢᵗ Army; TNA WO158/135.

[154] Salmon *et al., op cit*

[155] King (1921a, b) *op cit.*, see also King (1919) *op cit.*

[156] W.B.R. King (1921a,b) *op cit.*

[157] A map is given in King (1921a), giving the contours of the subsurface

[158] Institute of Royal Engineers (1922a) *op cit*, p. 13.

[159] Strahan (1917) *op cit.*, p. 70

[160] Strahan (1917) *op cit.*

[161] Manuscript account, *Bericht von Leutnant Kurt Trautner von der Somme-Schlacht* (Europeana, CC-BY-SA 3.0, courtesy Dr Jürgen Trautner, translated by Robin Schäfer).

[162] Trautner *Ibid*

[163] Masefield (1917) *op cit.*, p. 106.

[164] Lt Col Graham Seton Hutchison (1933) *Pilgrimage*. Rich & Cowan, London, p. 86.

[165] See Barton, M.E. (1987). The sunken lanes of southern England: engineering geological considerations. In: Culshaw, M.G., Bell, F.G., Cripps, J.C. & O'Hara, M. (eds) *Planning and Engineering Geology*, Engineering Geology Special Publication n. 4, pp. 411–418.

[166] Masefield (1917) *op cit.*, p. 41.

[167] Institution of Royal Engineers (1922a), *op cit.* p. 60.

[168] Johnson (1921) *op cit.*

Chapter 4: Geology and trench warfare

[169] Sir Max Aitkin (1916) *Canada in Flanders*, Hodder & Stoughton, London, p. 21.

[170] The *Oxford English Dictionary* has 'The making of a rampart or entrenchment round a place, esp. in besieging' which results in a 'line of circumvallation', meaning 'a line of

earth-works consisting of a rampart and trench surrounding a besieged place or camp of a besieging army'.

171 Those 'siege engines' would be: high trajectory howitzer and mortar fire (designed to smash defences); mine warfare (designed to undermine and destroy strongpoints); gas warfare (designed to kill the occupants); and tanks (designed to punch through defences).

172 Discussed by Anthony Saunders (2010) *Trench Warfare 1850–1950*. Pen & Sword, Barnsley, p. 51.

173 General Staff, War Office (1908) *Military Engineering (Part 1) Field Defences*. HMSO, London, p. 43

174 Carl von Clausewitz (1832) *On War*, English translation 1873.

175 Foch (1903) *op cit.* p. 283.

176 Discussed in William Philpott (2014) *Attrition. Fighting the First World War*. Abacus, London, see pp. 215–17.

177 Germany's war aims are discussed in Fritz Fischer (1967) *Germany's War Aims in the First World War*, W.W.Norton, New York; see in particular, chapter 6.

178 Pte Benn, manuscript diary, 16 June 1917

179 1st Coldstream Guards: Rowland Feilding (1929) *War Letters to a Wife France and Flanders, 1915–1919*. Medici Society, London, p. 26.

180 General Staff, War Office (1916) *Notes for Infantry Officers on Trench Warfare*, HMSO, London, p. 8.

181 General Staff (1917) *op cit*, pp.3–4

182 James Norman Hall (1917) *Kitchener's Mob*, Constable, London.

183 See Doyle, 1999; Doyle *et al.* 2001a

184 Major W.J. Johnston (ed, 1916). *The Royal Engineers Field Service Pocket-Book*, Royal Engineers Institute, Chatham, p. vii.

185 See: *French Trench Warfare, 1917–1918. A Reference Manual*. Imperial War Museum & Battery Press, 2002, reprinted from the French 'Manual of the Chief of Platoon of Infantry, 1918.

186 Major H. Hesketh-Pritchard (1994) *Sniping in France*. Leo Cooper, London, p. 13.

187 General Staff, War Office (1908) *op cit.*, p. 39.

188 Doyle *et al.* (2001a), *op cit.*, p. 5

189 Captain F.C. Hitchcock MC (1937) *'Stand To' A Diary of the Trenches 1915–1918*. Hurst & Blackett, London, p. 22.

190 General Staff, War Office (1908) *op cit.*, chapters 8 and 9.

191 As observed in archaeological investigations in the Ypres Salient, see below.

192 As above.

193 Seen in the excavations at Auchonvilliers, Somme, in 2000.

194 A.D. Gillespie (1916) *Letters from Flanders*, Smith Elder & Co, London, p. 58.

195 Field Marshal Sir John French (1919) *1914*, Constable & Co, London, pp. 288–289.

196 *Ibid*, p. 290

197 General Staff, War Office (1916) *Notes for Infantry Officers on Trench Warfare*, HMSO, London, p, 31.

198 War Office (1921) *Manual of Field Works (All Arms)*, HMSO, London, p. 65; see also War Office (1925) *Manual of Field Works (All Arms)*, HMSO, London, p. 73.

199 General Staff (1917) *The Construction of Field Positions (Stellungsbau)*. (1916) Translated from German by the General Staff, May 1917, p. 6.

200 Kranz (1913) *op cit.*

201 General Staff, War Office (1917) *Summary of Recent Information Regarding the German Army and its Methods*, HMSO, London, p. 12

202 *Ibid*, p. 12; see also War Office (1921) *Manual of Field Works (All Arms)*, HMSO, London, pp. 70–72. This extensive manual summarises the knowledge learned from four years of trench warfare.

203 General Staff, War Office (1917) *Notes for Infantry Officers on Trench Warfare*, March 1916, HMSO, London.

204 General Staff, War Office (1917) *Notes for Infantry Officers on Trench Warfare*, Revised Diagrams, December 1916, HMSO, London, Fig. 13; the same frames entered the *Manual of Field works (All Arms)*, War Office (1921) as 'Special deep revetting frames', see plate 69.

205 Cordite Reserve trench leading to Corfu Communication trench; Diary Major W.E. Buckingham RE, WO158/140.

206 F.C. Hitchcock (1937) *op cit.*, 184

207 Captain B.C. Lake (1916) *Knowledge for War. Every Officer's Handbook for the Front*, Harrison & Sons, London, p. 47.

208 General Staff, War Office (1908). *Military Defences (Part 1) Field Defences*. HMSO, London, p. 48.

209 General Staff, War Office (1917) *Summary of Recent Information Regarding the German Army and its Methods*, HMSO, London, p. 17.

210 J.H. Boraston (1919) *Sir Douglas Haig's Despatches*, J.M. Dent, London, p. 22.

211 'The first line must be constructed in such a manner…that the garrison is equal to dealing with any surprise attacks. The bulk of the garrison must be accommodated in the rearward lines.' The *Construction of Field Positions (Stellungsbau)*, Translated and Issued by the General Staff, 1917, p. 5

212 See: General Staff, War Office (1914) *Infantry Training (4-Company Organization)* HMSO, London, chapter XI.

213 'The first position, and the defences of the ground between it and the second, should be constructed by the garrison allotted to it…under special superintendance.' The *Construction of Field Positions (Stellungsbau)*, Translated and Issued by the General Staff, 1917, p.4

214 Anon (1915) *op cit*, p. 95.

215 See War Office (1921) *Manual of Field Works (All Arms)*, HMSO, London, Chapter Iv, pl. 14, 15; and H.A.S. Pressey (1919) Notes on trench war. *Royal Engineers Journal*, v. 29, pp. 297–315.

216 See War Office (1921) *Manual of Field Works (All Arms)*, HMSO, London for the advanced view of crater strengthening, and General Staff, War Office (1917) *Notes for Infantry Officers on Trench Warfare*, March 1916, HMSO, London.

217 General Staff, War Office (1917) *Summary of Recent Information Regarding the German Army and its Methods*, HMSO, London, p. 11

218 Lt Eugen Röcker, letter home, 3 November 1915, translation courtesy Robin Schäfer.

219 See Chasseaud, P. (1990). British artillery and trench maps on the Western Front, 1914–18. *Map Collector*, v. 51, pp. 24–32; and Chasseaud (1999) *op cit*.

220 See Lt-Col. H.S.L. Winterbotham (1919) Geographical work with the army in France. *Geographical Journal*, v.54, pp. 12–28 and Arthur R. Hinks (1919) German war maps and survey. *Geographical Journal*, v. 53, p. 31–44.

221 Cecil Lewis (1936) *Sagittarius Rising*. Peter Davies, London, p. 63

[222] Arthur R. Hinks (1919) German war maps and survey. *Geographical Journal*, v. 53, p. 33.

[223] See Nicolas J. Saunders (2011) *Killing Time: Archaeology and the Great War*. History Press, Stroud

[224] Saunders (2011), *ibid.*

[225] Saunders (2011), *Ibid*

[226] Comparison with the most modern geological map, published by the Belgian Geological Survey in 1999 (*Kaartblad (27-28-36), Proven–Ieper–Ploegsteert, 1:50,000*) shows correspondence of the old front line with the junction between the Ypres Clay (Kortrijk Formation) and the Paniselian sands (Tielt Formation).

[227] Stephen MacGreal (2011) *Boesinghe*. Pen & Sword, Barnsley, p. 73.

[228] Capt. E.V. Tempest (1921) *History of the Sixth Battalion West Yorkshire Regiment. Vol. 1, 1/6th Battalion*, Percy Lund, Humphries & Co, Bradford, p. 50.

[229] General Staff, War Office (1917) *Notes for Infantry Officers on Trench Warfare*, Revised Diagrams, December 1916, HMSO, London, Fig. 13.

[230] Lt John M.L. Grover K.S.L.I, quoted in Stephen MacGreal (2011) *Boesinghe*. Pen & Sword, Barnsley, pp. 109-110.

[231] See De Meyer & Pype (2004, 2009) *op cit.*

[232] Marc Dewide & Nicholas J. Saunders (2009) Archaeology of the Great War. The Flemish Experience. In N.J. Saunders & P. Cornish (eds) *Contested Objects. Material Memories of the Great War*. Routledge, London, p. 257.

[233] See Peter Chasseaud (2008) *Rat's Alley: Trench Names of the Western Front 1914–1918*. Spellmount

[234] Major-General T.O. Marden (1920) *A Short History of the 6th Division*, Hugh Rees, London. p. 17

[235] See Mattheieu de Meyer & Pedro Pype (2007) Scars of the Great War (Western Flanders, Belgium) In Douglas Scott et al. (eds) *Fields of Conflict, Volume 2*. Praeger, Westport, pp. 359–382.

[236] See S. Verdegem, J. Billemont & S. Genbrugge (2013) *Acheo Rapport 28. Mesen – Collector Aquafin*. AEDE, for full report of the excavations.

[237] The *Construction of Field Positions (Stellungsbau)*, Translated and Issued by the General Staff, 1917, p. 3

[238] See Peter Doyle *et al.* (2002) Terrain and the Messines Ridge, Belgium, 1914–1918, In P. Doyle & M.R. Bennett, *Fields of Battle: Terrain in Military History*, Kluwer, Dordrecht, pp. 205-224.

[239] See Rose & Rosenbaum (2011) *op cit.*, tables 2, 3; the recent map *Kaartblad (27-28-36), Proven–Ieper–Ploegsteert, 1:50,000*, has this as the Gent Formation, situated just to the west of the village. Messines sits on the Tielt Formation – the sands and clays of what was called the Paniselian.

[240] S. Verdegem, J. Billemont & S. Genbrugge (2013) *op cit*, p. 104 *et seq.*

[241] 1;10,000 Map Geological, Ploegsteert, 28SW4, May 1918. TNA WO297/2475.

[242] See Martin Brown & Richard Osgood (2009) *Digging Up Ploegsteert. The Archaeology of a Great War Battlefield*. Haynes, Yeovil.

[243] *Ibid*, p. 61

[244] The *Construction of Field Positions (Stellungsbau)*, Translated and Issued by the General Staff, 1917, p. 15

[245] *Ibid*, p. 7 'In building dug-outs in the front lines of positions, the main point to be borne in

mind is that the garrison, which should be kept small, should be able to reach the fire step quickly; protected posts for a few men, and not very deep (constructed of concrete, iron and baulks) are suitable.'

[246] S. Verdegem, J. Billemont & S. Genbrugge (2013) *op cit*, p. 150 *et seq.*

[247] *Ibid*, p. 157, fig. 126; geological detail from 1:10,000 Maps, Geological Ploegsteert 28 SW4, TNA WO297/2475.

[248] See www.laboisselleproject.com for details

[249] http://www.laboisselleproject.com/history/

[250] Charles Douie (1929) *The Weary Road. The Recollections of a Subaltern of Infantry.* John Murray, London, pp. 87-8.

[251] See https://simonjoneshistorian.com/2016/06/30/the-lochnagar-mine/

[252] War Diary 53 Infantry Brigade, Headquarters TNA WO95/2033

[253] Bureau de Recherches Géologiques et Minières (1982) *Carte Géologique de la France a 1/50,000, Albert XXIV-8.*

[254] Referred to in geological terms as 'solifluction'

[255] Attributed to back-fill and mine spoil by the La Boisselle Project group; see http://www.laboisselleproject.com/geophysics-site-clearance/

[256] Confirmed by the *Carte Géologique de la France a 1/50,000, Albert XXIV-8*

[257] See https://simonjoneshistorian.com/2016/06/30/the-lochnagar-mine/

[258] The nature of dug-outs in relation to geology has been outlined by Brooks (1919), King (1919), the Institution of Royal Engineers (1922), and more recently by Doyle (1999) and Doyle *et al.* (2001b).

[259] Described as such in the 1921 War Office *Manual of Field Works (All Arms)*, HMSO, London, p. 151. This was a summation of all the engineering knowledge accumulated during the war.

[260] See A.H. Brooks (1920), The use of geology on the Western Front. *United States Geological Survey Professional Papers*, v. 128-D, pp. 85-124; King (1919) *op cit*, the Institution of Royal Engineers (1922a) *op cit*; and more recently by Doyle (1999) and Doyle *et al.* (2001b).

[261] H.S. Clapham (1930) *Mud and Khaki.* Hutchinson, London, p.27

[262] General Staff, War Office (1917) *Notes for Infantry Officers on Trench Warfare*, HMSO, London, p. 28.

[263] Known as 'elephant iron', with smaller 'baby elephant', both in British usage.

[264] See General Staff, War Office (1921) *Manual of Field Works (All Arms)*, HMSO, London, p. 152–155.

[265] G.M Brown (1918) *If We Return. Letters of a Soldier of Kitchener's Army.* John Lane, London, pp 94–96

[266] Discussed by Brooks (1919), King (1919), the Institution of Royal Engineers (1922a) *op cit* and Institution of Royal Engineers (1922b), *The Work of the Royal Engineers in the European War, 1914-19. Military Mining.* Mackay & Co, Chatham, and more recently by Doyle *et al.* (2001b)

[267] The *in situ* pump at Cross Roads Farm and the dug-out at Boesinghe – uncovered by archaeologists – are examples of the necessity of providing pumping and drainage in this manner.

[268] See Tatham (1919) *op cit.*

[269] See Doyle *et al.* (2001) *op cit.*

270 Alfred H. Brooks (1920) *US Geological Survey Professional Paper* 128–D, pp.85–124.

271 Brooks (1920) *ibid*, p. 104. The same topic was discussed by Brooks in *Engineering and Mining Journal* (1920), Military Mining in France, v. 109, pp. 606–609.

272 See Verret (1980) for details of the clay; Institution of Royal Engineers (1922a) *op cit*, p.40

273 2Lt Arthur R. Stanley-Clarke, 1st Dorsetshire Regiment, 3 February 1915

274 Barton *et al*. (2004) *op cit*. chapter 11.

275 Records of trial bores on the Western Front' [1917] National Archives, Kew, WO 158/133; c. 1000 were logged in all (Institution of Royal Engineers 1922a)

276 See E.P.F. Rose & M.S. Rosenbaum (2011) British geological maps that guided excavation of military dug-outs in Belgium during World War 1. *Quarterly Journal of Engineering Geology and Hydrology*, v. 44, pp. 293–306.

277 S. Passarge (1917) *Geologie unde Minierkrieg bei Ypern*, Unpublished report, Heringen Collection, Euskirchen, reported in Willig *et al*. (2015), *op cit*. p. 142.

278 Institute of Royal Engineers (1921a) *op cit*, p, 38; Rose & Rosenbaum (2011) *op cit*., pp. 297–299.

279 Royal Engineers (1925) *op cit*., Barton *et al*. (2004) *op cit*.

280 Royal Engineers (1925), Institution of Royal Engineers (1952), p. 260, Barton *et al*. 2004

281 Stokes, R. S. G 'Assistant Inspector of Mines, Visit Diary' [1916] National Archives, Kew, WO 158/137

282 Data from Association for Battlefield Archaeology and Conservation.

283 Institution of Royal Engineers 1922b, 1952, Barton *et al*. 2004)

284 See Doyle *et al*. (2001b)

285 G.B. Manwaring [G.M. Brown] (1918) *If We Return. Letters of a Soldier of Kitchener's Army*. John Lane, London, p. 98.

286 A.H. Brooks (1921) *op cit*., p. 105

287 V.F. Eberle (1973) *My Sapper Venture*, Pittman, London, p. 69.

288 D.W. Johnson (1921) *op cit*. pp. 117–18.

289 'The first instinct of the men is to improve the protection afforded by the trench by burrowing out for themselves hollows in the front face, under the parapet ('undercutting'). This practice must be absolutely prohibited.' General Staff, War Office (1917) *Notes for Infantry Officers on Trench Warfare*, March 1916, HMSO, London, p. 28.

290 *Ibid*, p. 118, fig. 39.

291 See Doyle, P., Barton, P., Rosenbaum, M.S., Vandewalle, J. & Jacobs, K. (2002). Geo-environmental implications of military mining in Flanders, Belgium, 1914–1918. *Environmental Geology*, v. 43, pp. 57–71.

292 See, for example, M.G, Culshaw & A.C. Waltham (1987) Natural and artificial cavities as ground engineering hazards. *Quarterly Journal of Engineering Geology*, v. 20, pp. 139–150.

293 See review in Barton *et al*. (2004), chapter 12.

294 See Franky Bostyn (1999) *Beecham Dug-out Passchendaele 1914–1918*. Association for Battlefield Archaeology in Flanders, Studies 1, Zonnebeke Doyle, P., Barton, P & Vandewalle, J. (2006). Archaeology of a Great War dug-out: Beecham Farm, Passchendaele, Belgium. In: Pollard, T & Banks, I. (eds) *Past Tense: Studies in the Archaeology of Conflict*, pp. 45–66. Brill, Leiden.

295 The differences in depth was due to slight variations in slope; see Bostyn (1999) *op cit*.; Doyle et al. (2006) *op cit*.

296 Bostyn (1999) *op cit*; Doyle *et al*. (2006), p. 64

[297] See Bostyn (1999) op cit., Doyle *et al.* (2001b, 2006) *op cit.*; Barton *et al.* (2004) *op cit.*

[298] A function of the distinctively green clay mineral, glauconite.

[299] TNA WO158/133; this glauconitic level is most likely the lower part of the Gent Formation.

[300] 1:10,000 Map, Geological Zonnebeke 28NE1, November 1917, TNA WO 297/2470.

[301] As per regulations, see War Office (1921) *Manual of Field Works (All Arms)*, HMSO, London, pls 70, 71; the archaeology of this dug-out has been discussed by Bostyn (1999) and Doyle *et al.* (2006).

[302] With thanks to Tony Pollard, Peter Barton and Kristof Jacobs. See https://web.archive.org/web/20120308111159/http://www.polygonwood.com/Vampire%20Dug-out/Vampir%20Dug-out%20Zonnebeke.pdf. A preliminary report, Vampir Dug-out, was prepared by Tony Pollard.

[303] See detailed discussion in Barton *et al.* (2004) *op cit.*, chapter 11.

[304] T. Pollard (n.d.) *Vampir Dug-out*, Preliminary Report, GUARD.

[305] According to ABAC, this dug-out is one of some 350 known excavations in the Ypres Salient.

[306] T. Pollard (n.d.) *Vampir Dug-out*, Preliminary Report, GUARD.

[307] Results of the study are given in Institution of Royal Engineers (1922a), *op cit.*, pp. 40–43.

[308] Institution of Royal Engineers (1922a) *op cit.*, pp. 41–42

[309] See http://www.durandgroup.org.uk/maison%20blanche.html. I am grateful to the Durand Group for permission to use photographs of the site, and for conducting me around it in 2014.

[310] *Ibid*

[311] Kim Beattie (1932) *48ᵗʰ Highlanders of Canada, 1891–1928,* 48ᵗʰ Highlanders of Canada, Toronto, p.229. See http://15thbattalioncef.ca/regimental-history/

[312] For review, see Thomas E. Eastler (2004) Military use of underground terrain, In D.R. Caldwell *et al.* (eds) *Studies in Military Geography and Geology*, Kluwer, Dordrecht, pp. 21–37.

[313] For example, see Ball, (1919); Couthard, (1919); Reynolds, (1919); Woodward, (1920); the Institution of Royal Engineers, (1922b).

[314] For example, see Ball, (1919); Couthard, (1919); Reynolds, (1919); Woodward, (1920); the Institution of Royal Engineers, (1922b).

[315] Barton *et al.* (2004) *op cit*, p. 85

[316] Captain W. Grant Grieve and Bernard Newman (1936) *Tunnellers*, Herbert Jenkins, London, p. 115

[317] See Simon Jones (2010) *Underground Warfare 1914-1918*, Pen & Sword, Barnsley, chapter 9.

[318] See Anon (1919) Résumé de la causerie du général-major baron L. Greindl sur les inondations du front belge pendant la guerre 1914–1918. *Bulletin de la Société Belge de Geologie*, v. 29, pp. 15–61.

[319] See Captain A.C. Shortt (1933) A staff exercise in Belgium. *Royal Engineers Journal*, v.37, pp. 596–606.

[320] See Kristof Jacobs (2007) *Nieuwpoort Sector 1917*. De Krijger, Nieuwpoort; and Doyle *et al.* (2001a). Geohazards – last legacy of war? Geoscientist, v. 11, pp. 4–7.

[321] See Doyle *et al.* (2001a, 2002) *op cit.*; and for details of the tunnels see: War diary 257 Tunnelling Company TNA WO95/552; Nieuport Ville, 257 Tunnelling Company Plans,

Royal Engineers Museum, 2001-159/16; Nieuport, map shewing Tunnels and Lighting, Australian War Memorial DR5

[322] See Doyle *et al.* (2001, 2002) *op cit*; Barton *et al.* (2004) *op cit*.

[323] TNA WO158/133, Bore Trials, AEMMBC

[324] Institution of Royal Engineers, (1922a).

[325] Recent work on lateral variability of the strata of the region by Baeteman (1999) and Denys (1999) confirm these early findings.

[326] AWM DR5[54], Nieuport, Map Shewing Tunnels and Lighting; maps of Nieuport tunnels, 1917, in WO153/916 Fourth Army Schemes; and manuscript sketch map in TNA WO158/140, diary of Major W.E. Buckingham, R.E., Assistant to the Inspector of Mines.

[327] TNA WO158/140; diary of Major W.E. Buckingham, R.E., Assistant to the Inspector of Mines.

[328] See Doyle *et al.* (2001a). Geohazards – last legacy of war? Geoscientist, v. 11, pp. 4–7.

[329] Maps of dug-outs in the dune fields, 1917, in WO153/916 Fourth Army Schemes. Many are illustrated, and vary according to whether they are Headquarters, Signals Shelters, Infantry Shelters, etc.

[330] TNA WO158/140, diary of Major W.E. Buckingham, R.E., Assistant to the Inspector of Mines, 6 July 1917.

[331] Tatham (1919) *op cit.*, p. 259.

[332] TNA WO95/3294, Weekly Progress Reports, 257 Tunnelling Company.

[333] J.H. Boraston (ed.) (1919) *Sir Douglas Haig's Despatches*. J.M. Dent & Sons, London, p. 85.

[334] *Carte Géologique de la France, 1:50,000, no 26, Arras XXIV-6.*

[335] WO153/914 Mining First Army Offensive Schemes 1917, map of subways, 'Berthonval to Neuville St Vaast.'

[336] See http://www.durandgroup.org.uk/durand_group_vimy_ridge.html; H.S. Ball (1919) The work of the miner on the Western Front. *Transactions of the Institution of Mining and Metallurgy*, v.28, pp. 216–219; M.S. Rosenbaum (1989) Geological influence on tunneling under the Western Front at Vimy Ridge, *Proceedings of the Geologists' Association*, v. 100, pp 135–140; and Santarelli, N. (2015) Géologie de Grande Guerre. *Géochronique*, n. 135, p. 18.

[337] See Hutchinson *et al.* (2008) for details of the stability of chalk tunnels at Vimy.

[338] WO153/914 Mining First Army Offensive Schemes 1917, map of subways, 'Berthonval to Neuville St Vaast.' Illustrated are the 'Wombat' chambers at the head of the some of the tunnels, to fascilitate opening.

[339] Ball (1919*) op cit*, p. 217.

[340] Delattre *et al.* (1973) *op cit.*, p. 78; Santarelli, N. (2015) Géologie de Grande Guerre. *Géochronique*, n. 135, p. 19.

[341] Ball (1919*) op cit*, p. 218

[342] See Alain Jacques (ed., 1997) *La Bataille d'Arras, avril-mai 1917,* Documents d"Archéologie et d'Histoire du XXᵉ Siècle, No 5, Arras, p.8, *et seq*; J-M. Giradet *et al.* (2003) *Somewhere on the Western Front. Arras 1914–1918.* Documents d"Archéologie et d'Histoire du XXᵉ Siècle, No 8, Arras, p. 63 *et seq.*

[343] Quoted by Christopher Puglsley, The New Zealand Tunnellers at Arras 1916–18 . In A. Jacques (ed., 1997) *La Bataille d'Arras, avril-mai 1917,* Documents d"Archéologie et d'Histoire du XXᵉ Siècle, No 5, p. 16.

344 Institution of Royal Engineers (1922b), *op cit.*, fig. 15.

345 J-M. Giradet *et al.* (2003) *op cit.,* p. 74.

Chapter 5: Breaking the siege: artillery, mining, gas and tanks

346 Lt-Col. N.F. Fraser-Tyler (nd) *Field Guns in France.* Hutchinson, London, p. 81; this describes the bombardment prior to the Battle of the Somme.

347 Brig.-Gen. J.E. Edmonds, (1927) *History of the Great War, Military Operations France and Belgium 1915*, Macmillan, London, p. 4.

348 Defined by the application of mine warfare, the new tactics on land, and the competitive advantage given by new technology in the air.

349 Colonel J.F.C. Fuller (1920) *Tanks in the Great War*, John Murray, London, p. 15.

350 *Ibid*, p. 15

351 General Staff, War Office (1908) *Military Engineering (Part 1) Field Defences* HMSO, London, p. 8.

352 See P. Chasseaud (1999) *Artillery's Astrologers.* Mapbooks, Lewes for an account of the development of survey. See also Robin Prior & Trevor Wilson (1996) *Passchendaele – The Untold Story*, Yale University Press, New Haven, chapters 1, 2.

353 John R. Innes (1935) *Flash Spotters and Sound Rangers*, George Allen & Unwin, London, p. 30.

354 War Office (1921) *Manual of Field Works (All Arms)*, HMSO, London, pp. 36–7.

355 John H. Innes (1935) *op cit.* p. 27.

356 War Office (1921) *Manual of Field Works (All Arms)*, HMSO, London, p. 76, see pls 73–84 for the design of suitable emplacements. This manual was the result of experience on the Western Front.

357 Aubrey Wade (1936) *The War of the Guns*, Batsford, London, p. 45. The yellow clay was derived from the layers of the Paniselian at Hill 60.

358 Jonathan Bailey (1996) British artillery in the Great War. In: Griffith, P. (ed.) *British Fighting Methods in the Great War.* Frank Cass, London, p. 35.

359 See H.S. Ball (1919) The work of the miner on the Western Front. *Transactions of the Institution of Mining and Metallurgy*, v.28, p. 189.

360 General Staff, War Office (1910) *Military Engineering (Part IV) Mining and Demolitions* HMSO, London, p. 1.

361 *Ibid*, p. 1.

362 Brig.-Gen. J.E. Edmonds, (1927) *History of the Great War, Military Operations France and Belgium 1915*, Macmillan, London, pp. 32–33.

363 See Captain W. Grant Grieve and Bernard Newman (1936) *Tunnellers*, Herbert Jenkins, London; Alexander Barrie (1961, reprinted 1988) *War Underground. The Tunnellers of the Great War,* Tom Donovan , London; Barton *et al.* (2004) *op cit.*; Jones (2010) *op cit.*, and Dierck Willig (2015) German military mining on the Western and Eastern fronts, in Anthony Byledbal (ed.). *Les Taupes de la Grande Guerre*, Artois Presses Université, Arras, pp. 29–54, for summaries.

364 For an overview, see Simon Jones (2010) *Underground Warfare 1914–1918,* Pen & Sword, Barnsley.

365 See General Staff, War Office (1910) *Military Engineering (Part IV) Mining and Demolitions*, HMSO, London, pp. 19–21.

366 Captain Cecil Cropper, 250th Tunnelling Company, quoted in Jones (2010) *op cit.*, p. 92.

367 Brigadier J.A.C. Pennycuick (1965) Hill 60 and the mines at Messines. *The Royal Engineers Journal*, v. 79, p. 389; see also the description of working by Grant Grieve & Newman (1936) *op cit*, pp. 32–34.

368 Ball (1919) *op cit.*, p. 190.

369 King (1921a, b) *op cit.*

370 Table in Ball (1919), *op cit*, p.206. Ball does not give the units but identifies pick use in chalk ground as being identifiable at a unit of 125 (ear), 175 (seismo-microphone) and 250 (geophone); using the same instruments in sandy-clay gives the figures 50, 17 and 100. The use of the push-pick in sandy-clay is given at 15, 25 and 35.

371 Grant Grieve & Newman (1936) *op cit*, ch. V.

372 Jones (2010) *op cit*. p. 116.

373 Ball (1919) *op cit.*, p. 216.

374 Grant Grieve & Newman (1936) *op cit*, pp. 115–116.

375 Cecil Lewis (1936) *Sagittarius Rising*. Peter Davis, London, p. 104.

376 Sir William Orpen (1924) *An Onlooker in France*, Williams and Norgate, London, p. 48.

377 Barton *et al.* (2004) *op cit*, chapter V; Dierk Willig (2011) Mining warfare in the Wytschaete Ridge 1914–1917 – advantages and disadvantages of high ground emplacements. In: Häusler, H. & Mang, R. (eds) (2011) *International Handbook Military Geography, Volume 2.* Truppendienst, Vienna

378 Ball 1919, *op cit.*, pl. XXII

379 See: Section of the Passchendaele Ridge, WO297/2462.

380 Barton *et al.* (2004), *op cit.*, p. 79 et seq.

381 Otto Füsslein (1921) Die Mineur in Flandern. In G. von Dickhuth-Harrach (ed) *Im Felde unbesiegt, der Weltkrieg in 28 Einzeldarstellungen*. F. Lehman, Munich

382 See Ball (1919); Institution of Royal Engineers (1922b); Barton *et al.* (2004); Jones (2010)

383 Grant Grieve & Newman (1936) *op cit*, p. 41; see also Diary of Major W.E. Buckingham, RE, TNA WO158/140.

384 Barton *et al.* (2004) *op cit*, p. 80 *et seq*.

385 Ball (1919) *op cit*; Institution of Royal Engineers (1922a), *op cit.*; see 1;10,000 Map, Geological, Ploegsteert 28SW4, May 1918, for details of the local geology at large scale, TNA WO297/2475.

386 Diary of Major W.E. Buckingham, RE, noted 'work of getting back into the galleries has been discontinued here owing to the amount of sand that has run through into the shafts' TNA WO158/140.

387 *Carte Géologique de la Belgique, 1:40,000, no 95, Neuve-Eglise-Messines*, 1900.

388 See Rose & Rosenbaum (1993) *op cit.*; Doyle, P. (2012). Examples of the influence of groundwater on British military mining in Flanders, 1914–1917. In Rose, E.P.F. & Mather, J.D. (eds) *Military Aspects of Hydrology*, pp. 73-83. Geological Society Special Publication 362, Geological Society, London.

389 M. Edgeworth David (1938) *Professor David*. Edward Arnold, London, p. 222.

390 Barton *et al* (2004) *op cit*. p. 166.

391 See Willig (2011) *op cit*.

392 Otto Füsslein, 4th German Army (1921) *op cit*; in 2013 one of the water-filled timbered shafts was explored by remote underwater camera – it was intact and evidence of the German efforts to combat the running sands and take on the British tunnellers.

393 Manuscript diary, Pte J.H. Benn, 7th Loyal North Lancashire Regiment, 19th Division

394 International Committee of the Red Cross, Convention (IV) respecting the Laws and Customs of War on Land and its annex: Regulations concerning the Laws and Customs of War on Land. The Hague, 18 October 1907. https://ihl-databases.icrc.org

395 Jean Pascal Zanders (2016) The Road to Geneva in J.P. Zanders (ed.) *Innocence Slaughtered*, Uniform Press, London, p. 241; see also Major-General C.H. Foulkes (1934) *'Gas!' The Story of the Special Brigade*, William Blackwood, Edinburgh, p. 23.

396 Simon Jones (2007) *World War 1 Gas Warfare Tactics and Equipment*. Osprey, Oxford, p. 3

397 'Chlorine, the gas employed, has a powerful irritant action on the respiratory organs and all mucous membranes exposed to it, causing spasms of the glottis, a burning sensation in the eyes, nose and throat, followed by bronchitis and oedema of the lungs' Brigadier-General Sir James E. Edmonds (1927) *History of the Great War. Military Operations, France and Belgium, 1915, vol, 2*. Macmillan & Co, London, p. 177, fn.

398 The density of air at room temperature is 1.092 kg/m^3, the density of chlorine is 2.994 kg/m^3. The specific gravity of chlorine – the ratio of its density (mass per unit volume) with that of air – is 2.54.

399 https://emergency.cdc.gov/agent/chlorine/basics/facts.asp

400 Major-General C.H. Foulkes (1934) *'Gas!' The Story of the Special Brigade*, William Blackwood, Edinburgh, p. 58

401 Simon Jones (2007) *op cit.*, p. 5.

402 A continuation of the Steenbeek on some maps.

403 See Brigadier-General Sir James E. Edmonds (1927) *History of the Great War. Military Operations, France and Belgium, 1915, vol, 2*. Macmillan & Co, London

404 Field Marshal Sir John French, quoted in Oliver Lepick (2016) Towards total war: Langemarck, 22 April 1915, In J.P. Zanders (ed.) *Innocence Slaughtered*, Uniform Press, London, p. 51.

405 Brigadier-General Sir James E. Edmonds (1936) *History of the Great War. Military Operations, France and Belgium, 1915, vol, 1*. Macmillan & Co, London, p. 114.

406 *Ibid*, pp. 144–148.

407 For an account of the Battle of Loos, see Nick Lloyd (2006) *Loos 1915*, History Press, Stroud, and the book of the same name by Peter Doyle (2012), also History Press.

408 Gary Sheffield and John Bourne (eds, 2005) *Douglas Haig. War Diaries and Letters 1914–1918*. Weidenfield and Nicholson, London, p. 52.

409 *Ibid*, p, 153.

410 Major C.J.C. Street (1936) With the Guns at Loos, in J.A. Hammerton (ed) *The Great War I Was There*, vol. 1, Amalgamated Press, London, p. 467.

411 See overview in Jones (2007) *op cit.*

412 Col. J.F.C. Fuller (1920) *Tanks in the Great War*, 1914-1918, John Murray, London, p. 25.

413 *Ibid*, pp 26–7

414 Bureau de Recherches Géologiques et Miniéres, *Carte Géologique de la France a 1/50,000 Bapaume XXIV-7*.

415 David Fletcher (1994) *Tanks and Trenches*, Sutton, Stroud, pp. 5–7

416 Chris McCarthy (1998) *The Somme The Day-by-Day Account*, Brockhampton, London, p. 100-109

417 Lt E.A. Arnold, quoted in David Fletcher (1994) *Tanks and Trenches*, Sutton, Stroud, p. 10

418 Col. J.F.C. Fuller (1920) *Tanks in the Great War*, 1914-1918, John Murray, London,

p. 85.

[419] *Ibid*, p. 120

[420] Chris McCarthy (1998) *The Third Ypres Passchendaele. The Day-by-Day Account*, Arms & Armour Press, London, pp. 23, 27.

[421] '[Tank maps]… were prepared by the Tank Department itself, certain points only being referred to the geologists, and 'Tanks' being furnished with the maps published by the geologists, showing geological conditions for dug-outs and some details of surface soils and subsoils…' Institution of Royal Engineers (1921a), *op cit.*, p. 45.

[422] Colin Hardy's research into tank reconnaissance has uncovered a range of maps that were prepared by tank officers in advance of Third Ypres, including the 'swamp' maps prepared by Captain Frederick 'Boots' Hotblack, the Tank Corps GSO2 staff officer.

[423] TNA WO95/101, 2nd Bde., HQ., Feb.-Dec. 1917. I am grateful to Colin Hardy for bringing this to my attention.

[424] *Ibid*, Report on Reconnaisance work by 2nd Brigade, Tank Corps, 6. 8. 17.

[425] See Louis. L. Ray (1946) Problems of trafficability. *Bulletin of the Geological Society of America*, v. 57, pp. 1223–1224; Ray identifies five characteristics that need to be considered: Vehicle performance; topography; soil conditions; climate & weather; vegetation and land use. These were as applicable in the Great War as they were in the war that followed.

[426] Boraston (1919) *op cit.* p. 154.

[427] J.P. Harris (1996). The rise of armour. In: Griffith, P. (ed.) *British Fighting Methods in the Great War*. Frank Cass, London, p. 129.

[428] Col. H.C.B. Rogers (1965) *Tanks in Battle*. Seeley Service & Co, London, p. 55.

[429] Jean-Luc Gibot & Philippe Gorczynski (1999) *Following the Tanks, Cambrai 20 November–7th December 1917*, The Authors, Arras, separate map; *and Carte Géologique de la France, 1:50,000, no 36, Cambrai XXV-7*.

[430] Col. H.C.B. Rogers (1965) *Tanks in Battle*. Seeley Service & Co, London, p. 55.

[431] Boraston (1919) *op cit.* p. 261.

[432] The motto of the Tank Corps.

Chapter 6: Military resources: water supply and aggregates

[433] Alfred H. Brooks (1920) Use of Geology on the Western Front, *op cit.*, p. 115.

[434] 'Minerals and their products enter into almost every phase of … modern civilization… Our dependence upon minerals is even greater in times of war. No nation could hope to carry on war under present conditions without abundant resources of certain essential mineral materials.' H.E. Gregory (1918) *op cit.*, p. 253; see as an example Alfred H. Brooks (1920) The Lorraine iron field and the war. *Engineering and Mining Journal*, v. 109, pp. 1065–1069.

[435] See, for example Christopher A. Gellasch (2004) Groundwater. Past, present and future uses in military operations, in D.R, Caldwell et al. (eds) *Studies in Military Geography and Geology*, Kluwer, Dordrecht, pp. 307–319.

[436] See discussion in Doyle and Bennett (1999) *op cit*, p, 33 *et seq*; A. Beeby-Thompson, a civilian, was contracted to assist the Royal Engineers find water in Gallipoli, and subsequently, in Salonika and Africa. See A. Beeby-Thompson (1924) *Emergency Water Supplies for Military, Agricultural and Colonial Purposes*. Crosby, Lockwood & Son, London.

[437] A. Beeby Thompson (1926) Geology as applied to military requirements. *Royal Engineers*

Journal, v. 40, p.53.

438 H.E. Gregory (1918) *op cit.*, p. 108.

439 See Rose, E.P.F. (2009) Water supply maps for the Western Front (Belgium and northern France) developed by British, German and American military geologists during World War 1: pioneering studies in hydrogeology from trench warfare. *The Cartographic Journal*, v. 46, pp. 76–103; and Rose, E.P.F. (2012) Groundwater as a military resource: pioneering British military well boring and hydrogeology in World War 1. In Rose, E.P.F. & Mather, J.D. (eds) *Military Aspects of Hydrogeology*, Geological Society, London, pp. 49–72.

440 Institution of Royal Engineers (1921a), *op cit.* p. 9 *et seq.*

441 A.H. Brooks (1920) *op cit.* p. 115

442 Rose (2012) *op cit.*, p. 50.

443 G. Thiem (1916) *Keimfreies Wasser furs Heer.* Verlag der Internationalen Zeitschift für Wasser-Versorgung, Leizig; quoted in Willig, D. & Häusler, H. (2012) op cit., pp. 85–103

444 See Rose *et al.* (2000) *op cit.*

445 A.H. Brooks (1920) *op cit.* p. 116; King (1921a, b) *op cit.*; Rose & Rosenbaum (1993) *op cit*; Rose (2012) *op cit.*

446 Undated document, Depot RAMC, 1st London Division; papers of Dr Myer Coplans RAMC, author's archive.

447 Institution of Royal Engineers (1952) *op cit.*, p. 502.

448 *Memorandum on Advance Water Supplies* for the Third Army, issued in March 1917 in preparation for the Battle of Arras, made preparations for water supply in case of advance, following experience on the Somme in 1916. Papers of Dr Myer Coplans RAMC, author's archive.

449 Institution of Royal Engineers. (1921). *The Work of the Royal Engineers in the European War, 1914-19: Water Supply.* W & J Mackay, Chatham; Rose (2012) *op cit.*

450 Institution of Royal Engineers (1952) *op cit.*, p. 160.

451 See Rose (2009) *op cit* and Rose (2012) *op cit.* for more discussion; see also King (1919, 1921 a, b) for examples of his work.

452 Willig, D. & Häusler, H. (2012) *op cit*, pp. 85–86.

453 See Rose *et al.* (2000), *op cit.* p. 118.

454 Willig, D. & Häusler, H. (2012) *op cit*, p. 90

455 *Memorandum on Advance Water Supplies.* Third Army, March 1917, papers of Dr Myer Coplans RAMC, author's archive.

456 Brigadier General Liddell, discussion to W.B.R. King (1919), *op cit.*, p. 257; see also A.H. Brooks (1920), *op cit.* p. 116.

457 Joseph Förster of Jäger-Btl 12, manuscript letter, courtesy of Robin Schäfer.

458 L. Collis & R.A. Fox, (eds, 1985) *Aggregates, Geological Society, London*, p. 1.

459 J.H. Boraston (1919) *Sir Douglas Haig's Despatches*, J.M. Dent & Sons, London, p. 143.

460 See R. Thompson (2002) Mud, blood and wood: BEF operational and combat logistico-engineering during the Third Battle of Ypres. In P. Doyle & M.R. Bennett, *Fields of Battle: Terrain in Military History,* Kluwer, Dordrecht, pp. 237–255

461 Institution of Royal Engineers (1952), *History of the Corps of Royal Engineers, Volume V.* Institution of Royal Engineers, Chatham, p. 627.

462 Institute of Royal Engineers (1922a) *op cit.*, p. 58.

463 Herbert E, Gregory (ed., 1918) *Military Geology and Topography.* Yale University Press, New Haven, p. 41

464 Institution of Royal Engineers (1922a), *op cit.*, pp.58–9.

465 Institute of Royal Engineers (1922a) *op cit*, p. 62; Sabine (1991).

466 Capt. F.C. Hitchcock (1937) *op cit.*, p. 290.

467 Institution of Royal Engineers (1952), *History of the Corps of Royal Engineers, Volume V.* Institution of Royal Engineers, Chatham, p.312.

468 Frank Fox (1918) *The Battles of the Ridges Arras–Messines, March–April, 1917*. C. Arthur Pearson, London, p. 78.

469 V.F. Eberle (1973) *My Sapper Venture*, Pitman Publishing, London, p. 125.

470 Colonel E.G.L. Thurlow (1933) *The Pill-boxes of Flanders*, British Legion, London, p. 11.

471 Peter Oldham (1995) *Pill boxes on the Western Front*. Pen & Sword, Barnsley, p. 39.

472 Colonel E.G.L. Thurlow (1933) *The Pill-boxes of Flanders*, British Legion, London, p. 11.

473 *Ibid*

474 Peter Oldham (1995) *Pill boxes on the Western Front*. Pen & Sword, Barnsley, p. 67 (fn).

475 See *E-in-C Fieldwork Notes No 31*. German Concrete Structures on Messines Ridge and the Effect of Shellfire on Them.

476 See *E-in-C Fieldwork Notes Nos 31* and *43;* Thurlow (1933) *op cit.* p, 11: 'The best concrete shelters were quite capable of resisting direct hits by six-inch howitzers, heavy trench mortars and artillery of even greater calibre. In fact, in many cases the effect of shellfire on these structures was practically nill'

477 Oldham (1995) op cit; Franky Bostyn *et al.* (2000) *Bayernwald het Croonaertbos in de Eerste Wereldoorlog,* chapter 2.3.

478 Thurlow (1933) *op cit.* p, 11

479 *E-in-C's Fieldwork Note No 48*. Use of Ferro-Concrete in Construction Royal Engineers Library, Chatham

480 Peter Oldham (1995), *op cit.*, p. 47.

481 Institute of Royal Engineers (1922a) *op cit.,* Fig. 9.

482 See Institute of Royal Engineers (1922a) *op cit;* P.A. Sabine (1991) Geologists at War: a forensic investigation in the field of war-time diplomacy. *Proceedings of the Geologists' Association* v. 102, pp. 139–143; Oldham (1995) *op cit.*

483 Oldham (1995) *op cit.*, p. 139.

484 Thurlow (1933) *op cit.* p. 9.

Endword

485 This was an original aim identified as far back as 1915, with the publication of W. Salomon's book.

GLOSSARY

Adit: horizontal gallery access to a mine

Aggregate: rock particles, usually sand and gravel, often used in concrete

Alluvium/alluvials: sediments that have been transported and deposited by a river

Anticline: a geological structure in which strata are folded into an arch

Aquiclude: a layer of impermeable rock that prevents water from travelling through other strata

Aquifer: a layer of rock that is porous enough to hold groundwater

Argile à silex: see clay with flints

Argile des Flandres: Ypres Clay

Artesian water: groundwater that rises to the surface due to underground pressure

Batter: engineered slope

Beke: stream (Flemish)

Bentonite: a group of clay minerals

Bove: underground quarry (French)

Boyaux couverts: cut-and-cover tunnels

Boyaux enterées: mined tunnels

Box barrage: artillery barrage that creates a box-like 'wall' of shells to protect advancing infantry

Breastwork: trench wall raised above ground level

Bruxellien: an old subdivision of the Eocene geological time period

Burster course: layer used to cover underground fortifications, intended to force a shell to explode before it penetrates too deeply

Canalised: man-made river channels

Carboniferous: interval of geological time, approximately 359–299 million years ago

Chalk: pure limestone, characteristically white in colour, and typical of the Cretaceous period. In northern France, as in England, chalk may contain layers of hard flint

Clay: fine-grained, plastic, sedimentary rock made up of clay minerals

Clay kicking: technique used by military miners in clay, involving the kicker lying on his back and cutting out blocks of clay

Clay minerals: minerals that make up clay and which give this rock its plastic properties

Clay-with-flints: residue of the weathering of chalk, leaving behind typically a red-brown clay containing many nodules of flint

Coal: brittle black rock of organic origin that typically formed during the Carboniferous

Communication trench: military trench connecting the fire and support trenches with the rear areas

Confined aquifer: an aquifer (water-bearing layer) that has an impermeable layer that prevents water seeping into it from the surface

Corons: mine villages (French)

Craie blanche: pure white chalk (French)

Craie blanche à silex: white chalk with flint layers (French)

Crassier: heap of colliery waste (slag heap) (French)

Creeping barrage: artillery barrage that creating a screen that move forward slowly in front of advancing infantry

Cretaceous: interval of geological time, approximately 145–66 million years ago

Crown hole: holes that appear at the surface due to collapse of underground cavities or chambers

Cut-and-cover: method of creating tunnels that involves digging an open gallery, and then covering it

Defile: a narrow passage between mountains or hills; a narrow passage for troops to pass

Degree of protection: term referring to the capability of a military structure to withstand artillery bombardment

Diabase: American name for dolerite, a medium grained, relatively dark coloured, crystalline rock

Dip: the angle of a geological layer to the horizontal

Dissection: the manner in which valleys and streams cut through the landscape

Dry valley: valley created in chalk country; streams flow in these valleys only if the pore spaces in the chalk are saturated or frozen, otherwise they would soak away

Duck-board: slatted timber path laid down in muddy conditions

Dug-out: military shelter created by digging into the ground, variable in depth

Dug-out suitability map: map indicating the suitability of a region for the excavation of dug-outs, and relating to the water saturation of the underground strata

Dunefield: area of sand dunes

Elephant: prefabricated, heavy-duty, curved and corrugated iron sheets used in dug-outs and shelters

Enfilade: ability to fire along the line of a trench or fortification, thereby putting its occupants in grave risk

Engineering geology: application of geological principles in civil engineering

Eocene: interval of geological time, approximately 56–34 million years ago, and including the Ypresian

Escarpment: hill characterised by a steep front face and a more gently sloping rear

Fault: fracture in geological strata, in which one side moves relative to the other

Fault scarp: steep scarp created by the action of a fault

Ferro-concrete: concrete reinforced by iron, usually in bar form

Fire bay: part of a front line trench between two traverses

Fire step: step at the foot of a trench enabling men to look and fire over the parapet

Fire trench: frontline, fighting trench

Flexure: see fold

Flint: very hard, brittle rock commonly forming layers or nodules in chalk

Fold: bends or flexures of rock strata

Formation: term given to a group of strata that are distinctive enough to be plotted out on a map

Forward slope: sloping down towards the enemy

Fosse: coal mining pit-head (French)

Friction: those aspects of a military campaign that cannot be planned for, but which will inevitably slow down any advance

Frost-shattering: the breaking of rocks through the action of the repetitive freezing and thawing of ice in pore spaces and cavities

Funk-hole: term for a shallow dug-out shelter

Gallery: the horizontal tunnel components of a mine system, linked with shafts and inclines

Gent Formation: together with the Tielt Formation, the modern name for the Paniselian

Geologen Stellen: geological sections (German)

Geological map: map showing the distribution of rock units (formations) as they appear at the surface

Geology: the study of the composition, structure and history of the Earth

Geophone: listening device used to detect tunnelling activities

Glauconite: green clay mineral

Going: military term relating to the capability of men and machines to move across a surface

Going map: map showing the extent of the 'going surfaces' in a terrain

Ground: the surface of the Earth; used in military terms to describe the state of the terrain

Hydrography: the survey and study of bodies of water

Ice Age: period of the Earth's history with cooler temperatures and the growth of ice sheets and glaciers, commonly association with the most recent interval, which ended some 10,000 years ago

Impermeable: rocks that do not permit the passage of water

Incised: rock surfaces that have been deeply cut, mostly by water

Investment: surrounding a fort or fortification

Interbedded: layers of different rocks occurring together

Kaolinite: a common clay mineral

Kemmel Sands: water-saturated sands, part of the Paniselian, and an example of a perched or confined aquifer

Kortrijk Formation: modern name for the Ypres Clay

Kriegsgeologie: war geology (German)

Impervious: rocks devoid of, or possessing extremely fine, pore spaces

Incline: inclined tunnels or steps, part of the mine system

Inundation: deliberate flooding of low-lying land

Limestone: rock composed of lime (calcium carbonate) mostly derived from fossil shells

Limon/Limons de Plateaux: a mixture of loess and loam that caps the top of the chalk hills in Picardy

Loam: clay and silt rich soil

Loess: fine-grained sediment that was formed and wind-blown during the Ice Age

London Clay: clay of Eocene age that underlies the city of London; it is the equivalent of the Ypres Clay

Marl: lime-rich clay

Marnes crayeuses: clay-rich marl (French)

Marqueffles Fault: a major fracture (fault) that defines the line of the Vimy Ridge

MEBU: *Mannschafts Eisenbeton Unterstande* German concrete defensive posts commonly called 'pillboxes' by the British

Mesozoic: interval of geological time, approximately 252–66 million years ago, and including the Cretaceous

Metal (road): a term used for roadstone

Microgeography: the geography of the small scale

Militärgeologie: military geology (German)

Mined dugout: a deep dugout with galleries and tunnels

Mining case: see sett

Montmorillonite: a clay mineral

Mud: a wet mass of clayey material in a liquid or semi-liquid state

No Man's Land: the contested area between opposing trenches

Outcrop: the extent of a particular rock unit at the Earth's surface

Paniselian: a series of sedimentary layers, clay, silt and sand, first named after Mont Panisel near Mons; the Paniselian sediments are Eocene in age and lie on the Ypres Clay

Parados: linear mound of earth on the rim of the rear of the trench to protect its occupants

Parapet: linear mound of earth, sandbags or other materials on the rim of the front of the trench to protect its occupants

Passability: the extent to which men, animals and machines may pass over a particular surface

Perched aquifer: a water bearing layer above the normal water table, maintained in that position due to an impermeable layer

Percolation: the action of water passing through permeable rock layers

Permafrost: the more-or-less permanent freezing of the ground, associated with Ice Ages

Permeability: the degree to which a rock unit allows water and other fluids to pass through

Pillar and Stall: a type of underground quarrying which involves leaving intact pillars to support the roof, with the rock removed from the 'stalls' or rooms

Pillbox: British term for a MEBU

Pioneer Battalion: infantry unit equipped both to fight as infantrymen, and assist in construction and digging works

Phosphatised: the process of changing the lime minerals (calcium carbonate) into phosphate minerals (calcium phosphate)

Physiography: physical geography, and specifically the study of landforms

Plasticity: the ability to be moulded into another shape, typical of clay

Polder: low-lying lad reclaimed from the sea, and protected by drainage ditches and dykes

Pores: cavities between mineral grains typically containing water

Potable water: drinking water

Plateau: flat-topped hill

Puit: mine shaft (French)

Push-pick: a sharp bladed tool that is used to cut clay during clay-kicking

Quartz: hard mineral commonly found in sand

Quicksand: see running sand

Reserve trench: trench lines situated to the rear of the fire and support trenches

Reverse slope: sloping away from the enemy

Revetment: any material used for retaining earth at a steeper angle that it would normally assume

Rhine gravels: gravels obtained from the valley of the River Rhine

Roadstone: stone, usually crushed stone, used in the construction of roadways and surfaces

Running sand: fine, loose and water-saturated sand

Russian sap: shallow tunnel capable of being opened up to form a trench

Salient: bulge in the front line, usually jutting forward into enemy held territory.

Sand dune: mounds of sand accumulated by prevailing winds

Sandstone: sedimentary rock consisting of sand-sized particles, commonly quartz

Sarsen Stones: tough sandstone blocks resistant to weathering that are remnants of more extensive sand layers

Scarp: steep slope

Schwimmsands: 'swimming sands' (German), see running sands

Sedimentary: rocks formed by the accumulation of particles of sediment

Setts: pre-prepared wooden frames used in maintaining the dimensions of mine galleries

Shale: sedimentary rock consisting of fine-grained particles and which can be split into sheets

Siltstone: sedimentary rock consisting of silt-sized particles

Slabbing: the failure of slabs of rock in an open space such as a gallery or quarry

Slope: trench sides

Soil: accumulation of loose weathered particles on the Earth's surface, often mixed with organic material

Souterrains: underground chambers (French)

Spiling: a method of mining through soft or running sands which involves the use of timbers to support the face and the area being worked

Spur: distinctive positive landform between valleys

Stellungsbau: 'fortress building', the German manual of field fortifications

Strata/stratum: geological layers/layer

Stutzpunkt: strongpoint (German)

Subway: a tunnel providing access to other features, such as trenches

Support trench: trench lines situated to the rear of the fire trenches

Swelling pressure: the pressure exerted by the swelling of clay minerals due to the absorption of water

Terrain: tract of country considered with regard to its natural features, particularly in military use, as affecting its tactical advantages, etc

Terrain analysis: analysis of the suitability of terrain for military operations

Terrain evaluation: see terrain analysis

Terrain intelligence: the gathering of intelligence for use in terrain analysis

Tertiary: interval of geological time, approximately 66–2.6 million years ago, now divided into the Palaeogene and Neogene, and including the Eocene

Tielt Formation: together with the Gent Formation, the modern name for the Paniselian

Topography: detail of the physical features of a location

Trafficability: see going

Traverse: angles set into a frontline trench and separating firebays, intended to prevent enfilade fire

Trench: military fortification comprising a ditch-like structure intended to prevent the advance of an enemy and to provide protection to friendly troops

Trench feet: affliction allied to frost bite caused by prolonged immersion in freezing mud or water

Trench frame: pre-fabricated wooden frame used to support trench slopes

Tubbing: curved sections, usually of steel, used to combat running sands in the construction of mine shafts

Tunnelling Company: unit of engineers specifically organised to dig tunnels and dug-outs

Unconfined aquifer: an aquifer (water-bearing layer) that is capable of accepting water seeping into it from the surface

Wasserversorgungs-Karten: water supply maps (German)

Water supply map: map showing the sources of water supply

Water table: the upper surface of the zone of groundwater saturation

Wehrgeologie: defence geology (German)

Wombat: an explosive charge placed by boring

Wytschaete Sands: dry sands capping the top of the ridge at Wytschaete, part of the Paniselian

Ypres Clay: the Eocene clay that forms the base of the city of Ypres, equivalent to the London Clay, now the Kortrijk Formation

Ypresian: interval of geological time, approximately 56–47.6 million years ago, part of the Eocene

ACKNOWLEDGEMENTS

Putting together a book of this sort requires a great deal of support; I am grateful to all those who have assisted me on my journey to examine the detail of the role of terrain and geology in the Great War. Firstly I am indebted to Ted Rose and Mike Rosenbaum for initiating my work on this subject, linking two areas of great importance to me. Secondly, I acknowledge those who have assisted me along the way, including Matthew Bennett, Franky Bostyn Peter Chasseaud, Marc Dewilde, Kristof Jacobs, Simon Jones, Herman Häusler, Nick Saunders, Nigel Steele, the members of the International Committee on Military Geology (ICMG), and to the Faculty of Geography and Environmental Engineering at the US Military Academy, West Point (in particular Frank Galgano and Andy Lohman) at which institution I gave lectures on the topic in 2007 and 2014. I am grateful to Peter Barton for guiding me around the excavations at Vampir Dugout and La Boisselle. I thank the Association for Battlefield Archaeology and Conservation, the La Boisselle Study Group and the Durand Group for their support at various times. Colin Hardy kindly shared his research on tank reconnaissance with me, and Philip Robinson his work on Maison Blanche, for which I am grateful. I thank Ryan Gearing for his faith in the topic. Good friends Chris Foster, Tony Pollard, Paul Reed, Rob Schäfer, Johan Vandewalle, Simon Verdeghem, Dierk Willig and others provided illustrations and inspiration. Finally, I gain my greatest inspiration from those closest to me, Julie and James.

BIBLIOGRAPHY

Documents

The National Archives (TNA), London
WO 95/101 War Diary, 2nd Brigade HQ, Feb–Dec 1917
WO 95/335/1 War Diary, 171 Tunnelling Company
WO95/335/2 War Diary, 173 Tunnelling Company
WO95/492 War Diary, No 5 Water Boring Section RE
WO95/552 War diary 257 Tunnelling Company
WO95/1010 War Diary, AEMMBC
WO95/2033 War Diary 53 Infantry Brigade, Headquarters
WO95/3294, Weekly Progress Reports 257 Tunnelling Company
WO153/914 Mining First Army Offensive Schemes 1917
WO153/915 Records of Trial Bores
WO153/916 Fourth Army Schemes
WO153/982 Notes on the cross country conditions considered from a Geological
    Point of View
WO158/135 AEMMBC Weekly Progress Report on Borings
WO 158/137 Stokes, R. S. G 'Assistant Inspector of Mines, Visit Diary' [1916]
WO158/140 Diary of Major W.E. Buckingham RE
WO158/302 Preliminary Notes on the Operations of the Second Army, June 1917
WO158/306 The Battle of Messines June 1917 [Aerial Photographs]
WO297/2462 Diagrammatic Section Across Passchendaele Ridge
WO297/2463–2477 1:10,000 Maps, Geological

Royal Engineers Museum and Library, Chatham
Nieuport Ville, 257 Tunnelling Company Plans, 2001-159/16
E-in-C Fieldwork Notes No 31. German Concrete Structures on Messines Ridge and
    the Effect of Shellfire on Them
E-in-C Fieldwork Notes No 43. German Concrete Structures in the Area North of
    Ypres, Captured in August 1917, and the Effect of Shell Fire on Them
E-in-C Fieldwork Notes No 46. Effect of Bombing on Dug-outs
E-in-C's Fieldwork Note No 48. Use of Ferro-Concrete in Construction.

Australian War Memorial (AWM)
AWM DR5[54], Nieuport, Map Shewing Tunnels and Lighting

Heringen Collection, Euskirchen, Germany
S. Passarge (1917) *Geologie unde Minierkrieg bei Ypern*, Unpublished report.

Europeana, CC-BY-SA 3.

Manuscript account, *Bericht von Leutnant Kurt Trautner von der Somme-Schlacht,* courtesy Dr Jürgen Trautner, translated by Robin Schäfer).

2Lt Arthur R. Stanley-Clarke, 1ˢᵗ Dorsetshire Regiment, 3 February 1915

Other Archive Material

Pte Benn, manuscript diary, 1917

Joseph Förster of Jäger-Btl 12, manuscript letter, courtesy of Robin Schäfer

Capt Myers Coplans Papers

Lt Eugen Röcker, letter home, 3 November 1915, translation courtesy Robin Schäfer.

Official Manuals

Department of the Army (1952) US Army Technical Manual TM 5-545 *Geology and its Military Applications*, Washington D.C

General Staff, War Office (1908) *Military Engineering (Part 1) Field Defences.* HMSO, London

General Staff, War Office (1910) *Military Engineering (Part IV) Mining and Demolitions* HMSO, London

General Staff, War Office (1914) *Infantry Training (4-Company Organization)* HMSO, London

General Staff, War Office (1916) *Notes for Infantry Officers on Trench Warfare,* HMSO, London

General Staff, War Office (1917) *Notes for Infantry Officers on Trench Warfare,* Revised Diagrams, December 1916, HMSO, London

General Staff, War Office (1917) *Summary of Recent Information Regarding the German Army and its Methods*, HMSO, London

General Staff (1917) *The Construction of Field Positions (Stellungsbau).* (1916) Translated from German by the General Staff, May 1917, pp.3–4

Ministry of Defence (1976) *Military Engineering vol. XV Applied Geology for Engineers*, HMSO, London.

War Office (1921) *Manual of Field Works (All Arms)*, HMSO, London

War Office (1925) *Manual of Field Works (All Arms)*, HMSO, London

Maps

Carte Géologique de la Belgique, 1:40,000, no 81, Poperinghe-Ypres, 1897.

Carte Géologique de Belgique, 1:40 000 No. 82 Gheluvelt-Moorseele.

Carte Géologique de la Belgique, 1:40,000, no 95, Neuve-Eglise-Messines, 1900.

Belgian Geological Survey *Kaartblad (27-28-36), Proven–Ieper–Ploegsteert, 1:50,000,* 1999

Carte Géologique de la France, 1:50,000, no 3-4, Dunkerque Hondschoote .

Carte Géologique de la France, 1:50,000, no 8, Steenvoorde XXIV-3 .

Carte Géologique de la France, 1:50,000, no 26, Arras XXIV-6.

Carte Géologique de la France, 1:50,000, no 35, Bapaume XXIV-7.

Carte Géologique de la France, 1:50,000, no 36, Cambrai XXV-7.

Carte Géologique de la France, 1:50,000, no 47, Albert XXIV-8.

Books and reports

Aitkin Sir M. (1916) *Canada in Flanders*, Hodder & Stoughton, London.

Anon (2002) *French Trench Warfare, 1917–1918. A Reference Manual.* Imperial War Museum & Battery Press.

Baring, M. (1920) *Flying Corps Headquarters 1914–1918.* William Heinemann, London.

Barrie, A. (1988) *War Underground. The Tunnellers of the Great War,* Tom Donovan, London

Barton, P., Doyle, P. & Vanderwalle, J. (2004). *Beneath Flanders Fields. The Underground War 1914-1918.* Spellmount, Staplehurst.

Beattie, K. (1932) *48th Highlanders of Canada, 1891–1928,* 48th Highlanders of Canada, Toronto.

Beeby-Thompson, A. (1924) *Emergency Water Supplies for Military, Agricultural and Colonial Purposes.* Crosby, Lockwood & Son, London.

Belloc, H. (1914) *Warfare in England.* Williams and Norgate, London.

Boraston, J.H. (ed., 1919). *Sir Douglas Haig's Despatches.* J.M. Dent, London.

Borden, M. (1929) *The Forbidden Zone,* William Heinemann, London.

Bostyn, F (1999) *Beecham Dugout, Passchendaele 1914-1918.* Association for Battlefield Archaeology in Flanders, Studies 1: Zonnebeke.

Bostyn, F. *et al.* (2000) *Bayernwald het Croonaertbos in de Eerste Wereldoorlog.* Association for Battlefield Archaeology in Flanders, Studies 2: Zonnebeke

Brown, A. (1962). *Geology and the Gettysburg Campaign.* Pennsylvania Topographic & Geologic Survey Educational Series n.5, pp.1–15.

[Brown, G.M.] Manwaring, G.B. (1918) *If We Return. Letters of a Soldier of Kitchener's Army.* John Lane, London.

Brown, M. & Osgood, R. (2009). *Digging up Plugstreet.* Haynes, Yeovil.

Bulow, K. von Kranz, W. & Sonne, E. (1938) *Wehrgeologie,* Quelle und Meyer, Leipzig.

Chasseaud, P. (1999) *Artillery's Astrologers.* Mapbooks, Lewes.

Chasseaud, P. (2008) *Rat's Alley: Trench Names of the Western Front 1914–1918.* Spellmount, Staplehurst.

Chasseaud, P. (2013) *Mapping the First World War.* Collins, London.

Chasseaud, P. & Doyle, P. (2005). *Grasping Gallipoli. Terrain Intelligence, Maps and Failure at the Dardanelles, 1915.* Spellmount, Staplehurst.

Cherry, N. (2005) *Most Unfavourable Ground. The Battle of Loos 1915.* Helion, Solihull.

Clapham, H.S. (1930) *Mud and Khaki.* Hutchinson, London.

Clausewitz, Carl von (1873) *On War. Translated by Col. J.J. Graham* [from the 1832 original]. N. Trübner, London.

Cornélis, B. (2001). *Technical Overview of the SAFIR Report.* Nirond 2001-05 E, ONDRAF/NIRAS, Brussels.

Delattre, C. et al. (1973) *Région du Nord, Flandre, Artois, Boulonnais, Picardie.* Guides Géologiques Régionaux, Masson, Paris.

De Meyer, M. & Pype, P. (2004). *The A19 Project; Archaeological Research at Cross Roads.* Association for World War Archaeology.

Desfossés, Y., Jacques, A. & Prilaux, G. (2008). *L'archéologie de la Grande Geurre.* Editions Ouest–France, Rennes.

Douie, C. (1929) *The Weary Road. The Recollections of a Subaltern of Infantry.* John Murray, London.

Doyle, P. (1998). *Geology of the Western Front, 1914–18.* Geologists' Association Guide 61. Geologists' Association, London.

Doyle, P. (2012) *Loos 1915.* Spellmount, Stroud.

Doyle, P. & Bennett, M.R. (eds) (2002). *Fields of Battle, Terrain in Military History.* Kluwer, Dordrecht.

Dunn, Capt. J.C. (1994) *The War the Infantry Knew 1914–1919.* Abacus, London

Eberle, V.F. (1973) *My Sapper Venture*, Pittman, London.

Edgeworth David, M. (1937) *Professor David. The Life of Sir Edgeworth David KBE, DSO, FRS.* Edward Arnold, London.

Edmonds, Brigadier-General Sir James E. (1926) *History of the Great War. Military Operations, France and Belgium, 1915, vol. I.* Macmillan & Co, London.

Edmonds, Brigadier-General Sir James E. (1928) *History of the Great War. Military Operations, France and Belgium, 1915, vol. II.* Macmillan & Co, London.

Edmonds, Sir J.E. (1948) *Official History of the War, Military Operations, France and Belgium 1917 vol. II,* HMSO, London.

Falls, Capt. C. (1940) *Official History of the War, Military Operations, France and Belgium 1917 vol .I,* Macmillan, London.

Feilding, R. (1929) *War Letters to a Wife France and Flanders, 1915–1919.* Medici Society, London.

Finlayson, D. (2010) *Crumps and Camouflets. Australian Tunnelling Companies on the Western Front.* Big Sky, Newport.

Fischer, F. (1967) *Germany's War Aims in the First World War*, W.W.Norton, New York.

Fletcher, D. (1994) *Tanks and Trenches*, Sutton, Stroud.

Foch, Marshal F. (1903) *The Principles of War.* Translation, 1920, Henry Holt & Co, New York.

Foulkes. Maj-Gen. C.H. (1934) *'Gas!' The Story of the Special Brigade.* William Blackwood & Sons, Edinburgh.

Fox, F. (1918) *The Battles of the Ridges Arras–Messines, March–April, 1917.* C. Arthur Pearson, London.

Fraser-Tyler, Lt-Col. N.F. (nd) *Field Guns in France.* Hutchinson, London.

French, Field Marshal Sir J. (1919) *1914*, Constable & Co, London.

Fuller, Col. J.F.C. (1920) *Tanks in the Great War*, John Murray, London.

Gibbs, P. (1920) *Realities of War,* Heinemann, London.

Gibot, J.-L. & Gorczynski, P. (1999) *Following the Tanks, Cambrai 20 November–7ᵗʰ December 1917*, The Authors, Arras.

Gillespie, A.D. (1916*) Letters from Flanders*, Smith Elder & Co, London.

Giradet, J-M. *et al.* (2003) *Somewhere on the Western Front. Arras 1914–1918.* Documents d"Archéologie et d'Histoire du XXᵉ Siècle, No 8, Arras.

Gregory, H. E. (ed.) (1918) *Military Geology and Topography.* Yale University Press, New Haven.

Grieve, Capt. W. G. & Newman, B. (1936) *Tunnellers*. Herbert Jenkins, London.

Griffith, P. (ed.) (1996). *British Fighting Methods in the Great War*. Frank Cass, London.

Griffith, W. (1931) *Up to Mametz*, Faber & Faber, London.

Hall, J.N. (1917) *Kitchener's Mob*, Constable, London.

Hammerton, J.A. (ed) n.d. *The Great War I Was There*. Amalgamated Press, London.

Häusler, H. & Mang, R. (eds) (2011) *International Handbook Military geography, Volume 2.* Truppendienst, Vienna

Hesketh-Pritchard, Major H. (1994) *Sniping in France.* Leo Cooper, London.

Hitchcock, Capt. F.C., MC (1937) *'Stand To' A Diary of the Trenches 1915–1918.* Hurst & Blackett, London.

Innes, J.R. (1935) *Flash Spotters and Sound Rangers*, George Allen & Unwin, London.

Inners, J.D., Cuffey, R.J., Smith, R.C. II, Neubaum, J.C., Keen, R.C., Fleeger, G.M., Butts, L., Delano, H.L., Neubaum, V.A. & Howe, R.H. (2004). Rifts, Diabase, and the Topographic 'Fishhook': Terrain and Military Geology of the Battle of Gettysburg – July 1–3, 1863. Pre-Meeting Field Trip 4, Guidebook. Geological Society of America Northeast/ Southeast Sections.

Institution of Royal Engineers. (1921). The Work of the Royal Engineers in the European War, 1914-19: Water Supply. W & J Mackay, Chatham.

Institution of Royal Engineers (1922*a*) *The work of the Royal Engineers in the European War, 1914-19: geological work on the Western Front.* Institution of Royal Engineers, Chatham.

Institution of Royal Engineers (1922*b*) *The work of the Royal Engineers in the European War, 1914-19: military mining.* Institution of Royal Engineers, Chatham.

Institution of Royal Engineers (1927) *The work of the Royal Engineers in the European War, 1914–19: Miscellaneous.* W and J Mackay: Chatham.

Institution of Royal Engineers (1952) *History of the Corps of Royal Engineers. Volume V. The Home Front, France, Flanders and Italy in the First World War.* Institution of Royal Engineers: Chatham.

Jacques, A. (ed., 1997) *La Bataille d'Arras, avril-mai 1917,* Documents d"Archéologie et d'Histoire du XXᵉ Siècle, No 5, Arras.

Johnson, D.W. (1918), *Topography and Strategy in the War*, Constable, London.

Johnson, D.W. (1921), *Battlefields of the World War: Western and Southern fronts.* American Geographical Research Series 3, Oxford University Press, New York.

Johnston Maj. W.J. (ed.) (1916). *The Royal Engineers Field Service Pocket-Book*, Royal Engineers Institute, Chatham.

Jacobs, K. (2007) *Nieuwpoort Sector 1917.* De Krijger, Nieuwpoort.

Jones, S. (2010) *Underground Warfare 1914-1918*, Pen & Sword, Barnsley.

Keegan, J. (1991) *The Face of Battle.* Pimilico, London.

Kranz, W. (1927) *Die Geologie im Igenieur-Baufach* Enke-Verlag, Stuttgart.

Lake Captain B.C. (1916) *Knowledge for War. Every Officer's Handbook for the Front,* Harrison & Sons, London.

Lewis C. (1936) *Sagittarius Rising.* Peter Davies, London.

Liddle, P. (ed.) (1997) *Passchendaele in Perspective.* Pen & Sword. Barnsley.

Lloyd, N. (2008) *Loos 1915.* History Press, Stroud.

Lossberg, F. von (1939) *Meine Tätigkeit im Weltkriege*, E.S. Mittler & Sohn, Berlin.

Ludendorff, Gen. (n.d.) *My War Memories 1914–1918. Vol II.* Hutchinson & Co, London.

McCarthy, C. (1998) *The Somme The Day-by-Day Account*, Brockhampton, London.

McCarthy, C. (1998) *The Third Ypres Passchendaele. The Day-by-Day Account*, Arms & Armour Press, London.

Macdonald, L. (1978), *They Called it Passchendaele.* Penguin, Harmondsworth.

MacGreal, S. (2011) *Boesinghe.* Pen & Sword, Barnsley.

Marix Evans, M. (2000), *The Fall of France, Act with Daring.* Osprey, Oxford.

Masefield, J. (1917) *The Old Front Line*, Heinemann, London.

Miles, Capt. W. (1948) *Official History of the War, Military Operations, France and Belgium 1917 vol.III,* HMSO, London.

Mitchell, C. (1991) *Terrain Evaluation*, 2nd Edition. Longman, London.

Mottram, R.H. (1936) *Journey to the Western Front, Twenty Years After.* G. Bell, London.

Oldham, P. (1995) *Pillboxes on the Western Front,* Pen & Sword, Barnsley.

Orpen, Sir W. (1924) *An Onlooker in France*, Williams and Norgate, London.

Passingham, I. (1998) *Pillars of Fire, The Battle of Messines.* Sutton, Stroud.

Philpott, W. (2014) *Attrition. Fighting the First World War.* Abacus, London.

Pollard, T. (n.d.) *Vampir Dugout.* Unpublished preliminary Report, GUARD, University of Glasgow.

Portlock, Maj-Gen J.E. (1868), *A Rudimentary Treatise on Geology*, 5th Edn, London.

Prior, R. & Wilson, W. (1996) *Passchendaele the Untold Story*, Yale University Press, New Haven.

Pulteney, Lt-Gen Sir W. & Brice, B. (1925) *The Immortal Salient.* John Murray, London.

Robaszynski, F. & Dupuis, C. (1983). *Belgique.* Guides Géologiques Regionaux, Masson, Paris.

Robertshaw, A. & Kenyon, D. (2008). *Digging the trenches. The Archaeology of the Western Front.* Pen & Sword Military, Barnsley.

Rogers, Col. H.C.B. (1965) *Tanks in Battle.* Seeley Service & Co, London.

Salomon, W. (1915). *Kriegs-Geologie.* Carl Winters Universitätbuchhandlung, Heidelberg.

Saunders, A. (2010) *Trench Warfare 1850–1950.* Pen & Sword, Barnsley.

Saunders, N.J. (2011). *Killing Time. Archaeology and the First World War.* The History Press, Stroud.

Seton-Hutchinson, Lt-Col. G. (1935) *Pilgrimage.* Rich & Cowan, London.

Sheffield, G. (2011) *The Chief. Douglas Haig and the British Army.* Aurum, London

Sheffield, G. & Bourne, J. (eds) (2005) *Douglas Haig. War Diaries and Letters 1914–1918,* Weidenfield & Nicholson, London.

Stern, Sir A. (1919) *Tanks 1914–1918. Logbook of a Pioneer.* Hodder & Stoughton, London.

Sun Tzu [translated by Thomas Cleary (2009)] *The Art of War.* Shambhala, Boston.

Talbot House (1920) *The Pilgrim's Guide to the Ypres Salient.* Talbot House, Poperinge.

Tempest, Capt. E.V. (1921) *History of the Sixth Battalion West Yorkshire Regiment. Vol. 1, 1/6th Battalion,* Percy Lund, Humphries & Co, Bradford.

Thiem, G. (1916) *Keimfreies Wasser fürs Heer.* Verlag der Internationalen Zeitschift für Wasser-Versorgung, Leizig.

Thurlow, Col.l E.G.L. (1933) *The Pill-boxes of Flanders,* British Legion, London.

Treves, Sir F. (ed.) (1916). *Made in the Trenches.* George Allen & Unwin, London.

Verdegem, S., Billemont, J. & Genbrugge, S. (2013) *Acheo Rapport 28. Mesen – Collector Aquafin.* AEDE.

Wade, A. (1936) *The War of the Guns.* Batsford, London.

Watts, B.D. (2004) *Clausewitzian Friction and Future War. Revised edition.* McNair Paper 68, National Defense University, Washington.

Wiggins, K. (2003) *Siege Mines and Underground Warfare* Shire, Princes Risborough.

Williamson, H. (1987) *The Wet Flanders Plain.* Gliddon, Norwich.

Willig, D., Rose, E.P.F., Heyse, I, Allersmeir, C. & Doyle, P. (2015) *Militärhistorisch-Kriegsgeologischer Reiseführer zum Wytschaete-Bogen (Messines Ridge) bei Ypern (Belgien).* Geoinformationsdiesnt der Bundeswehr, Schiftenreihe.

Winters, H.A. (1998). *Battling the Elements. Weather and Terrain in the Conduct of War.* Johns Hopkins University Press, Baltimore.

Wolff, L. (1959) *In Flanders Fields.* Longmans, London.

Wood, C.E. (2006) *Mud, a Military History.* Potomac Books, Dulles.

Wood, R. (2017) *Miners at War 1914–1919. South Wales Miners in the Tunnelling Companies on the Western Front.* Helion, Solihull.

Zanders J.P. (ed.) (2016) *Innocence Slaughtered,* Uniform Press, London.

Papers and chapters

Anon [Steinmann] (1915) Geologie im Kriege. *Geologische Rundshau*, v. 6, pp.94–95.

Anon (1916) The geography of the Battle of the Marne. *Scottish Geographical Magazine*, v. 32, pp.31–35.

Anon (1919) Résumé de la causerie du général-major baron L. Greindl sur les inondations du front belge pendant la guerre 1914–1918. *Bulletin de la Société Belge de Geologie*, v. 29, pp. 15–61.

Bailey, J. (1996) British artillery in the Great War. In: Griffith, P. (ed.) *British Fighting Methods in the Great War*. Frank Cass, London, pp. 23–49.

Ball, H.S. (1919). The work of the miner on the Western Front, 1915-1918. *Transactions of the Institution of Mining and Metallurgy*, v.28, pp.189–248.

Baeteman, C. (1999) The Holocene depositional history of the Ijzer palaeovalley (Western Belgian coastal plain) with reference to the factors controlling the formation of intercalated peat beds. *Geologica Belgica*, v.2, pp.39–72.

Barton, M.E. (1987). The sunken lanes of southern England: engineering geological considerations. In: Culshaw, M.G., Bell, F.G., Cripps, J.C. & O'Hara, M. (eds) *Planning and Engineering Geology*, Engineering Geology Special Publication n. 4, pp. 411–418.

Bastin, E.S. (1918) War-time mineral activities in Washington. *Economic Geology*, v. 13, pp. 524–537.

Bateman, A.M. (1917) The geologist in war times–the training of artillery officers. *Economic Geology*, v.12, pp. 628–631.

Beeby Thompson, A. (1926). Geology as applied to military requirements. *Royal Engineers Journal*, v.40, pp.53–63.

Bergerat, F., Jacques, A., Vandycke, S., Amédro, F., Robaszynski, F. & Faÿ, O. (2015) Les carrières souterraines d'Arras: géologie, archéologie et histoire. *Bulletin d'Information des Geologiques du Bassin de Paris*, v. 52, 3–26.

Betz, F. (1984) Military Geology, In: Finkl, C.W. Jr (ed) (1984), *The Encyclopedia of Applied Geology. Encyclopedia of Earth Sciences, v.13*. Van Nostrand Rheinhold Co, NY.

Bradley, W.H. (1945). Military geology [abstract]. *Economic Geology*, v. 40, pp. 78–79.

Branagan, D. (1987) The Australian Mining Corps in World War 1. *Bulletin and Proceedings of the Australasian Institute of Mining and Metallurgy*, v. 292, 40–44.

Brooks, A.H. (1920). The use of geology on the Western Front. *US Geological Survey Professional Papers*, v. 128-D, pp. 85-124.

Brooks, A.H. (1920). Military mining in France. *Engineering and Mining Journal*, v.109, pp. 606–610.

Brooks, A.H. (1920). The application of geology to war. *Engineering and Mining Journal*, v.109, p. 794.

Brooks, A.H. (1920) The Lorraine iron field and the war. *Engineering and Mining Journal*, v. 109, pp. 1065–1069.

Burwash, E.M.J. (1940) Bomb craters in different soils. *Bulletin of the Geological Society of America*, v.51, pp.1922–1923.

Chasseaud, P. (1990). British artillery and trench maps on the Western Front, 1914–18. *Map Collector*, v. 51, pp. 24–32.

Cornish, V. (1915) Notes on the historical and physical geography of the theatres of war. *Geographical Journal*, v. 45, pp. 373–374.

Cotton, L.A. & Browne, W.R. (1934) Notes on the life of a great Australian Scientist. *Environment: a Magazine of Science*, v.2, pp.7–20.

Coulthard, R.W. (1919). Tunnelling at the Front. *Transactions of the Canadian Mining Institute*, v.22, pp. 444–461.

Cross, W. (1919) Geology in the world war and after. *Bulletin of the Geological Society of America*, v. 30, pp. 168–169.

Cuffey, R.J., Smith, R., II, Neubaum, J.C., Keen, R.C., Inners, J.D. & Neubaum, V.A. (2004), Lee vs. Meade at Gettysburg (July 1–3, 1863): The influence of topography and geology on command decisions and battlefield tactics. *Geological Society of America Abstracts with Programs*, v.36, n.2, p.48.

Culshaw, M.G. & Waltham, A.C. (1987) Natural and artificial cavities as ground engineering hazards. *Quarterly Journal of Engineering Geology*, v. 20, pp. 139–150

De Geyter, G., De Man, E., Herman, J. Moorkens, T., Steurbaut, E. & Vandenberghe, N. (2006). Disused Paleogene regional stages from Belgium: Montian, Heersian, Landenian, Paniselian, Bruxellian, Laekenian, Ledian, Wemmelian and Tongrian. *Geologica Belgica*, v. 9, pp. 203–213.

De Meyer, M. & Pype, P. (2009). Scars of the Great War (Western Flanders, Belgium). In: Scott, D., Babits, L. & Haecker, C. (eds) *Fields of Conflict. Battlefield Archaeology from the Roman Empire to the Korean War.* Potomac Books, Washington, pp. 359–382.

De Moor, G. & Heyse, I. (1978). Dépots quaternaires et géomorphologie dans le nord-Ouest de la Flandre. *Bulletin de la Société belge de Géologie,* v. 87, pp. 37–47.

Dewide, M. & Saunders, N.J. (2009) Archaeology of the Great War. The Flemish Experience. In N.J. Saunders & P. Cornish (eds) *Contested Objects. Material Memories of the Great War.* Routledge, London.

Doyle, P. (1999) The mud of Flanders. Geologists at war. *Military Illustrated*, n.139, pp. 44–47.

Doyle, P. (2001) 'Battlefield conservation: conserving the heritage of the underground war in Flanders' *Battlefields Review* v.12, pp. 50-51.

Doyle, P. (2001). Terrain and the Gallipoli Campaign, 1915. In: Celik, K. and Koc, C. (eds) *The Gallipoli Campaign, International Perspectives 85 years on.* Cannakale Onsekiz Mart University, Cannakale, 46-69.

Doyle, P. (2006). Military geology and the Battle of Gettysburg, July 1863. *Geology Today*, v.22, pp. 142–149.

Doyle, P. (2008). 'Six VCs before breakfast', terrain and the Gallipoli landings, 1915.

In: Nathanail, C.P., Abrahart, R.J. & Bradshaw, R.P. (eds) *Military Geography and Geology, History and Technology*, Land Quality Press, Nottingham.

Doyle, P. (2012). Examples of the influence of groundwater on British military mining in Flanders, 1914–1917. In: Rose, E.P.F. & Mather, J.D. (eds) *Military Aspects of Hydrology*, pp. 73-83. Geological Society Special Publication 362, Geological Society, London.

Doyle, P. (2014). Geology and the war on the Western Front, 1914-1918. *Geology Today*, v.30, pp. 183–191.

Doyle, P. (2015) Examples of the geo-archaeology of trench warfare in Flanders. In: Willig, D. (ed.) (2015) *Militärhistorisch-Kriegsgeologischer Reiseführer zum Wytschaete-Bogen (Messines Ridge) bei Ypern (Belgien).* Geoinformationsdiesnt der Bundeswehr, Schiftenreihe., v.4, pp. 193–202.

Doyle, P. (2016). An unfortunate accident of geography: badlands and the ANZAC Sector, Gallipoli, April–September 1915 *In* MacDonald, E.V. & Bullard, T. (eds) *Military Geosciences and Desert Warfare, Past Lessons and Modern Challenges*, Springer, Dordrecht, pp. 3–18.

Doyle, P. (2017) Trench construction and engineering geology on the Western Front, *1914–1918.* In: Rose, E.P.F., Ehlen, J. & Lawrence, U. (eds) *Military Aspects of Geology: Fortification, Excavation and Terrain Evaluation*, Geological Society Special Publication, Geological Society, London.

Doyle, P. & Bennett, M.R. (1997). Military geography: terrain evaluation and the British Western Front, 1914-1918. *Geographical Journal*, v.163, pp.1-24.

Doyle, P. & Bennett, M.R. (1999). Military geography: the influence of terrain on the outcome of the Gallipoli Campaign, 1915. *Geographical Journal*, v. 165, pp. 12-36.

Doyle, P. & Bennett, M.R. (2002). Terrain and the Gallipoli Campaign, 1915. In: Doyle, P. & Bennett, M.R. (eds) *Fields of Battle, Terrain in Military History.* Kluwer, Dordrecht, pp. 149-169.

Doyle, P., Bennett, M.R. & Cocks, F.M. (2000). Geology and warfare on the British sector of the Western Front, 1914-18. In: Rose, E.P.F. & Nathanail, C.P. (eds) *Geology and Warfare: Examples of the Influence of Terrain and Geologists on Military Operations.* Geological Society, London, pp. 179–235.

Doyle, P., Barton, P. & Rosenbaum, M.S. (2001) Geohazards – last legacy of war? *Geoscientist*, v. 11, pp. 4–7.

Doyle, P., Barton, P. & Rosenbaum, M.S. (2001). Archives and field observation as the basis for geohazard assessment of the legacy from warfare: the impact of military tunnels on the town of Nieuwpoort, Belgium. In: Nathanail, C.P., Rosenbaum, M.S. & Turner, A.K. (eds): *Characterisation of the shallow subsurface: Implications for urban infrastructure and environmental assessment.* TUD Publishers, Delft, 22.

Doyle, P., Barton, P & Vandewalle, J. (2006). Archaeology of a Great War dugout: Beecham Farm, Passchendaele, Belgium. In: Pollard, T & Banks, I. (eds) *Past Tense: Studies in the Archaeology of Conflict*, pp. 45–66. Brill, Leiden

Doyle, P., Bennett, M.R. & Cocks, F.M & Macleod, R. (2002) Terrain and the Messines Ridge, Belgium, 1914–1918, In: P. Doyle & M.R. Bennett, *Fields of Battle: Terrain in Military History,* Kluwer, Dordrecht, pp. 205-224.

Doyle, P., Bostyn, F., Barton, P. & Vandewalle, J. (2001). The underground war 1914-18: the geology of the Beecham dugout, Passchendaele, Belgium. *Proceedings of the Geologists' Association,* v. 112, pp. 263–274.

Doyle, P., Barton, P., Rosenbaum, M.S., Vandewalle, J. & Jacobs, K. (2002). Geo-environmental implications of military mining in Flanders, Belgium, 1914–1918. *Environmental Geology,* v. 43, pp. 57–71.

Eastler T.E. (2004) Military use of underground terrain, In: D.R. Caldwell *et al.* (eds) *Studies in Military Geography and Geology,* Kluwer, Dordrecht, pp. 21–37.

Ekins, A. (2001). A ridge too far: military objectives and the dominance of terrain in the Gallipoli Campaign, p. 7. In: Celik, K. and Koc, C. (eds) *The Gallipoli Campaign, International Perspectives 85 years on.* Cannakale Onsekiz Mart University, Cannakale, pp. 5-34.

Erdmann, C.E. (1943). Application of geology to the principles of war. *Bulletin of the Geological Society of America,* v.54, p. 1174.

Erdmann, C.E. (1944) Military geology: applications of geology to terrain intelligence. *Bulletin of the Geological Society of America,* v.55, pp. 783–788.

Füsslein, O. (1921) Die Mineur in Flandern. In: G. von Dickhuth-Harrach (ed) *Im Felde unbesiegt, der Weltkrieg in 28 Einzeldarstellungen.* F. Lehman, Munich.

Gellasch, C.A. (2004) Groundwater. Past, present and future uses in military operations. In: D.R, Caldwell *et al.* (eds) *Studies in Military Geography and Geology,* Kluwer, Dordrecht, pp. 307–319.

Gregory, J.W. (1916-18) The geological factors affecting the strategy of the war and the geology of the potash salts. *Transactions of the Geological Society of Glasgow,* v. 16, pp.1–33.

Haigh, R.H. (1978) The Battle of Messines Ridge–& June 1917. A view from the British ranks. *Royal Engineers Journal,* v. 92, pp. 227–239.

Hanot, F., Bergerat, F., Gély, J–P., Porchier, J.C. & Vicelli, J. (2015) La géologie du front occidental de la Grande Guerre des Flandres à la Champagne. Journées d'étude de Printemps – 29 au 31 Mai 2014. *Bulletin d'Information des Geologiques du Bassin de Paris,* v. 52, 27–43.

Harris, J.P. (1996) The rise of armour. In: Griffith, P. (ed.) *British Fighting Methods in the Great War.* Frank Cass, London, pp. 113–127.

Häusler, H. (2000) Die Österreichische und Deutsche Kriegsgeologie 1914– 1918. *Informationen des Militärischen Geo-Dienstes,* v. 75, pp. 1–161.

Häusler, H. (2003) Dr. Walter Kranz (1873–1953): Der erste Militärgeologedes 20. Jahrhunderts: *MILGEO: Organ des Militärischen Geowesens des* Österreichischen *Bundesheeres,* v. 12, p. 1–80.

Häusler, H. (2015) Military geology and comprehensive security geology – applied geologic contributions to new Austrian security strategy. *Austrian Journal of Earth Sciences*, v. 108, pp. 302–316.

Heyse, I. (2015) Geomorphology and geology of 'Flanders Fields' (the Ypres to Coastal Plain Region of West Flanders, Belgium) and their impact on military tunnelling and defensive flooding in the 1914-1918 world war. In: D. Willig *et al.* Militärhistorisch-kriegsgeologiischer Reiseführer zum Wytschaete-Bogen (Messines Ridge) bei Ypren (Belgien). *Schriftenreihe Geoinformationsdienst der Bundeswehr*, v.4, p. 54.

Hinks, A.R. (1919) German war maps and survey. *Geographical Journal*, v. 53, pp. 30–44.

Hussey, J. (1997) The Flanders battleground and the weather in 1917. In: Peter H. Liddle (ed.) *Passchendaele in Perspective. The Third Battle of Ypres*, Leo Cooper, London.

Hutchinson, D.J., Diederichs, M., Pehme, P., Sawyer, P., Robinson, P., Puxley, A. & Robichaud, H. (2008). Geomechanics stability assessment of World War 1 military excavations at the Canadian National Vimy Memorial Site, France. *International Journal of Rock Mechanics & Mining Sciences*, v.45, pp.59–77.

Kiersch, G.A. (1998) Engineering geosciences and military operations. *Engineering Geology*, v. 49, p. 124.

King, C. (1990) Stratigraphy of the Ieper Formation and Argile de Flandres (Early Eocene) in western Belgium and northern France. *Bulletin de la Société belge de Géologie*, v. 97, pp. 349-372.

King, W.B.R. (1919). Geological work on the Western Front. *Geographical Journal*, 54, 201–221.

King, W.B.R. (1921a) Résultants des sondages exécutés par les armées britanniques dans la Nord de la France. *Annales de la Société géologique du Nord*, v.45, pp.9–26

King, W.B.R. (1921b) The surface of the marls of the Middle Chalk in the Somme Valley and the neighbouring districts of northern France, and the effect on the hydrology. *Quarterly Journal of the Geological Society of London*, v. 77, pp. 135–143

Kranz, W. (1913) Militargeologie. *Kriegstechnische Zeitschrift* v. 16, pp.464–471.

Kranz, W. (1920) Beiträge zur Entwicklung der Kriegsgeologie. *Geologische Rundshau*, v. 11, pp.329–349.

Kranz, W. (1935) Minierkampf und Kriegsgeologie im Wytschaetebogen. *Vieteljahreshefte für Pionere*, v. 2/3, pp.161–181.

Laga, P., Louwye, S. & Geets, S. 2001. Paleogene and Neogene Lithostatigraphic units (Belgium). *Geologica Belgica*, v.4, pp.135–152.

Mercier-Castiaux, M. & Dupuis, C. (1990) Clay mineral association sin the Ypresian formations in the NW European basin, time and geographical variations – interpretations. *Bulletin de al Société Belgique des Géologie*, v.97, pp. 441–450.

Nolf, D. & Steurbaut, E. (1990). Stratigraphie de l'éocène en Flandre occidentale et dans les regions limitrophes. *Bulletin d'Information des Géologiques du Bassin de Paris*, v. 27, pp. 9–36.

Parry, J.T. (1984) Terrain evaluation, military purposes, in C.W. Finkl Jr (ed) *The*

Encyclopedia of Applied Geology. Encyclopedia of Earth Sciences, v.13. Van Nostrand Rheinhold Co, NY.

Pennycuick, Brig. J.A.C. (1965) Hill 60 and the mines at Messines. *The Royal Engineers Journal,* v. 79, p. 389.

Phillip, H. (1919) Die Entwicklung der Kriegsgeologie. *Technik und Wehrmacht,* v.22, pp.129–134.

Pogue, J.E. (1917) Military geology. *Science,* v.46, pp. 8–10.

Portlock, Maj. E.F. (1868) Geology and Geognosy, in *Aide-Mémoire to the Military Sciences, v. II.*

Pressey, H.A.S. (1919) Notes on trench war. *Royal Engineers Journal,* v. 29, pp. 297–315.

Price, P.H. & Woodward, H.P. (1942) Geology and war. *Bulletin of the American Association of Petroleum Geologists,* v. 26, pp.1832–1838.

Ray, L.L. (1946) Problems of trafficability. *Bulletin of the Geological Society of America,* v. 57, pp. 1223–1224

Reynolds, L.B. (1919). Mining in chalk on the Western Front. *Transactions of the Canadian Mining Institute,* v. 22, pp. 463–474.

Robinson, P. (1999). The abandoned Messines mines. *Battlefields Review,* v.3, pp.43–47.

Rose, E.P.F. (1978). Geology in war. *Royal Engineers Journal,* v.92, pp. 182-190.

Rose, E.P.F. (2004), Napoleon Bonaparte's Egyptian campaign of 1798: The first military operation to be assisted by geologists? *Geology Today,* v. 20, p. 24–29.

Rose, E.P.F. (2004) The contribution of geologists to the development of emergency groundwater supplies by the British Army. In: Mather, J.D. (ed) *200 Years of British Hydrogeology,* Geological Society, London, pp. 159–182.

Rose, E.P.F. (2009) Water supply maps for the Western Front (Belgium and northern France) developed by British, German and American military geologists during World War 1: pioneering studies in hydrogeology from trench warfare. *The Cartographic Journal,* v. 46, pp. 76–103.

Rose, E.P.F. (2012) Groundwater as a military resource: pioneering British military well boring and hydrogeology in World War 1. In: Rose, E.P.F. & Mather, J.D. (eds) *Military Aspects of Hydrogeology,* Geological Society, London, pp. 49–72.

Rose, E.P.F. (2014). Military geosciences before the twenty-first century. *Reviews in Engineering Geology,* v.22, pp.19–26.

Rose, E.P.F. & Rosenbaum, M.S. (1993). British military geologists: the formative years to the end of the First World War. *Proceedings of the Geologists' Association,* v.104, pp.41–50.

Rose, E.P.F. & Rosenbaum, M.S. (2011). British geological maps that guided excavation of military dug-outs in Belgium during World War 1. *Quarterly Journal of Engineering Geology and Hydrogeology,* v.44, pp.293–306.

Rose, E.P.F., Häusler, H. & Willig, D. (2000). Comparison of British and German applications of geology in world war. In: Rose, E.P.F. & Nathanail, C.P. (eds) *Geology and Warfare: Examples of the Influence of Terrain and Geologists on Military Operations*. Geological Society, London, pp. 108–140.

Rosenbaum, M.S. (1989). Geological influence on tunnelling under the Western Front at Vimy Ridge. *Proceedings of the Geologists' Association*, v.100, pp.135–140.

Rutledge, Capt. H. (1952). Some aspects of military geology [abstract]. *Transactions of the Edinburgh Geological Society*, v. 14, p. 427.

Sabine, P.A. (1991). Geologists at war: a forensic investigation in the field of war-time diplomacy. *Proceedings of the Geologists' Association*, v.102, pp.139-143.

Salmon, R. *et al.* (2001) Mine shafts in Nord Pas-de-Calais coalfield (France), Risk Assessment and treatment technique. In: *Confronting Change: North East England and East European Coalfield*, Conference Proceedings, Newcastle.

Santarelli, N. (2015) Géologie de Grande Guerre. *Géochronique*, n. 135, pp. 12–22.

Schiller, W. (1923) Die Geologie im Weltkriege. *Heerstechnik*, v. 1, pp. 25-29.

Seidlitz, W. von, (1922) Erfahrungen und Erfolge der Kriegsgeologie. *Fortschitte der Naturwissenschaftlichen Forschung*, v.11, pp.147–187.

Shortt, Capt. A.C. (1933) A staff exercise in Belgium. *Royal Engineers Journal*, v. 37, pp. 596–606.

Simpson, D.J. (1960) Water and warfare. *Transactions of the Geological Society of South Africa*, v. 63, pp. xix–xxxiv.

Smith, P.S. (1918) The geologist in war times: the United States Geological Survey's war work. *Economic Geology*, v. 13, pp. 392–399.

Stamp L.D. (1922) The Geology of Belgium. *Proceedings of the Geologists' Association*, v. 32, p.2.

Stamp, L.D. (1922) Long Excursion to Belgium. *Proceedings of the Geologists' Association*, v. 32,

Steurbaut, E. (1987). The Ypresian in the Belgian Basin. *Bulletin de la Société belge de Géologie*, 96, 339–351.

Steurbaut, E. & Nolf, D. (1986). Revision of the Ypresian stratigraphy of Belgium and northwestern France. *Mededelingenvan de Werkgroep voor Tertiarie en Kwartaire Geologie*, 23, 115–172.

Strahan, A. (1917). Geology at the seat of war. *Geological Magazine*, v.64, pp. 68-74.

Street Major C.J.C. (1936) With the Guns at Loos, in J.A. Hammerton (ed) *The Great War I Was There*, vol. 1, Amalgamated Press, London.

Tatham, H. 1919. Tunnelling in the sand dunes of the Belgian Coast. *Transactions of the Institution of Mining and Metallurgy*, v. 28, pp. 250–260.

Verrett, D.D. (1980) 'Etude statistique des résultats d'essais géotechniques réalises en laboratoire sur l'Argile des Flandres (nord de la France)' *Bulletin of the International Association of Engineering Geology* v. 22, pp. 253-255.

Whitmore, F.C. Jr (1960) Terrain intelligence and current military concepts. *American Journal of Science*, v. 258-A, pp. 375–387.

Willig, D. (2011) Mining warfare in the Wytschaete Ridge 1914–1917 – advantages and disadvantages of high ground emplacements. In: Häusler, H. & Mang, R. (eds) (2011) *International Handbook Military geography, Volume 2*. Truppendienst, Vienna, pp. 510–524.

Willig, D. (2015) German military mining on the Western and Eastern fronts. In: Anthony Byledbal (ed.). *Les Taupes de la Grande Guerre*, Artois Presses Université, Arras, pp. 29–54.

Willig, D. & Häusler, H. (2012) Aspects of military hydrogeology and groundwater development by Germany and its allies in World War 1. In: Rose, E.P.F. & Mather, J.D. (eds) *Military Aspects of Hydrogeology*, Geological Society, London, pp. 85–103

Winterbotham, Lt-Col. H.S.L. (1919) Geographical work with the army in France. *Geographical Journal*, v.54, pp. 12–28.

Woodward, O.H. (1920). Notes on the work of an Australian tunnelling company in France. *Proceedings of the Australasian Institute of Mining and Metallurgy*, 37, 1–54.

Web resources

https://simonjoneshistorian.com/2016/06/30/the-lochnagar-mine/

http://www.laboisselleproject.com/geophysics-site-clearance/

https://web.archive.org/web/20120308111159/http://www.polygonwood.com/Vampire%20Dugout/Vampir%20Dugout%20Zonnebeke.pdf.

http://www.durandgroup.org.uk/maison%20blanche.html.

http://www.durandgroup.org.uk/durand_group_vimy_ridge.html

INDEX